"From fairest creatures we desire increase,
That thereby beauty's rose might never die,
But as the riper should by time decease,
His tender heir might bear his memory..."

William Shakespeare, Sonnet 1, 1609

This book is dedicated in memory of Gian Paolo Bagnara,
Full Professor of Histology at the University of Bologna,
who motivated and inspired this book.

Gian Paolo Bagnara

STEM CELLS

Editors
Laura Bonsi and Francesco Alviano

SOCIETÀ EDITRICE ESCULAPIO

ISBN 978-88-9385-171-8
DOI: 10.15651/stem-cells

© Copyright 2020.
Società Editrice Esculapio s.r.l.
Via Terracini, 30 – 40131 Bologna
www.editrice-esculapio.com – info@editrice-esculapio.it

Cover layout: Laura Brugnoli
Editorial staff: Carlotta Lenzi, Laura Tondelli and Laura Brugnoli
Edited by Globe Group Milan

Authors

 Alviano Francesco
Unit of Histology, Embryology and Applied Biology, Department of Experimental, Diagnostic and Specialty Medicine, University of Bologna, Bologna, Italy.

Angeletti Andrea
Unit of Nephrology, Dialysis and Transplantation, Department of Experimental Diagnostic and Specialty Medicine, University of Bologna, S. Orsola-Malpighi Hospital, Bologna, Italy.

Baldassarro Vito Antonio
Department of Pharmacy and Biotechnology, University of Bologna; Fondazione IRET, Ozzano Emilia, Italy;

Baldini Nicola
Laboratory for Orthopedic Pathophysiology and Regenerative Medicine, IRCCS Istituto Ortopedico Rizzoli, Bologna, Italy. Department of Biomedical and Neuromotor Sciences, University of Bologna, Bologna, Italy.

Barbar Lilianne
The New York Stem Cell Foundation Research Institute, New York, NY, USA.

Bianchi Francesca
Unit of Nephrology, Dialysis and Transplantation, Department of Experimental Diagnostic and Specialty Medicine, University of Bologna, S. Orsola-Malpighi Hospital, Bologna, Italy.

Bonafè Massimiliano
Department of Experimental, Diagnostic and Specialty Medicine, University of Bologna, Bologna, Italy.

Bondioli Elena
Burns Center and Emilia-Romagna Regional Skin Bank, "M. Bufalini" Hospital - Cesena, AUSL Romagna, Italy.

Bonsi Laura

Unit of Histology, Embryology and Applied Biology, Department of Experimental, Diagnostic and Specialty Medicine, University of Bologna, Bologna, Italy.

Bortolotti Daria

Section of Microbiology and Medical Genetics, Department of Chemical and Pharmaceutical Sciences, University of Ferrara, Ferrara, Italy.

Burstein Suzanne

The New York Stem Cell Foundation Research Institute, New York, NY, USA.

Calzà Laura

Department of Pharmacy and Biotechnology, University of Bologna, Italy; Fondazione IRET, Ozzano Emilia, Italy.

Campioni Diana

Department of Specialist Biomedical and Surgical Sciences, University of Ferrara, Ferrara, Italy.

Cargnoni Anna

Centro di Ricerca E. Menni, Fondazione Poliambulanza, Brescia, Italy.

Cavallini Claudia

National Laboratory of Molecular Biology and Stem Cell Engineering - Eldor Lab, Istituto Nazionale di Biostrutture e Biosistemi (INBB) Innovation Accelerator CNR, Bologna, Italy.

Ciapetti Gabriela

Laboratory for Orthopedic Pathophysiology and Regenerative Medicine, IRCCS Istituto Ortopedico Rizzoli, Bologna, Italy. Department of Biomedical and Neuromotor Sciences, University of Bologna, Bologna, Italy.

Comai Giorgia

Unit of Nephrology, Dialysis and Transplantation, Department of Experimental Diagnostic and Specialty Medicine, University of Bologna, S. Orsola-Malpighi Hospital, Bologna, Italy.

Costa Roberta

Department of Biomedical and Neuromotor Sciences, University of Bologna, Bologna, Italy.

Di Pompo Gemma

Laboratory for Orthopedic Pathophysiology and Regenerative Medicine, IRCCS Istituto Ortopedico Rizzoli, Bologna, Italy. Department of Biomedical and Neuromotor Sciences, University of Bologna, Bologna, Italy.

Fossati Valentina

The New York Stem Cell Foundation Research Institute, New York, NY, USA.

Giardino Luciana
Department of Veterinary Medical Sciences, University of Bologna, Italy; Fondazione IRET, Ozzano Emilia, Italy.

Grigolo Brunella
RAMSES Laboratory, Dipartimento RIT IRCCS Istituto Ortopedico Rizzoli, Bologna.

Grossi Alberto
Italian Association against Leukemia-Lymphoma and Myeloma of Prato, Italy.

La Manna Gaetano
Unit of Nephrology, Dialysis and Transplantation, Department of Experimental Diagnostic and Specialty Medicine, University of Bologna, S. Orsola-Malpighi Hospital, Bologna, Italy.

Lanza Francesco
Section of Haematology, Hospital of Cremona, Cremona, Italy.

Lanzoni Giacomo
Diabetes Research Institute, University of Miami - Miller School of Medicine, Miami, FL; Department of Biochemistry and Molecular Biology, University of Miami - Miller School of Medicine, Miami, FL, USA.

Magatti Marta
Centro di Ricerca E. Menni, Fondazione Poliambulanza, Brescia, Italy

Marongiu Fabio
Department of Biomedical Sciences, Experimental Medicine Unit, University of Cagliari, Cagliari, Italy.

Melandri Davide
Burns Center and Emilia-Romagna Regional Skin Bank, "M. Bufalini" Hospital - Cesena, AUSL Romagna, Italy.

Minghetti Paola
Burns Center and Emilia-Romagna Regional Skin Bank, "M. Bufalini" Hospital - Cesena, AUSL Romagna, Italy.

Mitsiadis Thimios
Institute of Oral Biology, University of Zurich, Zurich, Switzerland.

Nijsure Madhura
The New York Stem Cell Foundation Research Institute, New York, NY, USA.

Olivi Elena
National Laboratory of Molecular Biology and Stem Cell Engineering - Eldor Lab, Istituto Nazionale di Biostrutture e Biosistemi (INBB) Innovation Accelerator CNR, Bologna, Italy.

Orlandi Catuscia

Burns Center and Emilia-Romagna Regional Skin Bank, "M. Bufalini" Hospital - Cesena, AUSL Romagna, Italy.

Orsini Giovanna

Polytechnic University of Marche Department of Clinical Sciences and Stomatology, Ancona, Italy.

Parolini Ornella

Centro di Ricerca E. Menni, Fondazione Poliambulanza, Brescia, Italy; Department of Life Science and Public Health, Università Cattolica del Sacro Cuore, Rome, Italy.

Pasquinelli Gianandrea

Clinical Pathology, Department of Experimental, Diagnostic and Specialty Medicine, University of Bologna, S. Orsola-Malpighi Hospital, Bologna, Italy.

Pozzo Enrico

Translational Cardiomyology Laboratory, Stem Cell Biology and Embryology Unit, Department of Development and Regeneration, KU Leuven, 3000 Leuven, Belgium.

Purpura Valeria

Burns Center and Emilia Romagna Regional Skin Bank, "M. Bufalini" Hospital - Cesena, AUSL Romagna, Italy.

Quattrocelli Mattia

Center for Genetic Medicine, Northwestern University Feinberg School of Medicine, Chicago, IL, USA.

Rizzo Roberta

Section of Microbiology and Medical Genetics, Department of Chemical and Pharmaceutical Sciences, University of Ferrara, Ferrara, Italy.

Rondelli Damiano

Division of Hematology/Oncology, Department of Medicine, University of Illinois, Chicago, IL, USA.

Roseti Livia

RAMSES Laboratory, Dipartimento RIT IRCCS Istituto Ortopedico Rizzoli, Bologna.

Rossi Martina

Unit of Histology, Embryology and Applied Biology, Department of Experimental, Diagnostic and Specialty Medicine, University of Bologna, Bologna, Italy.

Sampaolesi Maurilio

Translational Cardiomyology Laboratory, Stem Cell Biology and Embryology Unit, Department of Development and Regeneration, KU Leuven, 3000 Leuven, Belgium. Human Anatomy Unit,

Department of Public Health, Experimental and Forensic Medicine, University of Pavia, Pavia, Italy.

Silini Antonietta Rosa
Centro di Ricerca E. Menni, Fondazione Poliambulanza, Brescia, Italy.

Storci Gianluca
Department of Experimental, Diagnostic and Specialty Medicine, University of Bologna, Bologna, Italy.

Tassinari Riccardo
National Laboratory of Molecular Biology and Stem Cell Engineering - Eldor Lab, Istituto Nazionale di Biostrutture e Biosistemi (INBB) Innovation Accelerator CNR, Bologna, Italy.

Valente Sabrina
Clinical Pathology, Department of Experimental, Diagnostic and Specialty Medicine, University of Bologna, S. Orsola-Malpighi Hospital, Bologna, Italy.

Velasco Silvia
Department of Stem Cell and Regenerative Biology, Harvard University, Cambridge, MA, USA

Ventura Carlo
Department of Experimental, Diagnostic and Specialty Medicine, Italy. National Laboratory of Molecular Biology and Stem Cell Engineering - Eldor Lab, Istituto Nazionale di Biostrutture e Biosistemi (INBB)

Preface to the First Edition

Medicine is continuously evolving and one of its most recent advances is the science of regenerative medicine that provides therapeutic approaches for a variety of diseases, including those that lack efficient treatment. This book offers an update in regenerative medicine, it discusses the major principles concerning stem cells and cell therapy, starting from basic research up to the most recent clinical trials.

This volume discusses various stem cell populations and their therapeutic applications. As in any book of this type, this has been the combined efforts of many collaborators. They comprise a renowned group of scientists who provide studied contributions on the experimental studies and clinical trials of the biological, physiological, and pathophysiological properties of stem cells.

The book is dedicated to University students who are pursuing their degree in Biotechnology, Medicine, or Biology. It also represents a reference for those who are pursuing studies on stem cells. Each chapter has a wide and updated bibliography for further reading that includes review articles and original publications, thus offering the possibility to expand the reader's knowledge.

Laura Bonsi
Francesco Alviano

Foreword

Stem cell biology over the last 6 decades has become one of the most exciting, informative, rapidly changing and possibly clinically transformative areas of scientific and clinical investigation in the natural sciences. The clinical discipline of regenerative medicine has the potential of providing curative approaches for a whole host of genetic, malignant and age-related disorders that originate at the stem cell level. The new English edition of the book entitled "Stem Cells" which was edited by Drs Laura Bonsi and Francesco Alviano, provides a concise yet authoritative, timely and expert summary of our current understanding of stem cell biology. Although this field is rapidly changing, this textbook supplies its readers with a solid foundation by which to integrate and critically evaluate the almost daily onslaught of papers that deal with stem cells published in a numbing number of journals. Without the availability of a primer on stem cells these rapid advances are difficult to evaluate not only for the stem cell neophyte but also for the *aficionado*. This authoritative text was conceived as a collaboration between Drs. Bonsi and Alviano with Dr Gian Paolo Bagnara, who unfortunately passed away in 2014. Gian Paolo was a scholar, a good friend, a lover of the arts and a stem cell biologist. He was a Professor in Histology at the University of Bologna for over 3 decades. During his tenure in Bologna, he was one of the co-founders of their course in Biotechnology which helped many young scientists appreciate the science that was required to translate a stem cell product into the clinic. He was able to balance a robust laboratory-based stem cell research program with demanding teaching responsibilities. His understanding of the need to educate scientists and communicate the potential of stem cell science is best exemplified by this book His love of science was only exceeded by his love of his family and the University that he so faithfully served. The creation of this book represents a herculean task that outlines the fundamentals and nuances of stem cell biology. The text is provided by the talented editors and their carefully chosen team of authors. I am certain that Gian Paolo would smile and approve of this book and explain the need to continue to educate our colleagues and ourselves with the assistance of this well-timed volume. Access to a didactic approach, provided by this book, has surely been missing in the area of stem cell biology Admittedly, stem cell science and medicine change quickly but these advances can only be placed in proper perspective with the information provided by this wonderful volume. "Stem Cells" fills a void in educational tools available to educate the next generation of students of stem cell medicine. This marvelous book serves as a scientific companion and a resource for stem cell scientists, clinicians and students as our field continues to move incrementally forward.

Ronald Hoffman, MD
Albert A. and Vera G. List Professor of Medicine,
Director, Myeloproliferative Disorders Research Program,
Tisch Cancer Institute, Mount Sinai School of Medicine,
New York, NY, USA

Contents

Stem Cells

Francesco Alviano   Laura Bonsi

Fertilization is a series of processes during which the male gamete, the spermatozoon, penetrates the corona radiata of the female one, the oocyte, determining the formation of a single cell called a zygote. Genetic information, coded by DNA, which, together with the influence of the external environment, will determine the physical characteristics of a person, as well as their intelligence and personality, is present during fertilization. The zygote is the "ultimate" stem cell, referred to as the totipotent stem cell due to its high degree of plasticity. During the process of ontogenesis, the zygote gives rise, through successive cell divisions, to the embryonic stem cells of the inner cell mass and the outer epithelial layer (trophoblast) in the blastocyst. Therefore, the inner cell mass of the blastocyst consists of stem cells that combine a high capacity for self-renewal with the wide potential to generate several specialized cells. Following the process of gastrulation, the inner cell mass will generate the three germ layers (ectoderm, mesoderm and endoderm) and from these progressively more differentiated cells, including tissue-specific or somatic stem cells, which are responsible for the formation of the tissue in which they reside.

The number of somatic stem cells progressively declines with the development of the organism to a minimum and stable values in adulthood. At this stage, these cells assume the function of maintaining, both under physiological conditions and in possible pathological situations, the structural and functional integrity of the tissues by substituting the damaged mature cells. The adult organism, therefore, derives from a series of regulated processes involving the proliferation, migration, differentiation and maturation different cellular types (Figure 1.1).

In this context, the historical histological distinction of tissues in "labile", "stable" or "everlasting", is outdated as it is thought that there are stem cell populations upstream of all adult histotypes: these tissue-specific somatic stem cells or adult stem cells are characterized by different degrees of stemness and are able to duplicate each other maintaining the undifferentiated state or to differentiate into specialized cells of the tissue in which they reside.

1.1 Timeline of stem cell research milestones

1908   The Russian histologist Alexander Maksimov (1874-1928) proposes the term "stem cells" at the Congress of the Haematological Society in Berlin, postulating that all blood cells develop from a common precursor cell.

1960s Joseph Altman and Gopal Das present scientific evidence of neurogenesis in the adult, with a continuous activity of stem cells in the brain; because their

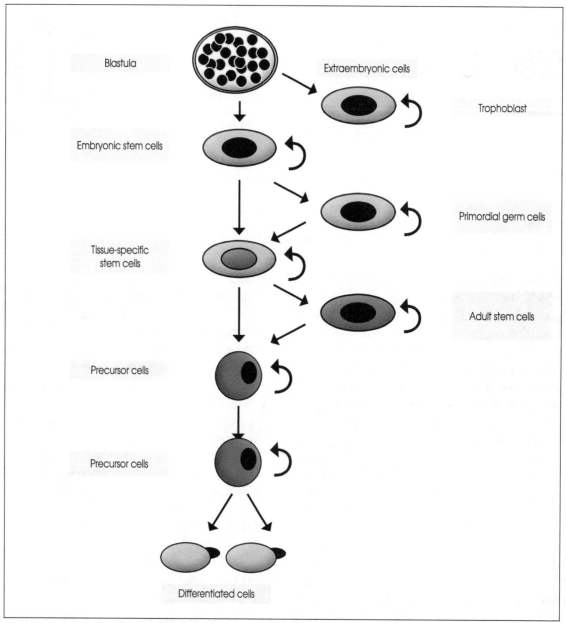

Figure 1.1. Hierarchical organization of stem cells.

results opposed Cajal's "no new neurons" dogma, they were neglected and marginalized.

1962 John Gurdon achieves the first cloning of an amphibious through the transfer of a nucleus, coming from a differentiated cell, into an oocyte, previously enucleated. This success demonstrated that the nuclei of differentiated cells retain their totipotency. The technique has been called "somatic cell nuclear transfer".

1963 McCulloch and Till show the presence of cells capable of self-renewal in the murine bone marrow.

1968 Bone marrow transplantation between two siblings successfully resolves SCID syndrome.

1970s Alexander Friedenstein describes a bone marrow-derived population, different from the haematopoietic cells, with the multipotent ability to generate several connective tissues.

1975 James Rheinwald and Howard Green describe the protocols for *in vitro* cultures of human epithelial cells for the creation of epidermal layers in the laboratory.

1978 January- Haematopoietic stem cells were discovered in human cord blood by Meulen's group.

1978 July- Louise Brown, the first test-tube baby, is born in England.

1981 Martin Evans, Matthew Kaufman and Gail R. Martin isolate mouse embryonic stem cells from the inner cell mass of the blastocyst. The origin of the term "embryonic stem cells" is attributed to Gail Martin.

1992 Brent A. Reynolds and Samuel Weiss establish neurospheres as a novel culture method to investigate neural progenitors and stem cells *in vitro*.

1996 Ian Wilmut and his research group successfully clone a mammal for the first time through the technique of somatic nuclear transfer: Dolly the sheep is born.

1997 The origin of leukaemia from haematopoietic stem cells is demonstrated: the first direct evidence of the existence of "cancer stem cells".

1998 James Thomson and his coworkers derive the first human embryonic stem cell lines.

2001 US Biotechnology company "Advanced Cell Technology" reports cloning of the first human embryos (four- to six-cell stage) to generate embryonic stem cells.

2003 Dr. Songtao Shi of the National Institutes of Health (NIH) discovers a new source of adult stem cells in deciduous teeth.

2004 The Korean researcher Hwang Woo-Suk reports having created several human embryonic stem cell lines by cell nuclear transfer using somatic cells from patients with different backgrounds. Later he will be found to have fabricated the data.

2005 Researchers at Kingston University (England) claim to have discovered a third category of stem cells, called embryonic-like stem cells derived from umbilical cord blood (Cord Blood Embryonic cells). The group of researchers argues that these cells are able to differentiate into more cell types than adult stem cells.

2006 August - Induced pluripotent stem cells (IPSC): The magazine *Cell* publishes the work of Kazutoshi Takahashi and Shinya Yamanaka, "Induction of Pluripotent Stem Cells from Mouse Embryonic and Adult fibroblast Cultures by Defined Factors".

2006 October - Newcastle University (England) Scientists create the first artificial liver cells using cord blood stem cells.

2007 January - Wake Forest University scientists, led by Dr Anthony Atala, and Harvard University report the discovery of a new type of stem cell in amniotic fluid. This could provide an alternative to the use of embryonic stem cells for research and therapy.

2007 June - Three different research groups show that skin cells can be reprogrammed at the stage of embryonic cells in mice. In the same month, Shoukhrat Mitalipov demonstrates the first creation of a primate stem cell line through the technique of somatic cell nuclear transfer.

2007 October - Mario Capecchi, Martin Evans and Oliver Smithies win the Nobel Prize in Medicine thanks to their studies on mouse embryonic stem cells that provided for the use of gene targeting strategies capable of creating genetically engineered mice (known as knockout mice) for genetic research.

2007   November - Human induced pluripotent stem cells: two similar articles, "Induction of Pluripotent Stem Cells from Adult Human Fibroblasts by Defined Factors" by Kazutoshi Takahashi and Shinya Yamanaka published in "Cells" and "Induced Pluripotent Stem Cell Lines Derived from Human Somatic Cells" by Junying Yu et al., of the research group of James Thomson published in " Science", report the generation of pluripotent stem cells from adult human fibroblasts. Now it is possible to produce a stem cell from almost all other human cells even if the risk of tumorigenesis due to c-Myc and the transfer of retroviral genes must be investigated and determined.

2008   January-Robert Lanza and colleagues at Advanced Cell Technology and UCSF obtain the first human embryonic stem cells without destroying the embryo.

2008   February - in the journal *Science*, the research group of Shinya Yamanaka describes the induction to pluripotention of stem cells from the liver and stomach of adult mice: these iPSCs seem more similar to embryonic stem cells than previously developed iPSCs and are not tumorigenic. Moreover, the genes required for producing iPSCs do not need to be inserted into specific sites so as to develop a reprogramming technique without the use of viral vectors.

2008   March - The first successful cartilage regeneration study was published. Human knee cartilage has been regenerated using autologous human mesenchymal stem cells. The work is published by clinicians of "Regenerative Sciences" medical centre.

2008   October - Sabine Conrad and colleagues in Tübingen (Germany) generate pluripotent stem cells from spermatogons of adult human testicle, by cultivating cells *in vitro* with the addition of LIF (Leukaemia Inhibitory Factor).

2009   March - Andras and collaborators set up a method for inserting specific genes into adult cells, reprogramming them to stem cells without the use of viral vectors.

2009   May - Kim and colleagues declare that the production of patient-specific "induced pluripotent stem cells" will be the definitive solution in regenerative medicine.

2010   October - in the Journal of *Experimental Medicine* Ishikawa writes that tissues created with the stem cells of a subject could be rejected because mitochondrial genomes tend to accumulate mitosis. In the same month, Vergano reports the first trial using embryonic stem cells in humans.

2011   An Israeli team produces stem cells from endangered animals.

2012   October - John Gurdon and Shinya Yamanaka are awarded the Nobel Prize in medicine for their work on iPSCs, somatic cells induced by nuclear reprogramming.

2013   August - Hannah Warren, born without a functional trachea, receives a transplant of a trachea engineered from her bone marrow stem cells.

2015   Several studies published on the *in vitro* creation of "organoid" models from human pluripotent stem cells. In particular, researchers obtained *in vitro* the first three-dimensional models of brain, pulmonary, hepatic and gastro-intestinal "organoids".

2015   February - Advanced therapy based on autologous stem cells able to restore sight to patients with severe burns of the cornea approved by the European Medicines Agency. Graziella Pellegrini e Michele De Luca (Center for Regenerative Medicine "Stefano Ferrari", University of Modena and Reggio, Italy) are the inventors of this technology.

2016 May - In the journal *Nature*, scientists of the The Rockefeller University (USA) reported the use of a novel *in vitro* system to study the post-implantation development of the human embryo. These findings could open a new understanding of early human embryonic development beyond the blastocyst stage and support the development of differentiation protocols for disease modelling and cell replacement therapy based on human embryonic stem cells.

2017 October - Scientists at the Wellcome Trust Sanger Institute created a new type of stem cell line that possesses a greater potential for development than current stem cell lines. These cells, known as Expanded Potential Stem Cells (EPSCs), can give rise to all three types of blastocyst stem cells - embryo, placenta and yolk sac.

2017 November - In the journal *Nature* Michele De Luca, together with colleagues of a multicentre collaboration, described an *ex-vivo* cell and gene therapy combined approach that permitted a regeneration of the entire human epidermis using transgenic stem cells in a young patient with a severe life-threatening form of junctional epidermolysis bullosa.

2018 Organoid technology leads a powerful way for application of stem cell research in personalized medicine based on patient-specific disease modelling and drug screening.

1.2 Definition of stem cell

Four criteria are used to define a stem cell. First, the cell must be able to divide in self-renewal to produce more of the same type of stem cells (a prerequisite to support a cellular population). Then the daughter cells, derived from a single stem cell, must be able to give rise to at least one differentiated cell type. The haematopoietic stem cells from which all the

haematopoietic progenitors originate have been known for a long time. Several stem cell types were recently discovered: nerve stem cells from which differentiate neurons, astrocytes and oligodendrocytes, myosatellite cells for regenerating skeletal muscle, perichondrium chondroblasts that can replenish cartilage, ovarian cells of the liver, preductal stem cells in pancreas, stem cells from the basal layer of epithelial tissue, stem cells of the cornea.

To date, numerous studies have focused on the mesenchymal stem cell population, discovered in the stroma of the bone marrow, which seems to be able to differentiate in fibroblasts, osteoblasts, chondroblasts, adipocytes and other cell types. The third criterion for stem cell capacity is to repopulate the tissue of origin if transplanted into a damaged recipient site. This ability has been extensively demonstrated for haematopoietic stem cells and, more recently, for hepatic progenitors and nerve stem cells. One last criterion, less shared and less consolidated, is that stem cells must contribute to a differentiated progeny *in vivo* even in the absence of tissue damage.

Recommended reading and references

1. Orkin S. *Embryonic stem cells and transgenic mice in the study of hematopoiesis.* Int J Dev Biol. 1998;42:927-934.
2. Svendsen CN, et al. *Human neural stem cells: Isolation, expansion and transplantation.* Brain Path. 1999;9:499-513.
3. Gage FH. *Mammalian neural stem cells.* Science. 2000;287:1433-1438.
4. Anderson DJ, et al. *Can stem cells cross lineage boundaries?* Nat Med. 2001;7:393-395.
5. Zhu Z, et al. *Human pluripotent stem cells: an emerging model in developmental biology.* Development. 2013 Feb;140(4):705-17. Review.
6. Hindley C, Philpott A. *The cell cycle and pluripotency.* Biochem J. 2013 Apr 15;451(2):135-43. Review.
7. Xu T, et al.. *Concise review: chemical approaches for modulating lineage-specific stem cells and*

progenitors. Stem Cells Transl Med. 2013 May;2(5):355-61. Review.

8. Liu S, et al. *Potential applications of induced pluripotent stem cells (iPSCs) in the modeling of gastrointestinal disorders.* Curr Stem Cell Res Ther. 2015;10(3):220-7.

9. Deglincerti A, et al. *Self-organization of the in vitro attached human embryo.* Nature. 2016 May 12;533(7602):251-4.

10. Yang J, et al. *Establishment of mouse expanded potential stem cells.* Nature. 2017 Oct 19;550(7676):393-397.

11. Hirsch T, et al. *Regeneration of the entire human epidermis using transgenic stem cells.* Nature. 2017 Nov 16;551(7680):327-332.

12. Perkhofer L, et al. *Importance of organoids for personalized medicine.* Per Med. 2018 Nov;15(6):461-465.

Pluripotent stem cells and reprogramming

2

Valentina Fossati   Suzanne Burstein
Madhura Nijsure   Lilianne Barbar   Silvia Velasco

2.1 Embryonic stem cells

Embryonic stem cells (ESCs) are isolated from the inner cell mass of the blastocyst and meet all the criteria for stemness previously described in Chapter 1. ESCs can be expanded virtually indefinitely while maintaining their undifferentiated state, and they can give rise to mature cells from all tissues and organs from any germ layer (ectoderm, mesoderm, or endoderm) when injected into a blastocyst. ESC research was built on previous studies using mouse testicular tumour germ cells, called embryonal carcinoma (EC) cells. When EC cells were injected into a mouse, they formed tumours; however, when they were injected into a developing blastocyst, they contributed to normal embryonic development. Thus, EC cells were considered pluripotent and expressed typical pluripotency markers in culture. Human pluripotent EC cells were also isolated soon after and, because they were easy to maintain in culture, became a powerful tool for the study of human development. However, one major limitation was the presence of chromosomal abnormalities in these cells, which prevented any potential translational application. The search for alternative sources of pluripotent stem cells led to the isolation of cells from the inner cell mass of early stage embryos. The first ESCs were isolated from

murine blastocysts by two independent laboratories (Martin Evans and Gail Martin) at the beginning of the 1980s.

Two decades later, in 1998, the laboratory of James Thomson announced the derivation of the first human ESC line. The development of human ESCs was made possible by the development of *in vitro* fertilization (IVF) clinics, that stored cryopreserved embryos from couples with fertility issues. Supernumerary embryos, which were not used by the couples and would have been otherwise discarded, were instead donated to research. The Thomson group was the first to identify the proper protocol and culture conditions to isolate the cells from the inner cell mass and expand them in a dish. Human ESCs were grown on top of gamma irradiated mouse embryonic fibroblasts, named "feeders", which are cells that are unable to proliferate (because of the irradiation), but secrete key nutrients required to expand and keep ESCs pluripotent (Figure 2.1). Under those conditions, ESCs can be expanded virtually infinitely while maintaining their undifferentiated state, which is regulated by three master transcription factors: Oct4, Nanog and Sox2. The POU5F1 gene, encoding for Oct-4 protein, was the first gene identified as the key regulator of pluripotency in murine and human ESCs. POU5F1 belongs to the POU family, which is comprised of transcription factors that regulate the expression of target genes by binding the ATGCAAAT octamer motif in promoter or enhancer regions. Nanog belongs to the family of the Homeobox proteins and is essential for early development; it is expressed in the blastocysts by the cells of the inner cell mass and later by the primordial germ cells. Sex determining region Y-box 2 (Sox2) is a member of the SoxB1 group of the Sox family, which is characterized by the high-mobility-group (HMG) DNA binding domain. It is expressed from the morula stage of development and its zygotic deletion is lethal because the embryo fails to form the epiblast. Other ESC markers expressed on the cellular surface are SSEA-3 and 4, TRA-1-60 and TRA-1-81. Moreover, ESCs are characterized by high telomerase activity and, unlike EC cells, can be

maintained in culture while preserving a stable diploid karyotype, except for possible trisomies (especially of chromosome 12 and chromosome 17), occurring after prolonged expansion. Gene expression and epigenetic analyses have revealed many differences between distinct ESC lines derived in independent laboratories and this likely reflects the different culture methods used. Thus, research has focused on the standardization of the methods of isolation, expansion and maintenance, with the goal of achieving a reproducible product that could eventually be used as a cell therapy.

In vitro, by withdrawing the key pluripotency factors from the culture medium, ESCs can be induced to generate three-dimensional spheroids named embryoid bodies (EB), disorganized masses of mature cells of ectoder-

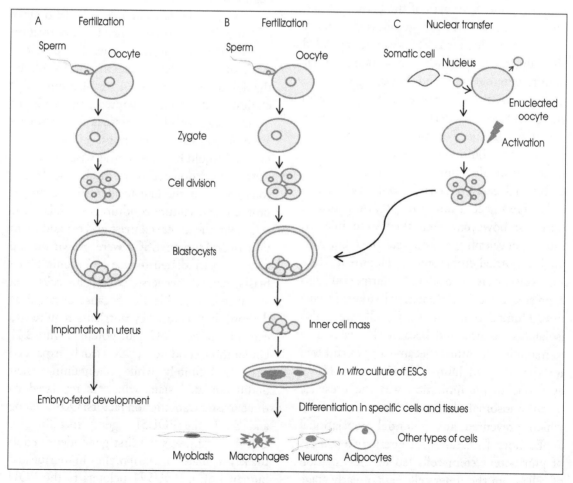

Figure 2.1. Pluripotent stem cells. A: normal development of the zygote; B: ESCs isolation and *in vitro* culture; C: somatic nuclear transfer.

mal, mesodermal and endodermal derivation. When EBs are transplanted into immuno-suppressed mice, they give rise to teratomas, disorganized masses that are comprised of mature cells of different tissues. This makes ESCs extremely powerful as a potential thera-peutic tool for regenerative medicine to replace damaged organs, but at the same time makes their use dangerous due to their tumorigenic potential or the development of uncontrolled differentiations.

Finally, it should be noted that ESCs are immunogenic; therefore, any potential therapy developed with ESC-derived cells requires an immunosuppressive treatment to avoid rejec-tion.

2.1.1 Optimization of the culture conditions

As previously described, ESCs were ini-tially isolated and expanded onto a feeder layer of mouse fibroblasts, with a culture medium containing fetal bovine serum. However, alter-native culture conditions without animal com-ponents were soon developed for therapeutic applications. The feeder layer can be replaced by extracellular matrices, secreted by tumour lines, which mimic the laminin-rich micro-en-vironment *in vivo* (e.g. Matrigel®, Geltrex®), or by synthetic substances whose formulation is chemically defined and whose production does not involve any purification process from animals (e.g. recombinant human vitronectin). Similarly, fetal bovine serum has been replaced by chemically defined media, such as the one developed by the group of James Thomson, that identified the eight minimum compo-nents to support stem cell growth in an undif-ferentiated state.

2.2 Induced Pluripotent Stem Cells (iPSC)

In 2006, the stem cell field witnessed a groundbreaking discovery when Kazutoshi Takahashi and Shinya Yamanaka published the successful reprogramming of murine somatic cells (embryonic and adult) to stem cells equivalent to ESCs. The two scientists discov-ered that the expression of 24 genes, selected for their roles in the maintenance of the ESC undifferentiated state, led to the transforma-tion of fibroblasts into cells that looked very similar and aggregated into colonies like ESCs. By eliminating one gene at a time, Takahashi and Yamanaka identified the four factors that were necessary and sufficient to reprogram somatic cells to so-called "induced pluripotent stem cells" (iPSC). These factors, known as the "Yamanaka factors" are: Oct4, Sox2, Klf4 and cMyc. Shortly after the first publication, Yamanaka reproduced the results from mouse cells and reprogrammed human somatic cells to iPSCs (Figure 2.2).

The striking potential of such a discovery in the context of regenerative medicine was immediately evident to the scientific commu-nity. For the first time, it became possible to generate stem cells from living patients, using a minimally invasive skin biopsy to expand and reprogram skin fibroblasts. Thus, patient-spe-cific iPSCs could be differentiated to any desired cell type (i.e. the cell type affected in the specific disease), following the differentia-tion protocols previously developed for ESCs. iPSCs present many advantages compared to ESCs: they do not raise ethical issues related to the use of embryos, they allow research on cells derived from patients with a known clin-ical history and genetic background, and they can be used for autologous cell transplantation, without need for immunosuppression. For his revolutionary discovery, Shinya Yamanaka was awarded the Nobel Prize in Medicine in 2012, only six years after the first publication.

The studies comparing iPSCs to ESCs ini-tially had controversial results, but there is now a consensus that iPSCs are equivalent to ESCs, and that any differences in their differentiation potential are attributable to intrinsic properties of the single lines, rather than to how they were derived. It has been shown that distinct stem cell lines have specific propensities to form dif-ferentiated cells belonging to one or another embryonic germ layer (ectoderm rather than endoderm, or mesoderm, for example). iPSCs are similar to the ESCs in their microRNA and DNA methylation profiles. However, it was shown that iPSCs retain some epigenetic features of the somatic cells from which they have been reprogrammed. This phenomenon, described as epigenetic memory, is still poorly understood, and more in-depth studies will be needed to evaluate potential consequences.

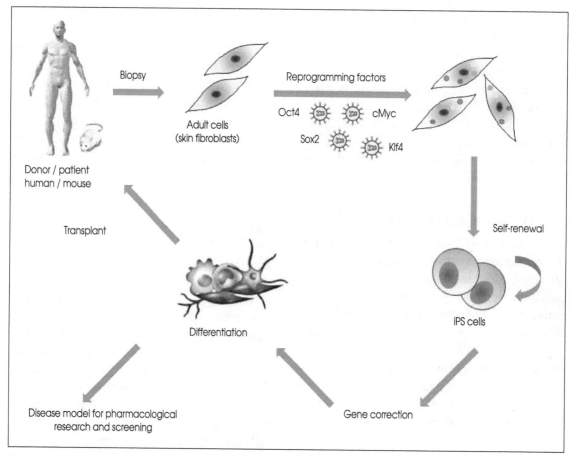

Figure 2.2. Derivation and applications of induced pluripotent stem cells (iPSCs).

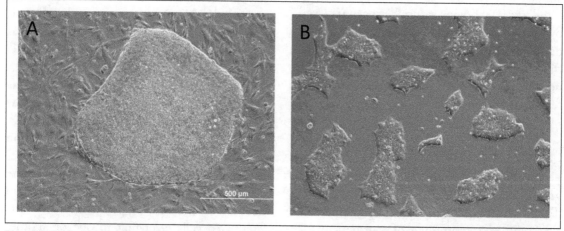

Figure 2.3. Morphological characteristics of iPSCs grown *in vitro*. A: example of iPSC colony cultivated on feeder layer of murine embryonic fibroblasts (MEF); B: iPSC colonies adapted for growth on Matrigel (feeder-free condition). Image courtesy of the New York Stem Cell Foundation Research Institute.

Reprogramming techniques have improved over the years: cMyc can be omitted and other factors have been identified, such as Lin28, Nanog, valproic acid, butyrate and other histone acetylases and methyltransferases, that increase the efficiency of reprogramming. Because the original protocol required expressing the Yamanaka factors using retroviral vectors, which integrate into the DNA, several studies aimed at developing integration-free approaches that were more suitable for clinical application. Thus, adult somatic cells have been reprogrammed using the Sendai virus (a non-integrating RNA virus), the adenovirus,

episomal vectors, and a cocktail of mRNAs coding for the Yamanaka factors.

In addition to skin fibroblasts, other somatic cell types have been successfully converted to iPSCs, with the goal of identifying alternative and less invasive sources of cells to replace the skin biopsy procedure. Blood samples are slowly replacing skin biopsies as the prominent source, because they are considered a less invasive procedure for the patient; thousands of patient blood samples are already being stored. Successful reprogramming has also been reported from non-invasive sources, such as epithelial renal cells isolated from urine and keratino-

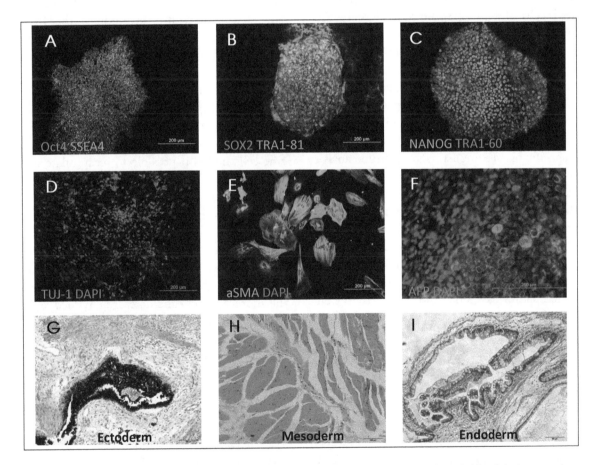

Figure 2.4. Molecular and functional characterization of a human iPSC line. (A-C) Expression of characteristic pluripotency markers: transcription factors Oct4, Sox2 and Nanog; surface molecules: SSEA4, TRA-1-81 and TRA-1 60. (D-F) Spontaneous differentiation *in vitro*: immunofluorescence for tissue markers of ectodermal derivation (neurons, TUJ-1 ectoderm-neuron-specific class III β-tubulin), of mesodermal derivation (muscle tissue, ASMA - alpha smooth muscle actin), of endodermic derivation (hepatic progenitors AFP: alpha-fetetotein). (G-I) Teratoma formation after injection of iPSCs in immunodeficient mice: histological analysis (hematoxylin – eosin) to highlight ectodermal derivation tissues (pigmented epithelium - G), mesodermal (muscle tissue - H) and endodermic (pseudo-glandular tissue - I) (from the laboratory of the New York Stem Cell Foundation Research Institute).

cytes derived from the scalp. The efficiency of the reprogramming with the original retroviral vectors is rather low, between 0.02% and 0.08%, but it has been improved with other methods, reaching 0.6-4.4% with mRNAs. On the other hand, a single iPSC colony can be expanded rapidly and can generate billions of cells in just one month. The duration of the reprogramming process depends on the method used, but on average it takes about two weeks for the first iPSC colonies to appear and a few months to expand and characterize them. The characterization of human iPSCs is based on the same assays performed with ESCs: in particular the colonies must have a round morphology, with well-defined margins and without differentiated cells (Figure 2.3). Immunofluorescence analysis must show that the cells express the typical markers, e.g. Nanog, Oct4, Sox2, and the surface molecules TRA-1 60, TRA-1-81, SSEA4. The differentiation potential is evaluated by an EB assay with gene expression analysis to show spontaneous differentiation into cells from all three germ layers (without a specific bias to one). This gene profile analysis has replaced the traditional teratoma *in vivo* assays. Finally, it is important to confirm that the cells maintained in culture retain a normal karyotype. An example of the characterization of a human iPSC line is provided in Figure 2.4. iPSC lines can now be generated in large scale (from hundreds of individuals) using fully automated platforms, such as the Global Stem Cell Array®, developed by the New York Stem Cell Foudation Research Institute.

2.3 Applications of pluripotent stem cells

a. Disease modelling

Pluripotent stem cells (PSC), which include both ESCs and iPSCs, have become a new tool for *in vitro* disease modelling of previously incurable diseases with unknown aetiology. Until a decade ago, bioptic and autoptic specimens were the only sources of human cells. Organs or tissues were not easily accessible because of highly invasive biopsy proce-

dures. With the advent of stem cell technology, patient-specific PSCs can now be differentiated to numerous cell types. Differentiation protocols are continuously being improved, generating mature cell types more similar to their *in vivo* phenotype. Because many diseases of the nervous system affect humans exclusively and lack good animal models, PSC technology has been largely applied to the field of neuroscience. In particular, PSC studies have been applied to the study of neurodegenerative disorders, an area of urgent unmet need. The incidence of neurodegenerative diseases, such as Alzheimer's or Parkinson's, is dramatically increasing in Western societies, in parallel with increasing life expectancy, but current therapies are only focused on treating symptoms rather than stopping or reverting the disease. For instance, iPSCs have been generated from patients with amyotrophic lateral sclerosis (ALS), Alzheimer's disease, Parkinson's disease, Huntington's disease, multiple sclerosis, adrenoleukodystrophies, schizophrenia, fragile X syndrome and some rare diseases. Using patient-specific cells makes it possible to recapitulate the fundamental characteristics of a disease and can help identify new mechanisms for disease pathogenesis. For example, for ALS, which is an incurable neurodegenerative disease where motor neurons are rapidly lost, iPSC modelling has identified a previously unknown role for astrocytes in the death of motor neurons. Furthermore, a novel candidate drug, named kenpaullone, has been shown to be effective as neuroprotective treatment when tested directly in human iPSC-motor neurons. Similarly, iPSCs have been used for *in vitro* disease modelling of cardiac arrhythmias. A prominent study by the group of Lior Gepstein showed successful modelling of the long QT syndrome, a rare disease characterized by sudden cardiac arrhythmia, and recapitulated the abnormal disease phenotype in a dish. One limitation of using iPSCs to model diseases is that iPSC-derived cell types show a partially immature phenotype. With the continuous improvements in differentiation protocols, however, there is tremendous promise in using iPSCs as a platform for disease modelling and drug screening.

b. Drug screen and toxicology

Over 90% of drug candidates that are tested in animals fail in clinical trials, either due to unforeseen toxicity or lack of efficacy in human cells. This is where human PSC-derived cells can be useful in allowing researchers to test novel compounds *in vitro* and to assess efficacy and toxicity on human cells before subjecting any individual to the compound. Such studies can serve as strong pre-clinical tools to better predict which compounds are likely to succeed in clinical trials.

<u>Drug screening for therapeutic compounds</u>

Human PSC-derived cells can be used to test for potential therapeutic compounds that efficiently modulate the *in vitro* disease phenotype. This is particularly useful in genetic disorders, where patient iPSC-derived cells can be used to generate the disease-affected cell type. Once an *in vitro* phenotype has been identified, a screen could be performed to identify novel therapeutic compounds that successfully reverse this phenotype. The tested compounds could be selected to target a specific pathway known to be involved in the disease (targeted screen), or to target multiple different pathways in an unbiased manner (large collection), which could lead to the identification of novel disease mechanisms. The patient iPSC-derived cells could also be used to validate the efficacy of animal-tested compounds before proceeding to the clinic (post-screen validation).

Given the value of using patient hiPSC-derived cells that successfully recapitulate the disease phenotype *in vitro* in order to perform drug testing, many different groups from various fields have taken this approach (see Table 1).

<u>Drug toxicity screening</u>

iPSC drug screens allow not only the identification of potential therapeutic compounds, but also the prediction of potential toxicity in patients. A very large number of therapeutic candidates fail during clinical trials because of toxicity issues, generally to the liver, heart, or nervous system. One of the main reasons this happens is the increased tolerability to drugs in animal models such as mice, rats and dogs (10-100-fold higher than in humans). As such, one of the main advantages of human PSC-derived cells is the ability to derive hepatocytes, cardiomyocytes, or neural cells in order to test the toxicity of novel drugs. This approach has been shown not only to successfully predict toxicity in human patients*, but also to reflect patient-to-patient variability in drug response, which proves promising in the future of personalized medicine.

c. Cell replacement therapy

Another important application of PSCs is cell therapy, which is the transplantation of functional cells differentiated from PSCs to replace those damaged by an injury or disease. Multiple studies on safety are required before the various regulatory agencies worldwide can approve the transplantation of PSC-derived cells, but the field has advanced remarkably over the last few years and there are now at least a dozen planned and ongoing clinical trials. Cellular therapies have been proposed for macular degeneration, Parkinson's disease, dystrophic epidermolysis bullosa, diabetes, myocardial infarction, and others. A clinical trial in the United Kingdom to treat age-related macular degeneration has been very successful and two patients who received a patch coated with ESC-derived retinal pigment epithelial cells (RPE) achieved a visual acuity gain of 29 and 21 letters respectively over one year. A similar study performed in Japan with RPEs derived from autologous iPSCs from two patients did not show any improvement or worsening in visual acuity, at least in the one-year follow-up, and the procedure was deemed safe without serious side effects. In 2014, the company ViaCyte announced that the first type 1 diabetes patient was treated with pancreatic islet cells derived from ESCs in a phase

Table 1. Summary of screens based on iPSC-derived cells

Genetic disease	iPSC-derived cell type	*In vitro* phenotype(s)	Screen type(s)
Age-related macular degeneration	Retinal pigment epithelium	↑ disease markers	Targeted testing
Amyotrophic lateral sclerosis	Neurons	Cell death, ↑ ER stress markers, ↑ poly(GP) protein	Targeted testing, post-screen validation, and large collection
Arterial calcification	Mesenchymal stromal cells	↑ calcification, ↓ adenosine production	Targeted testing
Autism spectrum disorder	Neurons	↓ neurite length, branch points and calcium signalling	Post-screen validation
Alzheimer's disease	Neurons	↑ amyloid beta, ↑P-tau	Targeted testing, large collection
Behçet's disease	Haematopoietic precursor cells	Differential gene expression	Targeted testing
BH4 metabolism disorders	Neurons	↓BH4, ↓neurons	Targeted testing
Catecholaminergic polymorphic ventricular tachycardia	Cardiomyocytes	Abnormal calcium signalling, induced arrhythmia, delayed afterdepolarizations	Targeted testing
Diamond-Blackfan anaemia	Haematopoietic stem cells and erythroid progenitors	↓ erythroid progenitors	Large collection
Inherited erythromelalgia	Neurons	↑ excitability	Targeted testing
Familial hypercholesteraemia	Hepatocyte-like cells	↑ apoB levels in culture media, inefficient LDL-cholesterol clearance	Large collection
Fibrodysplasia ossificans progressiva	Mesenchymal stromal cells, osteogenic cells	-	Large collection and targeted testing
Fragile X syndrome	Neural progenitor cells	↓ *FMR1* expression	Large collection
Friedreich ataxia	Neurons	↓ frataxin, ↑ oxidative stress and cell death	Targeted testing
Frontotemporal dementia	Neurons	↑ tau, ↑ER stress, ↓PGRN, ↑ cell death	Targeted testing and post-screen validation
Gaucher disease	Neurons	↓ gluco-cerebrosidase activity, ↑-synuclein	Targeted testing
Huntington's disease	Neurons	↑ cell death, differential gene expression	Targeted testing
	Brain microvascular endothelial cells	↑ migration, abnormal blood-brain barrier function	
Long QT syndrome	Cardiomyocytes	↑ QT interval, pronounced late sodium current	Targeted testing
MECP2 duplication syndrome	Neurons	↑ synaptogenesis and arborizations	Targeted testing
Mitochondrial disorders	Neural progenitor cells	↓ ATP, mitochondrial hyperpolarization, altered calcium	Large collection
Neuronal ceroid lipofuscinoses	Neural stem cells	↑ lysosomal lipid accumulation, enlarged lysosomes	Targeted testing
Neutropenia	Neutrophils	↓ Neutrophils	Targeted testing
Parkinson's disease	Neurons	↑ mitochondrial oxidant stress, oxidized dopamine, α-synuclein	Targeted testing
Pelizaeus-Merzbacher disease	Oligodendrocytes	↑ process length and number, differentiation defects, myelination deficits, PLP ER retention	Targeted testing
Pulmonary arterial hypertension	Endothelial cells	Angiogenesis and wound closure abnormalities, ↓ BMPR2	Targeted testing
Retinitis pigmentosa	Retinal pigment epithelium	↓ phagocytosis	Targeted testing
Short QT syndrome	Cardiomyocytes	↑ KCNH2, ↑ AP duration, ↑ arrhythmic events	Targeted testing
Spinal muscular atrophy	Neurons	↓ dendrite length and branching, ↑ apoptosis	Targeted testing
Spinocerebellar ataxia type 6	Purkinje cells	↓ cell survival, ↑ Cav2.1, dendrite deficits	Targeted testing
Timothy syndrome	Cardiomyocytes	↓ beating rate, ↑ contraction irregularity	Targeted testing
VCP-associated disease	Myogenic lineage cells	↑ TDP-43, ↑ ubiquitin	Targeted testing
Wolman disease	Neural stem cells	↓ lysosomal acid lipase activity, ↑ lysosomal content and lipids	Targeted testing

1/2 clinical trial and is continuing to work on cell replacement therapies. In 2014, leading international Parkinson's disease centers funded GforcePD, in a coordinated effort to advance cell replacement therapies for PD. Different teams are investigating alternative strategies for injecting dopaminergic neurons (which are dying in PD) derived either from ESCs, allogeneic iPSCs or autologous iPSCs. The autologous iPSC-neurons will not require an immunosuppressive regime, while the other strategies include 1-2 years of treatment with immunosuppressive drugs. Clinical trials are planned to begin in 2019-2020. The first clinical studies for PD cell therapies have already started outside of the GforcePD consortium, one led by an academic group in China that uses ESC-derived neural precursor cells and one led by the company ISCO using human parthenogenetic stem cell-derived neural stem cells (ISC-hpNSC®).

2.4 Somatic Cell Nuclear Transfer - SCNT

The concept of reprogramming a somatic cell to an undifferentiated state equivalent to that of ESCs was explored for a long time prior to Yamanaka's discovery. For over fifty years, researchers tried to reprogram the genome of a somatic cell by inserting it into an oocyte, the only cell type able to develop into an embryo. When the oocyte in metaphase II is enucleated and its nucleus is replaced with that of an adult somatic cell, the cytoplasmic factors of the oocyte allow the development of an embryo genetically identical to the somatic cell. This technique, called somatic cell nuclear transfer (SCNT), was initially developed in amphibious cells by Sir John Gurdon (who shared the Nobel prize with Yamanaka for his pioneering studies) in 1962 and was successfully applied to other animals, including mammals, in the following decades. The SCNT technology is the foundation for reproductive cloning, which brought to life Dolly the sheep, the first mammal cloned in 1996 in the United Kingdom through the research of Sir Ian Wilmut.

Despite many successes with oocytes from animals of different species, SCNT failed to work on human cells for a long time.

In 2013, the group of Shoukhrat Mitalipov in the United States generated for the first time human pluripotent stem cell colonies (defined as NT-ESCs, nuclear transfer-ESCs) by nuclear transfer of skin fibroblasts; similar results were obtained shortly after by the group of Dieter Egli, also in the US. It should be noted that SCNT research is limited to a few laboratories worldwide, as it raises some important ethical issues: first, although reproductive cloning in humans is forbidden, the possibility to generate NT-ESC lines is seen as risky because it could lead to improper applications that go far beyond disease modelling or cell therapy. Secondly, the SCNT protocol requires human oocytes, which are currently donated to research by female volunteers, for free or with monetary compensation, in accordance with the legislation of the country where the research takes place. For these reasons, iPSC research has developed much faster than SCNT research. Whether NT-ESCs are equivalent to or have some advantages when compared to iPSCs has yet to be verified, but the comparison of the two reprogramming methods may be useful to advance our knowledge of the molecular mechanisms of cell differentiation. A therapeutic application that derived from SCNT research involves the prevention of mitochondrial diseases. Mitochondrial diseases are chronic, genetic disorders, presenting with a wide range of severity, and inherited from the maternal oocyte that carries mutations in the mitochondrial DNA. Mitochondrial replacement therapy (MRT) is a technological innovation that could help female carriers of mtDNA mutations by using a healthy oocyte as a source of healthy mitochondria and replacing the nucleus with the mother's nucleus. Thus, through consequent *in vitro* fertilization it is possible to derive an embryo that contains nuclear DNA from the parents and mitochondrial DNA from the healthy donor.

In 2016, the Human Fertilisation and Embryology Authority (HFEA) in the UK approved the use of MRT in specific cases and in 2017 granted the first clinical mitochondrial donation license to the Newcastle Fertility Centre at the International Centre for Life in Newcastle-upon-Tyne, United Kingdom. In the United States, the Food and Drug Administration has not yet approved the procedure (as of 2018); however, in 2016, an American doctor announced the birth of a child by MRT/IVF performed in Mexico to prevent the transmission of the Leigh Syndrome. Per the statement, the newborn boy had fewer than 1% mitochondria carrying the Leigh Syndrome mutation, and this should keep the child healthy, although the risk that the mutant mitochondria could proliferate and expand cannot be ruled out.

2.5 Direct Reprogramming of Adult Somatic Cells

The finding that an adult somatic cell could be reprogrammed into a pluripotent stem cell led researchers to wonder whether it was also possible to directly transdifferentiate an adult somatic cell into another somatic cell type of a different tissue. Based on pioneering studies on the conversion of fibroblasts to muscle cells and B-lymphocytes to macrophages, the laboratory of Marius Wernig showed in 2010 that murine fibroblasts can be reprogrammed to cells derived from a different germ layer, such as neurons (called iN, or induced neurons). Following this work, murine and human fibroblasts were directly differentiated into cardiomyocytes, blood cells, hepatocytes, and others. The direct differentiation is achieved by forced expression of specific exogenous transcription factors, for example Brn2, Ascl1 and Myt1l (denoted BAM) in the earliest protocols for iN generation. Neurons derived by direct reprogramming are morphologically identical to primary neurons, express typical neuronal markers, develop action potentials and form synapses. In the past few years, studies on direct reprogramming have multiplied, and scientists have aimed to narrow down the minimum transcription factors required to achieve particular cell fates. Protocols have been developed to obtain specific neuronal subtypes, such as dopaminergic neurons, which degenerate in Parkinson's disease, as well as various types of glial cells, using different cocktails of transcription factor expression.

The use of direct reprogramming to generate the cell type of interest bypasses a pluripotent stage, and thus may better preserve epigenetic signatures and reduce phenotypic variability. Despite rapid progress in this field in recent years, some challenges still remain. As is the case for the reprogramming of iPSCs, the forced expression of transcription factors was initially obtained via viral vectors, but there has been extensive research and development of alternative methodologies that can make the cells generated in this manner more suitable for clinical use. The efficiency of direct reprogramming varies greatly and depends on the starting cell type: in particular, human cells have lower efficiencies than murine cells, and blood cells are more difficult to reprogram than skin fibroblasts. Furthermore, reprogramming efficiency decreases from embryonic cells to neonatal cells to adult cells. The PSC field as a whole still faces the challenge of generating authentic, fully mature cell types that are equivalent to adult primary cells. Whether these problems can be overcome in the future with the advancement of culture techniques and the optimization of the present protocols remains to be demonstrated. In the case of the nervous system, for example, the complex three-dimensional microenvironment provides fundamental signals for the maturation and functioning of the different neuronal types, signals that cannot be faithfully reproduced *in vitro* in a classical monolayer culture system. This concern is relevant for cells generated by both direct reprogramming and differentiation from PSCs and has led to the development and optimization of 3D culture systems.

2.5.1   3D Organoids

Stem Cells show an intrinsic ability to self-organize and differentiate *in vitro* to generate a variety of complex three-dimensional (3D) structures that resemble organs of different types, and are therefore collectively referred to as "3D organoids". 3D Organoids can be derived from pluripotent stem cells (PSCs), including embryonic stem cells (ESCs) and induced pluripotent stem cells (iPSCs), and also from adult stem cells. Since the first human intestinal organoids were developed in 2009 in the laboratory of Hans Clevers, the technique has rapidly improved, leading to protocols for the generation of organoids resembling the majority of human organs, such as the stomach, pancreas, prostate, breast, liver, eyes, lungs, heart, and brain.

Brain organoids hold great promise for recapitulating key features of human brain development and function, the study of which *in vivo* poses major challenges. Mammalian brain development occurs largely *in utero*, and important ethical considerations limit access to the developing human brain. In addition, due to the limited regenerative capacity of the brain, brain tissue cannot easily be grown and expanded *in vitro*.

Human brain organoids have been generated using a variety of protocols that produce tissue with different identities and properties; some take advantage of the intrinsic capacity of stem cells to self-organize and orchestrate early neural developmental steps (self-organized organoids), while others involve the use of exogenous factors that activate specific signalling pathways to drive selected developmental programs (pre-patterned organoids). While self-organized organoids generally produce tissue with broad regional identities (whole-brain organoids), the use of exogenous factors in pre-patterned models can promote the formation of specific brain regions, such as the cerebral cortex, hippocampus, midbrain, hypothalamus, cerebellum, anterior pituitary, or retina. Among the variety of brain organoid protocols developed during the past few years, many focus on modelling cortical development. The generation of human cortical organoids allows the study of human-specific features of brain development that cannot be studied in animal models, due to inter-species differences and the uniqueness of the human cerebral cortex. For instance, cortical organoids can produce human-relevant cell types, such as outer radial glia (oRG) progenitors; oRGs are not found in the mouse but are present in large numbers in gyrencephalic primates, and have been suggested to have played an essential role in the evolutionary increase in human cortex size and complexity.

The recent development of single cell RNA-sequencing (scRNA-seq) provides a great opportunity to characterize organoids at an unprecedented molecular level and, importantly, to understand the extent to which *in vitro* derived cells resemble their *in vivo* human counterparts. Comparison of gene expression profiles in whole-brain organoids and human fetal brains showed that the transcriptional profiles of organoids, cultured for up to 100 days, correlate with early to mid-gestational stages of brain development.

One important issue, which particularly affects organoids designed to self-assemble with minimal addition of extrinsic factors, is poor reproducibility, across individual organoids, of the variety of cell types produced and their relative proportions. Models involving the use of exogenous factors to influence patterning, however, show promise with regard to better reproducibility. Another concern is that cortical organoids contain mostly cells deriving from the dorsal telencephalon (pallium) and lack cells from other embryonic regions; for instance, GABAergic interneurons, which originate from the ventral telencephalon. The presence of GABAergic interneurons in addition to glutamatergic neurons is essential for the potential formation of cortical circuits in brain organoids. Recent studies have addressed this issue by fusing organoids patterned to dorsal and ventral regional identities. Microglia, immune cells that regulate synaptic pruning and thus contribute to the development and maintenance of neural circuits, are also missing in most of the current cortical models. Finally, the lack of endothelial cells and vasculature limits the diffusion of nutrients and oxygen, and thus the prolonged growth potential of organoids. Recently, researchers combined human PSC-derived neural progenitors, endothelial cells, mesenchymal stem cells, and microglia precursors on chemically defined polyethylene glycol hydrogels to establish 3D neural constructs with microglia and vascular networks, pointing towards a possible solution to these obstacles. Finally, additional levels of organization, such as cortical layering and the specificity of neuronal connections, will need to be established in order to fully recapitulate brain function and to generate cortical circuits.

Despite these limitations, several studies have shown that *in vitro* organoids, by recapitulating key features of *in vivo* human brain development, can be used to model brain diseases in a 3D, multicellular environment. For instance, organoids generated from patient-derived iPSCs have been used to investigate the molecular mechanisms underlying neurodevelopmental disorders, such as microcephaly and Miller Dieker syndrome, a

severe congenital form of lissencephaly. Brain organoids have also been employed to study microcephaly induced by Zika virus infection. Moreover, patient-derived organoids hold promise for modelling complex polygenic disorders, including those with unidentified risk loci, such as autism spectrum disorder (ASD) or schizophrenia. A comparison between organoids from patients with severe idiopathic ASD and their unaffected relatives suggested molecular and cellular alterations that may underlie this disorder. Brain organoids have also been used to model Timothy syndrome, a severe neurodevelopmental disease characterized by ASD and epilepsy. One open question is whether brain organoids can be used to study late-onset neurodevelopmental and neurodegenerative diseases that appear postnatally and require years to mature. Remarkably, recent studies have suggested that brain organoids can recapitulate some aspects, perhaps the earliest events, of late-onset neurodegenerative diseases such as Alzheimer's disease (AD).

The opportunities for disease modelling have further expanded with the introduction of genome editing technologies, such as CRISPR/Cas9. Patient-derived organoids

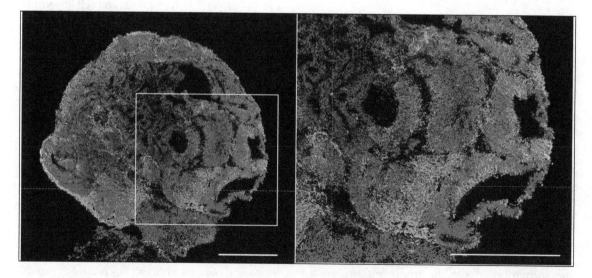

Figure 2.5. Immunohistochemical analysis showing the expression of the dorsal forebrain progenitor marker PAX6 (long red) and the pan-neuronal marker MAP2 (green) in a brain organoid derived from the H9 (WA09) ESC line. Note the organized progenitor zone where PAX6 positive cells line ventricle-like cavities. The "whole-brain organoid" was generated according to a method previously described (Quadrato G. et al., *Nature* 2017) and imaged 30 days after initiation of the protocol. DAPI (blue) labels nuclei. Scale bar is 500 μm. Image from Silvia Velasco (Paola Arlotta laboratory, Department of Stem Cell and Regenerative Biology, Harvard University).

where disease loci have been repaired using genome-editing techniques might, eventually, be a potential option for replacing impaired brain tissue via transplantation.

Organoids have also been grown from primary cancers, providing a unique opportunity to investigate how individual genetic backgrounds affect tumour properties, such as drug response. In principle, organoids could allow rapid *ex vivo* testing of drug efficacy on affected tissue from individual patients, to allow selection of the best-suited treatment regime.

Moreover, organoids provide a platform for the development of novel therapeutic strategies: high throughput screening enables a large number of compounds to be tested on brain organoids, and there are a variety of disease phenotypes that can be evaluated using automated methods. Furthermore, transcriptome sequencing of patient-derived organoids may both allow the identification of novel diagnostic biomarkers and enable more personalized treatment strategies (Figure 2.5).

To conclude, despite their reductionist nature, 3D organoids replicate key features of organ development and function and thus represent an invaluable tool to model human physiological and pathological processes, identify new therapeutic targets and diagnostic biomarkers for neurological diseases, and eventually, develop novel personalized cell-based therapies.

2.5.2 Bioreactors, microfluidics and organs-on-a-chip

Engineering the cell microenvironment using bioreactors has been proven to be an effective tool for truly modelling the stem cell niche, with greater control over regulatory factors, such as oxygen, paracrine and autocrine signalling, extracellular matrix, and mechanical, electrical and shear forces. Bioreactors are developed based on the understanding of physiological systems and tissue dynamics. Examples of some bioreactors used to culture cell layers or organoids include spinner flasks, rotating wall bioreactors and perfusion bioreactors. Incor-

poration of bioreactors that can recapitulate physiological mechanical loading in connective tissues has been shown to promote osteogenic, tenogenic or chondrogenic differentiation. The landmark study of brain organoids by Lancaster involves the use of spinner flasks to facilitate nutrient flow through stem cell-derived brain organoids. Several groups have adapted spinning bioreactors to their organoid models because they improve oxygen and nutrient perfusion. One issue that limits the use of bioreactors is that they consume large volumes of cell culture media, thereby making the process of generating functional tissue very expensive. To circumvent this problem, more labs are turning towards miniaturizing these systems to be less expensive and more efficient. For instance, Qian et al. recently developed cost-effective miniature spinning bioreactors for developing brain-region-specific organoids that can fit a regular 12-well tissue culture plate. These models can potentially be adapted to high-throughput screening systems. Microfluidic systems are another alternative that provides spatio-temporal control over 2D or 3D stem cell microenvironments. Micro-Electro-Mechanical Systems (MEMS) can be used to control specific electrical and mechanical features of cell microenvironments to direct stem cell differentiation. Miniaturization of complex stem cell-derived tissue systems has also paved a way for organ-on-a-chip systems that simulate the physiological activities of whole organs; models have been developed for heart, kidney, lung, liver, intestine, retina, bone, brain, and multiorgan chips (for example containing lung, liver and heart cells) have been devised to evaluate the metabolism and toxicity of a given drug.

In summary, the pluripotent stem cell field has made tremendous progress in a relatively short time and constantly continues to grow. Over time, PSCs have proven to be of great value for disease modelling, drug screening and various forms of cell therapy, and the potential of these cells will continue to expand even further as newer 3D models and reprogramming strategies are improved.

Recommended reading and references

1. Evans MJ, Kaufman MH. *Establishment in culture of pluripotential cells from mouse embryos.* Nature. 1981;292:154–156.

2. Martin GR. *Isolation of a pluripotent cell line from early mouse embryos cultured in medium conditioned by teratocarcinoma stem cells.* Proc Natl Acad Sci USA. 1981;78:7634–7638.

3. Thomson JA, Itskovitz-Eldor J, Shapiro SS, *et al. Embryonic stem cell lines derived from human blastocysts.* Science. 1998;282:1145–1147.

4. Takahashi K1, Yamanaka S. *Induction of pluripotent stem cells from mouse embryonic and adult fibroblast cultures by defined factors.* Cell. 2006 Aug 25;126(4):663-76. Epub 2006 Aug 10.

5. Takahashi K1, Tanabe K, Ohnuki M, Narita M, Ichisaka T, Tomoda K, Yamanaka S. *Induction of pluripotent stem cells from adult human fibroblasts by defined factors.* Cell. 2007 Nov 30;131(5):861-72.

6. Tachibana M, Amato P, Sparman M, Gutierrez NM, Tippner-Hedges R, Ma H, Kang E, Fulati A, Lee HS, Sritanaudomchai H, Masterson K, Larson J, Eaton D, Sadler-Fredd K, Battaglia D, Lee D, Wu D, Jensen J, Patton P, Gokhale S, Stouffer RL, Wolf D, Mitalipov S. *Human embryonic stem cells derived by somatic cell nuclear transfer.* Cell. 2013 Jun 6;153(6):1228-38. doi: 10.1016/j.cell.2013.05.006

7. Di Giorgio FP, Carrasco MA, Siao MC, Maniatis T, Eggan K. *Non-cell autonomous effect of glia on motor neurons in an embryonic stem cell-based ALS model.* Nat Neurosci. 2007 May;10(5):608-14

8. Maroof AM, Keros S, Tyson JA, Ying SW, Ganat YM, Merkle FT, Liu B, Goulburn A, Stanley EG, Elefanty AG, Widmer HR, Eggan K, Goldstein PA, Anderson SA, Studer L. *Directed differentiation and functional maturation of cortical interneurons from human embryonic stem cells.* Cell Stem Cell. 2013 May 2;12(5):559-72. doi: 10.1016/j.stem.2013.04.008.

9. Yang YM1, Gupta SK, Kim KJ, Powers BE, Cerqueira A, Wainger BJ, Ngo HD, Rosowski KA, Schein PA, Ackeifi CA, Arvanites AC, Davidow LS, Woolf CJ, Rubin LL. *A small molecule screen in stem-cell-derived motor neurons identifies a kinase inhibitor as a candidate therapeutic for ALS.* Cell Stem Cell. 2013 Jun 6;12(6):713-26. doi: 10.1016/j.stem.2013.04.003. Epub 2013 Apr 18.

10. Zhang Y, Pak C, Han Y, Ahlenius H, Zhang Z, Chanda S, Marro S, Patzke C, Acuna C, Covy J, Xu W, Yang N, Danko T, Chen L, Wernig M, Südhof TC. *Rapid single-step induction of functional neurons from human pluripotent stem cells.* Neuron. 2013 Jun 5;78(5):785-98. doi: 10.1016/j.neuron.2013.05.029.

11. Elitt MS, Barbar L, Tesar PJ. *Drug screening for human genetic diseases using iPSC models.* Hum Mol Genet. 2018 Aug 1;27(R2):R89-R98. doi: 10.1093/hmg/ddy186.

12. Barker RA1, Parmar M2, Studer L3, Takahashi J4. *Human Trials of Stem Cell-Derived Dopamine Neurons for Parkinson's Disease: Dawn of a New Era.* Cell Stem Cell. 2017 Nov 2;21(5):569-573. doi: 10.1016/j.stem.2017.09.014.

13. Drost J, Clevers H. *Organoids in cancer research.* Nat Rev Cancer. 2018 Jul;18(7):407-418. doi: 10.1038/s41568-018-0007-6. Review.

14. Ronaldson-Bouchard K, Ma SP, Yeager K, Chen T, Song L, Sirabella D, Morikawa K, Teles D, Yazawa M, Vunjak-Novakovic G. *Advanced maturation of human cardiac tissue grown from pluripotent stem cells.* Nature. 2018 Apr;556(7700):239-243. doi: 10.1038/s41586-018-0016-3.

15. Boj SF, Hwang CI, Baker LA, Chio II, Engle DD, Corbo V, Jager M, Ponz-Sarvise M, Tiriac H, Spector MS, Gracanin A, Oni T, Yu KH, van Boxtel R, Huch M, Rivera KD, Wilson JP, Feigin ME, Öhlund D, Handly-Santana A, Ardito-Abraham CM, Ludwig M, Elyada E, Alagesan B, Biffi G, Yordanov GN, Delcuze B, Creighton B, Wright K, Park Y, Morsink FH, Molenaar IQ, Borel Rinkes IH, Cuppen E, Hao Y, Jin Y, Nijman IJ, Iacobuzio-Donahue C, Leach SD, Pappin DJ, Hammell M, Klimstra DS, Basturk O, Hruban RH, Offerhaus GJ, Vries RG, Clevers H, Tuveson DA. *Organoid models of human and mouse ductal pancreatic cancer.* Cell. 2015 Jan 15;160(1-2):324-38. doi: 10.1016/j.cell.2014.12.021.

16. Clevers H. Modeling *Development and Disease with Organoids.* Cell. 2016 Jun 16;165(7):1586-1597. doi: 10.1016/j.cell.2016.05.082.

17. Brown J, Quadrato G, Arlotta P. *Studying the Brain in a Dish: 3D Cell Culture Models of Human Brain Development and Disease.* Curr Top Dev Biol. 2018;129:99-122. doi: 10.1016/bs.ctdb.2018.03.002.

18. Kelava 1, Lancaster MA. *Dishing out mini-brains: Current progress and future prospects*

in brain organoid research. Dev Biol. 2016 Dec 15;420(2):199-209. doi: 10.1016/j.ydbio.2016.06.037.

19. Di Lullo E, Kriegstein AR. *The use of brain organoids to investigate neural development and disease.* Nat Rev Neurosci. 2017 Oct;18(10):573-584. doi: 10.1038/nrn.2017.107.

20. Paşca SP. *The rise of three-dimensional human brain cultures.* Nature. 2018 Jan 24;553(7689):437-445. doi: 10.1038/nature25032.

Adult Stem Cells

3

Francesco Alviano   Laura Bonsi

General considerations

The ethical concerns specific to embryonic stem cell research and its possible implications have led scientists to find alternative sources, such as somatic stem cells.

Somatic stem cells, for convenience defined as "Adult Stem Cells", are responsible for producing mature cells of the tissue in which they reside. These cells are present in the human organism from the earliest stages of development following those of embryonic stem cells and, therefore, in theory not comparable to the latter.

Compared to embryonic stem cells, adult stem cells have differences in *in vitro* self-renewal: while embryonic stem cells can be cultivated for more than 150 passages maintaining an undifferentiated stage, adult stem cells undergo an irreversible proliferation arrest known as senescence that involves progressive differentiation up to a mature stage. This is believed to be due to levels of telomerase activity lower than those of embryonic cells. Moreover, compared to the ESCs, called pluripotent, in general the adult stem cells show a reduced range of possible differentiations.

Since a stem cell component can exist in every tissue, it could mean the existence in the organism of multiple sources of stem cells usable in autologous transplants. It is therefore important to investigate the actual proliferative and differentiative potentials of these cells, in order to understand their actual ability to generate multiple cellular histotypes characteristic of different tissues and organs.

Examples of cells able to reconstruct the tissue in which they reside include myosatellite cells in skeletal muscle, chondroprogenitors in the perichondrium, osteoprogenitors in the periosteum, adipose progenitor cells in vascular stromal fraction, oval cells in the liver, preductal stem cells in the pancreas, basal stem cells of epithelial tissue and neural stem cells in the brain. In addition, some studies have shown that some of these types of cells can differentiate into cell types of other tissues.

For example, bone marrow-derived mesenchymal stem cells can differentiate not only in cartilage, bone and adipose tissue but also in haematopoietic stem cells, even in neurons and glia cells, restore the expression of dystrophin in skeletal muscle, give origin to hepatic cells, and provide cells for neovascularization.

Moreover, it has been shown that stem cells derived from nervous tissue and muscle tissue can differentiate into blood cells. Finally, stem cells derived from the dermis can differentiate into skeletal muscle, adipose tissue, cartilage and bone. Several papers seem to demonstrate a greater "plasticity" of these cells, although the actual differentiative potential is still under discussion. Therefore, these characteristics make adult stem cells an important object of study because the degree of "plasticity" of somatic stem cells must still be defined. The hope of using these cells for the treatment of many diseases could be concrete, despite the stemness not being equal to embryonic stem cells.

The proliferative and differentiative potentials of stem cells residing in different adult tissues will be treated extensively in the following paragraphs.

3.1 Biological characteristics

The criteria described in Chapter 1 for defining stemness have been used to characterize haematopoietic stem cells (HSCs). A single HSC can undergo self-maintenance divisions by generating a clone that can give rise to all the blood cytotypes: it can replace, after transplantation, the haematopoietic system of recipients that were lethally irradiated; it can engraft and differentiate even if the recipients were healthy. In mice, HSCs have been purified to obtain a homogeneous population using antigenic characteristics of the cell surface: HSCs express CD45, Thy1, C-Kit and SCA-1 but not the *lineage* antigens (Lin). Interestingly, murine HSCs do not even express significant levels of typical stem cell markers, such as the CD34 antigen.

Moreover, HSCs can be purified by fluorescence-activated cell sorting (FACS), because of their ability to eliminate Hoechst dye by using the transporter ABC/breast cancer receptor protein (BCRP-1). This Hoechst^{low} population is generally called Side Population (SP). In humans the purification of HSCs can be achieved using a similar criterion. Human HSCs also do not express *lineage* antigens, do not express CD 38, but are positive for CD45, C-Kit and Thy1. Unlike mouse HSCs, the majority of human HSCs are present in the CD34$^+$ fraction of bone marrow, peripheral blood, and umbilical cord blood. It is unclear whether human HSCs have been purified to almost reach homogeneity, as it has been done for murine HSCs, since the characterization of human HSCs depends on a xenograft. A minimum of 200-500 cells are required to obtain a haematopoietic progeny in immunodeficient mice or sheep and it has not yet been demonstrated whether this depends on the xenotropic

nature of the transplant assay or whether it can reflect the purity deficiency of human HSCs. A test of the fact that a single HSC can differentiate into multiple haematopoietic lineages comes from transplants of a single HSC in mice. Even more reliable are the data obtained through a retroviral marking technique. As retroviruses integrate into random regions of host cell DNA, the flanking sequences of the integrating virus are cell-specific and can be used to follow the offspring of single cells *in vitro* and *in vivo*. This approach has been exploited to demonstrate that a single cell of both mice and humans can give rise to multiple progeny cells.

In addition, this technique has allowed to show that single HSCs undergo self-renewal divisions and that these daughter cells have multiple differentiative potentiality in various lineages (see Chapter 4).

These criteria have recently been applied to identify other adult stem cells. For example, neural stem cells can be purified from the human brain by using a combination of antibodies against CD133 and CD24. The CD133$^+$ CD24$^-$ cells generate neural spheres that can be further cultivated and can give rise to astrocytes, oligodendrocytes and neurons.

Unlike ESCs, adult stem cells have a lower self-renewal capacity, partly due to a lack of high levels of telomerase activity. Moreover, the range of possible differentiated cells that can be generated by an adult stem cell is reduced; generally, adult stem cells generate daughter cells that can differentiate into cells belonging to the tissue of origin and not in other cell types.

3.2 Mesenchymal Stem Cells

Within the study of haematopoiesis, at the end of the 1960s, pioneering works highlighted the presence in the bone marrow stroma of an interesting stem cell population, different from that of the HSCs. The interest of researchers has shifted from the role of the stroma as a mere support to haematopoiesis to the potential of the "new" stem cells contained in it.

Alexander Friedenstein, Maureen Owen and their collaborators were the first to use *in vitro* cultures and transplants in animal models to characterize the bone marrow stromal cells. Since the extracellular matrix layer is very thin, a single-cell suspension of stromal and haematopoietic bone marrow cells can be easily obtained by aspiration from the iliac crest. Once they are seeded at low-density, marrow stromal cells (Bone Marrow Stromal Cells-BMSCs) adhere quickly and can then be separated from non-adherent haematopoietic cells by repeated washings. In appropriate cultural conditions, every single precursor will form a distinct colony, which was initially defined as CFU-F (Colony Forming Unit-Fibroblast).

The terms CFU-F or marrow stromal fibroblasts have mostly been abandoned and have now been replaced by others, such as marrow stromal cells, mesenchymal stem cells (MSCs), mesenchymal progenitor cells (MPCs); there is not yet a single nomenclature, but all the definitions refer to a particular type of adherent, mononuclear cell, derived from marrow, grown in a classical medium supplemented only with FBS (Fetal Bovine Serum). Such cells have a fibroblast-like morphology, with a limited amount of cytoplasm, few mitochondria and a poorly developed Golgi apparatus; they can be expanded *ex vivo* and have a differentiation potential towards cytotypes of mesenchymal origin, such as osteocytes, chondrocytes, adipocytes, tendon cells, myotubes, astrocytes and stroma to support haematopoiesis (Figure 3.1).

Using the fibroblast clonogenic assay (CFU-F), the estimated frequency of mesenchymal cells in the bone marrow nucleated cells was 1 in 10^4 to 10^5 mononuclear cells. In order to verify the homogeneity of the colonies, *in vitro* differentiation tests were performed, which showed the presence of subpopulations in the mesenchymal stromal population, including cells with only osteogenic potential

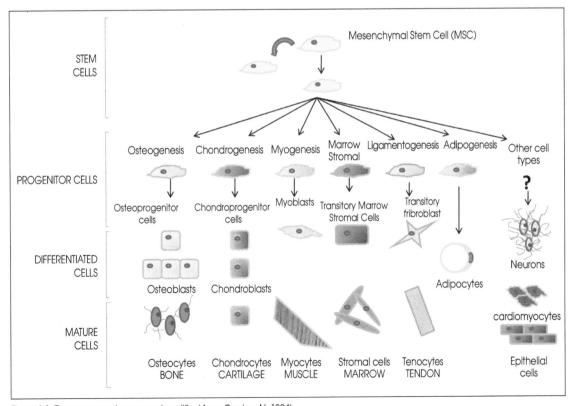

Figure 3.1. The mesengenic process (modified from Caplan AI, 1994)

or cells capable of differentiating also in the adipogenic or chondrogenic direction.

The heterogeneity of the bone marrow stromal cell population was also confirmed by *in vivo* studies showing that only some colonies derive from mesenchymal stem cells, while the others originate from more mature precursors, with a limited differentiation potential. Hence the need for a phenotypic characterization that allows to identify and isolate the true mesenchymal stem cells.

Already in 1992, studies conducted on foetal liver cells had hypothesized the existence of a precursor common to the mesenchymal and haematopoietic progeny, characterized as CD34+, CD38-, HLA DR-. In the bone marrow microenvironment, stromal cells produce the growth factors necessary to promote the activation, proliferation and differentiation of the responsive stem cells. Most stem cells are, in fact, quiescent (i.e. in G0) and only a small fraction responds to paracrine messages, by differentiating into the commissioned haematopoietic CD34+ or into mesenchymal stem cells.

The CD34 marker, identified as a sialomucin, is expressed in haematopoietic progenitors and vascular endothelial cells but is not present on *ex vivo* expanded mesenchymal stem cells. It is possible that this antigen is expressed in cells directly isolated from the bone marrow, but is "downregulated" or modified in a molecule not reacting with the anti-CD34 after *in vitro* culture. Moreover, the antigen could be present in the cells derived from the fetal liver and is not, however, very expressed in adult marrow cells. It should be emphasized that *in vitro* culture conditions, such as flask surface adhesion, fetal bovine serum or growth factors, may result in loss or acquisition of surface receptors, thus altering the pattern of markers. In fact, it is believed that the phenotypic fingerprint undergoes continuous modifications in response to the microenvironment both *in vitro* and *in vivo*; this is why a clear and unequivocal characterization has not yet been obtained.

In general, mesenchymal stem cells express numerous receptors that are important for cell adhesion and interaction with haematopoietic cells. They express adhesion molecules, growth factor receptors and cytokines, integrins and other markers, while they are negative for haematopoietic markers, such as CD45, expressed on myeloid cells, and LPS receptor (CD14), expressed on monocytes.

In order to characterize mesenchymal stem cells, the simultaneous presence of three specific monoclonal cell surface markers was described in the late 1980s.

The first of these is called SH2 and represents a specific epitope of a glycoprotein of molecular mass 92kDa, known as Endoglin CD105 or TGFbeta IIIr. This growth factor receptor binds TGFbetaI and III to high affinity, but not TGFbetaII; it plays a fundamental role in the cell-to-cell interactions of endothelial cells and during the vasculogenic process. Moreover, it mediates interactions between MSCs and haematopoietic cells in the marrow and finally could play a key role in chondrogenic differentiation by signal transduction. The other two markers are known as SH3 and SH4, two different epitopes of CD73, an antigen present in many cellular types and in particular in lymphoid tissue but not in haematopoietic precursors or osteocytes. CD73 is a membrane protein of 67 kDa, anchored by glycophosphatidylinositol, with nucleotidasic activity and the ability to transduce the signal. It catalyzes the dephosphorylation of ribo/desoxy ribonucleotides in the corresponding nucleosides; this activity could be important in the recovery of purines and pyrimidines presumably in all the cells where CD73 is expressed. In the marrow microenvironment, the CD73 could mediate cell-to-cell interactions and represents a common element between stromal and lymphocytic development.

Subsequentially, interesting markers of mesenchymal cells emerged, such as the antigen recognized by the monoclonal antibody SB10, identified as ALCAM (Activated leukocyte-cell adesion molecule), or CD166, a glycoprotein involved in osteogenic differentiation.

More recent studies have described that mesenchymal stem cells can express the low-affinity receptor for the nerve growth factor (LNGFR). This feature has recently been successfully utilized to develop a method of cell selection by immunomagnetic sorting; the binding to the anti-LNGFR allows to obtain a phenotypically and functionally homogeneous population, able to proliferate *in vitro*, to self-maintain, to differentiate in all the mesenchymal progeny and to support haematopoiesis.

3.3 Plasticity: what is it?

"It seems like everyone wants to be the first to show that an arm can give rise to a leg, and a nose to an ear."

(S.J. Morrison. Stem cell potential: Can anything make anything? Current Biology 2001; 11:R7-R9)

Several articles have been published in recent years suggesting that the previous dogma of tissue-specificity for adult stem cells may be surpassed. The alleged ability of stem cells to acquire the fate of cell types other than those of the source tissue has been termed "adult stem cell plasticity". These articles have generated considerable excitement in the scientific community, as well as significant skepticism: the majority of the studies still wait for an independent confirmation.

Most studies showed plasticity using cells derived from bone marrow.

It has been shown that human MSCs have osteogenic, adipogenic and chondrogenic *in vitro* potential. The necessary factors for induction in these lineages are known, although the biochemical pathways that underlie these processes have not yet been clarified. But the differentiative potential of MSCs would seem not to stop here. The possibility has been highlighted that, under the action of specific differentiating factors, it is possible to obtain *in vitro* cells apparently commissioned in myocyte lineages, morphologically similar to the multinucleate muscle striated cells and expressing transcription factors implicated in myogenic commitment, such as Myo-D and myogenin, as well as muscle-specific proteins, such as desmin, skeletal myosin, alpha-actinin. In endothelial lineages, characterized by the expression of proteins such as the Von Willebrand factor and the functional ability to create capillary-like structures in the basal membrane matrix assay (Matrigel); in neural lineages, with the expression of high levels of specific proteins and with the adoption of the characteristic morphology of the neuronal cells; in hepatocyte lineage, with the functional (uptake of di-Ac-LDL, release of albumin) and morphological characteristics of hepatic cells.

In vivo studies are based largely on the analysis of animal tissues that have received lethal doses of radiation and a bone marrow transplant or bone marrow-derived cells from a donor. In fact, numerous studies have shown the presence in the various tissues of the recipient, though with very low efficiencies, of donor-derived cells belonging to mesodermal lineages different from the haematopoietic lineage. Tissues in which donor contribution has been observed include the skeletal muscle, the endothelium and the cardiac muscle. Studies suggesting that bone marrow cells can differentiate *in vivo* in tissue cells from different germ layers are even more surprising. In fact, various articles have been published suggesting that bone marrow cells could differentiate *in vivo* in cells with neuroectodermal morphology and phenotype. The differentiation of these mesodermal cells into cells with endodermal morphology and phenotype has also been shown. Petersen and collaborators were the first to show that the oval cells in a regenerating liver could derive from bone marrow. Similar discoveries have since been reported by numerous groups: cells derived from donor bone marrow have been found in epithelial tissues belonging to the recipient, such as the skin and the lungs. In summary, these studies suggest that multipotent cells with a remarkable "plasticity" are present in the bone marrow and possibly in other tissues.

3.3.1. Plasticity: possible mechanisms

"(…) consolidated laws are not dogmas (which elicited the comment that germ layers are more important to embryologists than to embryos) (…)"

(P. Bianco, Bone Marrow Stromal Stem Cells: Nature Biology and Potential Applications. Stem Cells 2001;19:180-192)

Many mechanisms may be subject to this apparent plasticity: tissue-specific stem cells may be present in different organs. Plasticity, then, could be the result of the fusion of donor cells with cells residing in an organ; cells could go through de-and redifferentiation processes; or stem cells could persist in post-natal life. There are data supporting each of the four models and the issue is still extensively debated.

3.3.2. Tissue-specific stem cells present in different organs

It is well known that HSCs come out of the bone marrow space, circulate in peripheral blood and can find a "home" in organs or tissues other than bone marrow. This appears to be the case of the muscle, as demonstrated by two studies in which the transplantation of muscle cells in lethally irradiated mice was able to repopulate the haematopoietic system due to HSC persistence in the muscle. A further example is the presence of cells with the characteristics of the oval cells, as the progenitors for the hepatic and biliary epithelial cells, in the bone marrow. Or vice versa, the contribution of bone marrow-derived cells to liver regeneration could be the result of the infusion of hepatic oval cells resident in the marrow. Given the enormous therapeutic potential of cells with such characteristics, it is important to clarify the possible *in vitro* and *in vivo* differentiation of the stem cell population residing in the bone marrow stroma.

3.3.3. Plasticity as a result of the fusion of donor cells with resident cells

The notion that cellular fusion can change the fate of a cell is not new. Studies of heterokaryons were carried out already at the beginning of the twentieth century; many studies had shown that the fate of cells can be changed by the formation of heterokaryons. For example, the fusion of a myoblast with a fibroblast induces the expression of muscle proteins in the fibroblast. This indicates that the cytoplasm of myoblasts contains factors that induce muscle differentiation in non-muscle cells. Two recent studies have documented that co-culture of adult tissue cells with embryonic stem cells leads to cellular fusion. In fact, the co-culture of murine bone marrow with Embryonic Stem Cells causes the "transdifferentiation" of bone marrow cells into ESCs. Although several *in vitro* studies have shown that the "switch" of lineage is also possible without the co-culture of adult stem cells with ESCs, no single study has excluded the possibility of cellular fusion as a phenomenon of plasticity *in vivo*. The "switch" shown by Terada and collaborators and by Ying and collaborators is rare (the fusion between adult and embryonic cells occurs at a frequency of 0.001% – 0.0001%) and requires considerable selective pressure for the fused cells. More interesting data emerge from the studies of Shi and co-workers: *in vitro* and *in vivo* experiments showed that the myogenic fusion is related to bone marrow stromal cells and not haematopoietic cells. Subpopulations of human bone marrow (stromal cells, haematopoietic stem cells, haematopoietic progenitors and monocytes) were tested for their ability to fuse with mouse C2C12 myoblast cells. A high fusion efficiency was obtained in the co-culture with stromal marrow cells, highlighting the existence of human nuclei aligned with murine nuclei in the heterokaryonic cells and the existence of transcripts for human muscle-specific genes. The cells belonging to the other lineages were found to be more refractory to fusion. Injection of stromal cells marked with the green fluorescent protein (GFP) gene into the anterior tibial muscle of NOD/SCID B2M-/-damaged cardiotoxin mice resulted in the regeneration of the mouse muscle with human nuclei (detected by immunohistochemistry by monoclonal antibodies against human nuclei) expressing GFP. A fraction of between 0.45% and 0.02% of the injected cells was incorporated into the myotubes. The rarity of the cell fusion event could explain the very low frequency of transdifferentiations *in vivo*. This mechanism could, however, be subject to plasticity *in vivo*, especially in those situations of high selective pressure as in the case of an acute crisis of an organ with extensive tissue death, and especially in tissues that tolerate polyploidy, such as muscle, liver or Purkinje cells.

3.3.4. Dedifferentiation and redifferentiation

Now that cloning is a reality, it is clear that the genetic information of a cell can be reprogrammed and that somatic cells can dedifferentiate into pluripotent cells. It has long been known that phenomena of dedifferentiation and redifferentiation occur in amphibians like urodeles, which can regenerate whole limbs. Numerous studies have suggested that similar processes, though less impressive, could cause the dedifferentiation of somatic cells. For example, oligodendrocyte progenitors derived from the optic nerve can acquire the characteristics of NSCs when maintained in culture conditions of absence of serum and low cell density. Other studies have suggested that cells commissioned towards the pancreatic epithelium may be directed to assume a hepatic phenotype, although the functional properties of the hepatocytic lineage have not been defined.

These findings suggest that dedifferentiation and redifferentiation could be a third explanation for adult stem cell plasticity. Therefore, adult stem cells or progenitor cells could be reprogrammed when removed from their usual microenvironment and introduced into a different niche, which gives the signals necessary to activate the new genetic program for the new cell destiny. Studies of the molecular mechanisms underlying nuclear reprogramming during the cloning process could thus help us to better understand the phenomenon of adult stem cell plasticity. These results

could therefore be exploited to induce lineage "switch" even without nucleus transfer. Similarly, analyses of the molecular mechanisms underlying dedifferentiation and redifferentiation in amphibians and fish that regenerate a limb could help to understand the plasticity of adult stem cells. For example, the MSX1 gene is a gene expressed in the blastema that regenerates. A recent study has shown that the overexpression of this gene in myotubes derived from the C2C12 cell line induces the regression from myotubes to mononucleated myoblasts, which then proliferate and reach the ability to differentiate into osteoblasts, chondrocytes and adipocytes. It is therefore necessary to define whether there are biochemical pathways which can play a role in the plasticity of adult stem cells in higher mammals.

3.3.5. Stem cells that persist in post-natal life

There is evidence of the persistence of somatic stem cells beyond the first steps of embryologic development. For example, Suzuki and collaborators have isolated fetal liver cells that can be clonally expanded *in vitro* and can reconstruct not only the liver and biliary epithelium, but also the epithelium of the pancreas and of the gastrointestinal tract. This study suggests that stem cells could persist in an organ and, under the influence of the environment, could differentiate into cells different from those of the organ of origin. Jiang and collaborators have demonstrated that bone marrow MSCs as single cells derived through clonogenic assays are able to differentiate *in vitro* in cells with characteristics of the mesodermal, neuroectodermal and endodermal lineage. These cells injected into a blastocyst can also contribute towards most cell types of the developing organism.

In another case, a somatic stem cell population, such as the Multipotent Adult Progenitor Cells derived from bone marrow stroma (MAPC), has shown expression of typical molecular markers of pluripotent cells, such as Oct-4 and Rex-1, albeit at levels significantly lower than the embryonic stem cells.

In particular, Oct-4 is a transcription factor expressed in the pre-gastrula embryo, in the cells of the inner cell mass of the blastocyst and in embryonic carcinoma cells. Oct-4 is required to maintain the undifferentiated phenotype of ESCs and plays an important role in defining the first steps of embryogenesis and differentiation, and is negatively modulated when cells are induced to differentiate *in vitro*. In the adult organism, the Oct-4 transcript is only present in germ cells.

Since it has not yet been clarified whether MAPCs already possess the differentiative potential *in vivo* or whether they are MSCs that are going to dedifferentiate *in vitro*, there is still no definitive evidence to assert that pluripotent stem cells exist *in vivo* during post-natal life.

3.4 Adipose tissue as a source of stem cells

Human adipose tissue has been revalued as an important organ after the discovery in 2001 of a population of mesenchymal stem cells within its stromal compartment, called Adipose-derived Stem Cells (ASCs). In mammals there are two different types of adipose tissue that differ for structure, function and localization: white adipose tissue, very widespread in the human body, especially in adults; brown adipose tissue, rare in adults, except in the perinatal period as used for thermogenesis, while it is characteristic of small mammals, rodents and hibernating animals.

Adipose tissue derives from the mesodermal germ layer and develops both in the prenatal and postnatal period. It begins to appear towards the second trimester of pregnancy, while preadipocyte precursors can be identified at the 8th and 10th week of gestation. Adipose tissue plays multiple functions:
- energy storage and energy release;
- mechanical role in preventing physical stress of other tissues. It also covers the nerves, the vessels, the muscles and fills some interstices of the bone marrow;
- heat insulation;
- metabolic activity by regulating appetite and metabolism.

As a storage compartment, adipose tissue can also undergo changes due to the nutritional status of the individual.

The localization of adipose tissue progenitor cells has remained controversial for a long time because of doubts concerning its possible endothelial, pericyte or stromal origin.

Pre-adipocytes and endothelial cells share surface antigens, in accordance with a common derivation. Experimental studies and clinical practices have shown that stem cells isolated from adipose tissue belong to the Stromal Vascular Fraction (SVF), a component consisting of a heterogeneous cellular population, which includes circulating blood cells, resident or infiltrate $CD14^+/CD31^+$ macrophages, fibroblasts, pericytes, endothelial cells, $CD34^+/CD31^+$ and $CD34^+/CD31^-$ preadipocytes.

Similarly to mesenchymal stem cells, ASCs, when subjected to induction with specific culture media, can differentiate *in vitro* in the three classical mesenchymal commissions: adipogenic, osteogenic and chondrogenic. *In vitro* and *in vivo* studies have also highlighted high plasticity by ASCs, which have proved their ability to differentiate even in the myogenic, cardiomyogenic, neurogenic, angiogenic, hepatic, pancreatic and epithelial lineages.

Adipose tissue can be collected from various anatomical sites, through diverse methods of isolation. Numerous studies have been conducted to determine the most appropriate site and technique to achieve optimum recovery of this stem population, but the specific differences that seem to occur at different districts, regarding the content and quality of resident stem cells, have not yet been clarified.

The first uses of adipose tissue for self-/homografts date back to the end of the 19th century.

The introduction of the modern liposuction technique, at the end of the 1970s, allowed to remove excess subcutaneous adipose tissue by using variable diameter cannulas, through small incisions in the area of interest. This technique has the advantage of being able to recovery large quantities of adipose tissue, with minimally invasive techniques, simplifying isolation and making the procedure less traumatic. Many advances in instrumentation, techniques and devices followed. However, the real breakthrough came with Sidney R. Coleman, a pioneer of the "purified and atraumatic" period of liposuction and adipose grafts. He set up a new technique, later called "Liposculpting", which he published in 1994, codifying in detail the steps of tissue harvesting, purification and reinjection. Coleman focused attention on the importance of preserving the adipose tissue from mechanical and chemical insults, emphasizing in this way the influence of the technique used on the survival of the transplant tissue and consequently on the achievable aesthetic results.

These guidelines are perfectly in line with the discovery, in the early 1990s, of stem cells residing in adipose tissue, which therefore assumes a potential role in regenerative approaches of plastic surgery. A recent study by Tonnard and collaborators proposes a new method of liposuction, different from the methods suggested by Coleman. The clinical samples obtained by the classic Coleman procedure are called "Macrofat"; when 3 mm diameter cannulas with multiple lateral openings of 1 mm diameter to increase the harvest yield are used they are defined as "Microfat". If the Microfat lipoaspirate sample is mechanically emulsified, obtaining a liquid tissue of viscous consistency, then it is classified as "Nanofat". The results of this study showed that in Nanofat-type specimens most adipocytes are destroyed during mechanical emulsion, limiting the volumetric effect of this preparation and therefore its use as filler. However, the effect of the processing does not affect the stem cell component (ASCs) present in the aspirated tissue, which remains viable and may be involved in the improvement of the quality of the dermis observed as a result of the re-injection into *in vivo* applications of cosmetic bio-stimulation.

The isolation of the stem cell component resident in adipose tissue involves a mechanical shredding mechanism followed by enzymatic digestion.

In general, the recovery of the stem cell component from adipose tissue is higher than in other classical adult sources such as bone marrow: ASCs constitute 2% of cells from lipoaspirate cells while MSCs in the marrow represent less than 0.01%. Apart from the advantages linked to the isolation, there are still a series of problems related to the difficulty of *ex vivo* cell expansion, to the low survival after freezing and thawing of the lipoaspirates, to the low efficiency of grafing *in vivo* (less of 5% of transplanted cells is maintained after transplantation).

With a view to the translation of the use of these cells on humans, the transition to the clinical practice of cells subjected to manipulation requires a very accurate treatment in accordance with CGMP guidelines (acronym for "Current Good Manufacturing Practices", i.e. good manipulation practices). To minimize the manipulation of the possible cellular product, in order to maintain also the native characteristics of the tissue, an innovative technique has been developed by Tremolada and collaborators. This technique is based on a method of non-enzymatic processing of lipoaspirates to obtain a mechanically disintegrated, minimally manipulated preparation containing ASCs with increased viability.

This new device, called Lipogems, is a sterile disposable kit, developed to collect, process and reinject, in a closed-loop machining system, human or animal lipoaspirates. It is a simple device that progressively reduces the adipose tissue clusters from 1-3.5 mm fragments to 0.2-0.8 mm fragments, eliminating the liquid part (oil) and the residual blood. The procedure takes about 20 minutes; starting from 100-130 ml of lipoaspirate, 60-100 ml of the final product is obtained. The purpose of Lipogems is to optimize Coleman's classic lipofilling method to obtain fragments of lipoaspirates of reduced measure and to improve post-transplant establishment. Immunophenotypic analysis, differential ability to classical lineage, and immunomodulatory ability have shown that the cellular product obtained through Lipogems could be an excellent candidate in regenerative medicine approaches. Also, unlike previously described lipoaspirates, this product can be frozen without losing the viable and functional stem cell population.

3.4.1 ASC clinical applications

The discovery of a resident population of stromal/stem cells in adipose tissue, able to differentiate into mesodermal lineages, but potentially also into endodermal and ectodermal lineages, paved the way for various possible applications of Lipoaspirate in the field of regenerative and reparative medicine, extending its use not only as filling material to compensate for the loss of soft tissue volume or for body remodelling in the cosmetic field. Stem cells derived from adipose tissue have been shown to improve the healing of wounds, ulcers and skin defects; they can be used for the regenerative treatment of extended cranial and facial defects due to trauma or simply ageing or used for regeneration in degenerative joint disease, such as osteoarthritis. Furthermore, use of adipose tissue is very promising in the breast reconstruction after breast surgery.

In addition, Klinger and collaborators have obtained excellent results also in the treatment of several cases of extended facial scars due to second- and third-degree burns. After the infiltration of adipose tissue, a clear improvement was noted due to the deposition of new collagen, cutaneous hypervascularization and dermis hyperplasia. The autologous stem cells present in the transplanted adipose tissue appear to be responsible for these effects, and thus able to improve the quality of the scars.

The immunomodulatory capacity of ASCs has been exploited to treat, in the murine model, allergic pathologies (e.g. allergic rhinitis) and autoimmune pathologies (e.g. rheumatoid arthritis), obtaining a reduction of symptoms; ASC co-transplantation may also play an important role in preventing the onset of or combatting Graft versus Host Disease (GVHD), one of the most frequent clinical complications of allogeneic bone marrow transplant rejection.

Finally, ASCs can be used in combination with gene therapy: they can be engineered with retroviral vectors to express molecules of therapeutic interest *in vivo*.

For the many reasons listed above, adipose tissue can be considered an ideal source of stem cells that can be used for tissue regeneration and reconstruction.

3.5 Potential use of adult stem cells

3.5.1 Basic stem cell biology

Adult stem cells are a very powerful tool for the study of self-renewal and differentiation. In the studies mentioned above, scientists used stem cells and committed progenitor cells to evaluate the effects of growth factors and other required signals on their development. Now, with the completion of the human and murine genome project, stem cells and their commissioned progeny can be used to define which genetic programs need to be activated or inactivated to lead to cellular differentiation. Because some plasticity phenomena could be caused by dedifferentiation and redifferentiation processes, studies aimed at understanding the genetic mechanisms underlying these processes could give important results. Better understanding and defining the factors governing these processes should lead to an improvement in methods for the induction and control of differentiation, making this phenomenon clinically relevant. Some experimental observations on plasticity, recently described in adult stem cell populations, may reflect the persistence of more primitive stem cells in post-natal life; the comparative analysis of gene and protein expression profiling, of specific tissue stem cells, such as HSCs or NSCs, with the most primitive stem cells (MSCs) or with pluripotent cells (ESCs) could add relevant information on the factors important for stemness maintenance or for control of lineage commitment.

3.5.2 Adult stem cells for the treatment of degenerative diseases

HSCs have been already used over the last decades for the treatment of haematologic disorders or to treat patients with malignant tumours undergoing chemotherapy or intensive radiotherapy. It is conceivable that with the progress achieved in characterizing stem cell populations for other tissues - such as NSCs, keratinocyte stem cells and corneal stem cells - stem cell therapy could become a foundation for the treatment of hereditary or acquired defects in such tissues. There are already some

tests in murine models of the usefulness of NSCs in the treatment of Parkinson's disease. If these studies, indicating that adult stem cells could have a greater differentiation potential than believed, are confirmed and extended, adult stem cells could be used to treat a wider range of genetic or degenerative disorders. In addition, numerous studies will be needed to determine how such cells could be used in clinical practice. Since there is no evidence of the tumorigenicity of these cells, if is proven that *in vivo* signals may be enough to induce organ-and tissue-specific differentiation, adult stem cells could be used without *in vitro* predifferentiation. We still know little about the "homing" of adult stem cells towards non-hae-

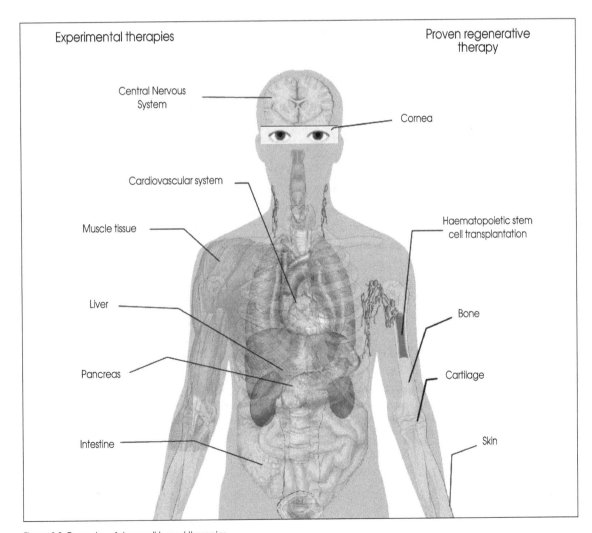

Figure 3.2. Examples of stem cell-based therapies.

matopoietic microenvironments; it will therefore be necessary to determine whether undifferentiated cells capable of lineage "switch" should be infused intravenously or locally to obtain sufficient engraftment to replace a damaged tissue. Moreover, since it may be possible that local microenvironment signals are not sufficiently strong to efficiently mediate the lineage "switch", it will be necessary to test whether stem cells should be predifferentiated *in vitro* before infusion to obtain optimal tissue repair and, if so, whether they should be used as commissioned or completely differentiated progenitor cells. Contrary to pluripotent cells such as ESCs, adult stem cells could be used for autologous transplants. However, for acute diseases, such as heart attacks, or diseases with an immunological basis, such as diabetes, allogeneic therapy may be necessary; in this case, strategies will be needed to avoid immune rejection. Nowadays, we have a plethora of data from clinical trials for the use of MSCs on humans: these cells have already proved useful in the treatment of bone and cartilage defects and in improving the engraftment of transplanted HSCs. Moreover, thanks to their immunomodulatory and trophic properties, MSCs could also be useful in the control of autoimmune diseases (e.g. multiple sclerosis) and retransplantation rejection; in the repair of metabolic pathologies (e.g. juvenile diabetes), in diseases of the cardiovascular apparatus (e.g. infarction, stroke) and of the nervous system (e.g. Alzheimer's and Parkinson's) (Figure 3.2).

Recommended reading and references

1. Eglitis MA, et al. *Haematopoietic cells differentiate into both microglia and macroglia in the brains of adult mice.* Proc Natl Acad Sci U S A 1997 Apr 15;94(8):4080-4085.

2. Yotsuyanagi T et al. *Reconstruction of a three-dimensional structure using cartilage regenerated from the perichondrium of rabbits.* Plast Reconstr Surg 1999 Apr;103(4):1120-1123.

3. Kopen GC et al. *Marrow stromal cells migrate throughout forebrain and cerebellum, and they differentiate into astrocytes after injection into neonatal mouse brains.* Proc Natl Acad Sci U S A 1999 Sep 14;96(19):10711-10716.

4. Gussoni E et al. *Dystrophin expression in the mdx mouse restored by stem cell transplantation.* Nature 1999 Sep 23;401(6751):390-394

5. Grounds MD. *Muscle regeneration: molecular aspects and therapeutic implications.* Curr Opin Neurol 1999 Oct;12(5):535-543.

6. Watt FM et al. *Out of Eden: stem cells and their niches.* Science. 2000 Feb 25; 287(5457): 1427-1430.

7. Slack JM. *Stem cells in epithelial tissues.* Science. 2000 Feb 25;287(5457):1431-1433.

8. Gage FH. *Mammalian neural stem cells.* Science. 2000 Feb 25;287(5457):1433-1438.

9. Bianco P et al. *Bone Marrow Stromal Stem Cells: Nature, Biology, and Potential Applications.* Stem Cells 2001;19:180-192.

10. Jiang Y et al. *Pluripotency of mesenchymal stem cells derived from adult marrow.* Nature. 2002 Jul 4;418(6893):41-49.

11. Bianco P et al. *Mesenchymal stem cells: revisiting history, concepts, and assays.* Cell Stem Cell. 2008 Apr 10;2(4):313-319.

12. Bianco P. et al. *The meaning, the sense and the significance: translating the science of mesenchymal stem cells into medicine.* Nature Medicine 2013 19;35–42.

13. Szöke K et al. *Concise review: therapeutic potential of adipose tissue derived angiogenic cells.* Stem Cells Transl Med 2012 1;658–667.

14. Stosich MS et al. *Adipose tissue engineering from human adult stem cells: clinical implications in plastic and reconstructive surgery.* Plast Reconstr Surg 2007 119, 71–83; discussion 84–85.

15. Tonnard, P et al. Nanofat *Grafting: Basic Research and Clinical Applications.* Plast Reconstr Surg 2013 Oct;132(4):1017-1026.

Haematopoietic Stem Cell Transplantation

Alberto Grossi   Damiano Rondelli

4

4.1. The Haematopoietic Stem Cell

Haematopoiesis is the process of formation of blood cellular components. In embryonic development, this process has the purpose of allowing the transport of oxygen through the erythrocytes, and, in the adult, maintains the blood system. In embryogenesis the first cells that appear are nucleated erythrocytes and macrophages. These cells appear in the extra-embryonic islands of the yolk sac at day 7-7.5 (E7-7.5) in the mouse and at day 18 in human embryogenesis. This is followed by the appearance of progenitors with multipotent activity in clonogenic assays and limited *in vivo* repopulation capacity. Mature haematopoiesis is supported by haematopoietic stem cells (HSC), pluripotent elements capable of giving origin to all blood cells of the adult organism and located in the

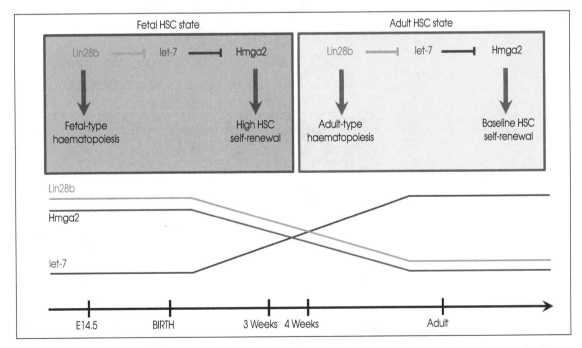

Figure 4.1. Scheme of proteins regulating the activity of HSCs at fetal and adult level. Lin28b is an mRNA binding protein, a fundamental regulator of fetal stem cells. In this phase, unlike in adults, at high levels of Lin28b there are reduced levels of let-7 mRNA (miRNAs) and this allows to maintain a high expression of Hmga2, a transcription factor that regulates the high self-renewal activity of fetal HSCs, compared to adult ones.

AMG region (Aorta/Gonad/Mesonephros) in the embryonic life. By the sixth week of gestation, the haematopoietic process shifts into the liver and the spleen, while it begins in the bone marrow by the end of the second trimester.

Figure 4.1 schematizes the activity of proteins regulating the activity of the HSCs at fetal level and in the adult.

Two factors, Gata1 and Pu.1, are the main transcriptional regulators of haematopoiesis for erythropoiesis and granulocyte/macrophage production, respectively.

Adult human haematopoiesis occurs in the axial skeleton (the sternum, ribs and vertebrae) and in the pelvis, which is the site from which it would be better to obtain a sample of liquid marrow (bone marrow aspiration) or a histological sample (biopsy) for examination of its function. Examples of a smear of liquid marrow and histological bone marrow sample are shown in Figures 4.2 and 4.3, respectively. The shift from prenatal haematopoiesis to postnatal haematopoiesis is completed in the ninth - tenth month of life and haematopoietic activity in the liver and spleen, typical of the fetal phase, finishes in the adult (with possible reactivation in some diseases – extramedullary haematopoiesis). This process is different from

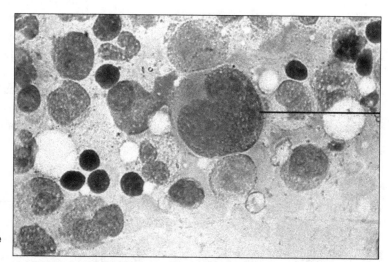

Figure 4.2. Stained bone marrow aspirate smear.

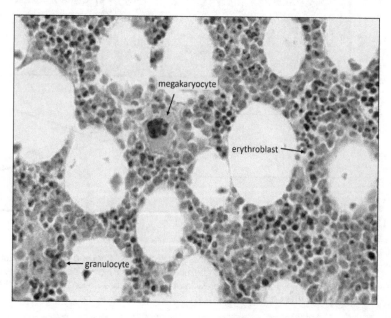

Figure 4.3 Photomicrograph of spongy bone tissue.

the murine model widely used in the studies on haematopoiesis.

HSCs are characterized by an unlimited capacity of self-renewal, the ability to give origin to an identical cellular progeny, and to express a surface glycoprotein, identified according to cluster designation (CD) as CD34, which allows them to be recognised within cellular populations derived from bone marrow blood or peripheral blood. Another protein associated with stemness is CD133, but it is not specific to HSCs, because it is also expressed by cells of other tissues, such as the brain, liver, prostate, and by neoplastic stem cells. In relation to the action of transcription factors, cytokines and interleukins with specific or pleiotropic activity, HSCs undergo a differentiation process towards cellular progenitors named "committed", which express receptors for the growth factors that allow their proliferation and maturation.

Figure 4.4 shows a diagram of the process which, starting with haematopoietic stem cells (HSC), generates both myeloid (Common Myeloid Progenitor-CMP) and lymphoid (Common Lymphoid Progenitor-CLP) lines; this mechanism maintains the homeostasis of a system that provides for cell production equal

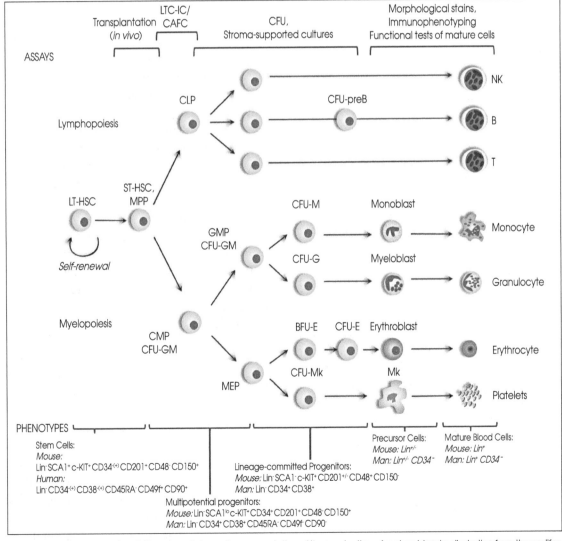

Figure 4.4. Lympho-haematopoietic system. Schematic representation of the production of mature blood cells starting from the proliferation and differentiation of haematopoietic stem cells.

to the amount that every day is eliminated by senescence or increases its activity in relation to conditions that result in increased cellular loss.

The CMP cells give rise to progenitors that are further restricted in their potentialities ("lineage restricted") that have been studied with the experimental method of the formation of cell clones in semi-solid medium cultures.

The identification of surface proteins, surface antigenic markers through specific antibodies, and their analysis by cytofluorimetry are fundamental for identifying stem cells and those cells resulting from the differentiation/maturation process, both in experimental studies and in the clinical diagnosis of haemopathies (Table 4.1).

Table 4.1 Immunophenotype of lympho-haematopoietic progenitors.	
Cell type	CD markers
Stem Cell	CD34+,CD31-
Leukocytes	CD45+
Granulocytes	CD45+,CD15+
Monocytes	CD45+,CD14+
T lymphocytes	CD45+,CD3+
T helper cells	CD45+,CD3+,CD4+
Cytotoxic T lymphocytes	CD45+,CD3+,CD8+
B lymphocytes	CD45+,CD19+ or CD45+,CD20+
Natural Killer	CD16+,CD56+,CD3-
Erythrocytes	CD235+
Megakaryocytes - Thrombocytes	CD45+,CD61+

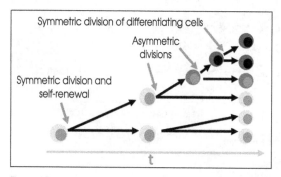

Figure 4.5. Symmetric and asymmetric cell division model.

The possibility that a stem cell is able to give origin to the progeny and at the same time maintain its capacity of self-renewal supposes an asymmetric model of cell division (Figure 4.5) which has not been definitively demonstrated in the adult.

4.2. Study of HSC proliferation/differentiation

Semi-solid cell cultures are used to evaluate the ability of HSCs and progenitors to proliferate in response to haematopoietic factors and inhibitors, and to study their interaction with stromal cells in the haematopoietic microenvironment (see below). Semi-solid culture conditions may change in relation to the cell line of interest (erythroid, monocyte-granulocyte, megakariocyte, lymphocyte lines). The method is applied both for the study of totipotent cells, such as HSCs, and of cells with reduced proliferative capacity which are at various stages of differentiation. In addition, proliferative/differentiative capacity can be assessed on cells under different conditions (cryopreserved cells, *ex vivo* expansion, genetic modification, etc.). Mononucleated cells obtained from bone marrow or peripheral blood that are cultured *in vitro* usually contain progenitors with reduced self-renewal characteristics, thus more differentiated. The culture conditions allow the growth of colonies by the progenitors, so-called Colony Forming Unit cells, identifiable on the basis of morphological and phenotypic characteristics.

Erythroid colonies derived from more mature progenitors (CFU-E), which require a 7-day incubation time for their formation, can be identified by the red colour derived from the presence of haemoglobin, while colonies derived from a more immature progenitor (Burst Forming Unit BFU-E) require 2-3 weeks for their formation, consist of "bursts" of smaller erythroid colonies and are made up of cells that have not yet acquired this differentiation capacity, so they usually have a less intense colour compared to CFU-E. The survival and proliferation of CFU-E depends on the presence of erythropoietin (Epo) in the culture medium, while a combination of Epo with other cytokines (stem cell factor-SCF; interleukin 3 -IL-3; granulocyte/macrophage Colony-Stimulating Factor – GM-CSF) is required for BFU-E growth. Except for the Epo, the above-mentioned cytokines are also necessary for the survival and proliferation of the CFU-G (Granulocyte progenitor), CFU-GM (granulocyte and monocyte progenitors), and CFU-M (monocyte progenitor). The Megakaryocyte colonies (CFU-MK) are generally obtained on collagen-containing culture media.

Long-term culture assays (several weeks of culture), in which the haematopoietic cells grow on a monolayer of adherent primary stromal or immortalized cells, allow to study the survival, proliferation and self-renewal characteristics of HSCs. Culture media containing adequate cytokines/interleukins are commercially available for the study of haematopoietic progenitors.

4.3 The Haematopoietic Niche

The self-renewal ability, the undifferentiated state, or the proliferation/differentiation potentials, and escape from the marrow environment of HSCs require that these multipotent progenitors reside in a particular environment consisting of stromal cells without haematopoietic potentiality, defined as a haematopoietic niche (Figure 4.6). Therefore, the haematopoietic niche is the microenvironment in which the HSCs reside as represented in Figure 4.6.

On the basis of an image representation of the bone marrow, this niche can include different regions, in one of which the osteoblasts are in close proximity of the vascular endothelium (to form the trabecular structure of the niche). In fact, the surface of the endosteum (the layer of vascular connective tissue lining the inner surface of bone medullary cavities) is highly vascularized, and vascular and perivas-

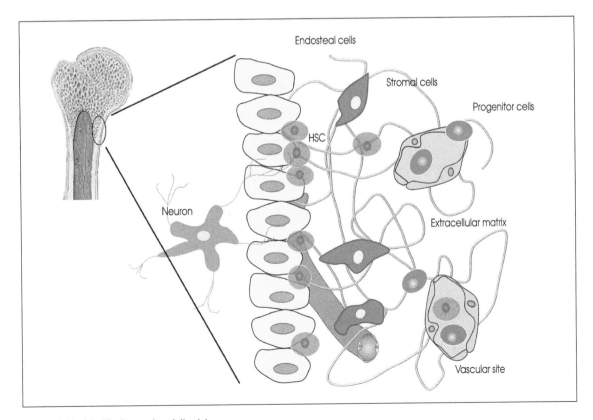

Figure 4.6. Model of the haematopoietic niche.

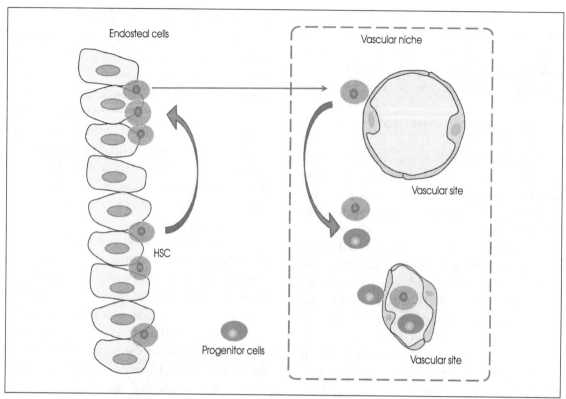

Figure 4.7. Representative scheme of the role of the vascular niche in haematopoiesis.

cular cells (reticular cells, adipocytes and mesenchymal cells) contribute to the formation of the haematopoietic niche at the endosteum level. The passage of haematopoietic cells from the niche to the marrow environment occurs through the endothelium of the vascular system (Figure 4.7).

4.4 Cellular structure and molecular mechanisms of the microenvironment

The morphological examination of the bone marrow (obtained by biopsy or aspiration), used in the diagnosis of several pathological conditions, allows to evaluate the percentage, the location and the stage of maturation of its various cellular components. This investigation does not give us a three-dimensional representation of the microenvironment in which haematopoiesis takes place, that is of the "haematopoietic niche", in which the interaction between cellular components and

the stroma occurs. The cellular structure of the microenvironment where the HCSs reside consists of osteoblasts, osteoclasts, endothelial cells, fat cells and sympathetic nervous system cells, determining the fate of stem cells through molecular and humoral mechanisms. The interaction between HSCs and the microenvironment, in particular their permanence, is allowed by the binding of CD44 (transmembrane protein binding hyaluronic acid and other extracellular matrix glycoproteins) and of the integrins to the osteopontine, and by the fundamental binding of the integrins to the fibronectin and to the Vascular endothelial Cell Adesion Molecule 1 (VCAM1). The binding through the integrins, heterodimers expressed on the cellular surface, is important to prevent apoptosis and the maintenance the HSC quiescence . VLA-4 and VLA-5 (Very Late Antigen) appear to play a role in maintaining an undifferentiated state of the cells, while alpha-integrin maintains the functional capacity of LTC-IC (long term culture – initiating cells) within the HSC population.

In a murine model of osteoblastic stimulation it has been shown that the Notch (transmembrane receptor) signalling pathway regulates HSC self-renewal through the binding with the Jagged1 notch ligand, which leads to an increase in the activated form of the receptor, while the inhibition of beta-secretase, able to cleave the membrane-spanning domain of Notch, reduces the increase in the HSC number.

Other regulators possibly involved in the permanence of HSCs in the microenvironment are annexin II, expressed by osteoblasts and endothelial cells, and the receptor tyrosinkinase Tie2 and its angiopoietin ligand -1, produced by osteoblasts. The signal resulting from the Tie2 and angio-1 binomials increases the expression of alpha-integrins that maintain LTC-IC functional capacity. The mechanisms that regulate the adhesion of HSCs to the microenvironment are the same as those regulating and maintaining the pool of so-called neoplastic stem cells that are believed to be protected by

the activity of anti-neoplastic treatments; they may be one of the reasons for the therapeutic failures of antineoplastic chemotherapies. Notch and beta-secretase, angiopoietin 1, the SDF1/CXCR4 complex, described in the next paragraph, are just some of the possible targets of so-called "targeted therapy" which constitutes an important part of the therapeutic research in the field of oncology.

4.5 Soluble factors acting within the niche

The interaction between CXCL12 (SDF-1) and its CXCR4 receptor (chemokine receptor 4) is involved in the localization of HSCs and their permanence within the niche. There is evidence that CXCL12 has a role in maintaining the state of quiescence of the stem cell, and its concentration within osteoblasts is regulated by the parathyroid hormone (PTH) that, in synergy with the PTH-related protein, is also able to increase the number of these cells. Deletions of the CXCR4 receptor lead to an increase of cycling HSCs.

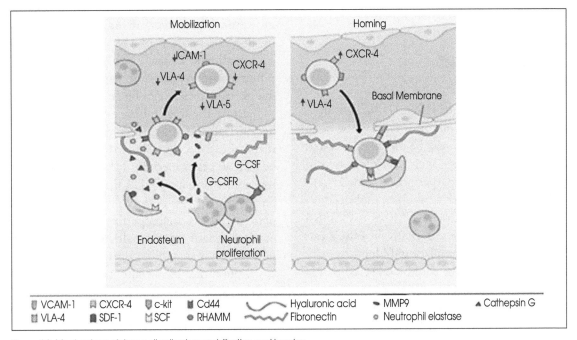

Figure 4.8. Mechanisms of stem cell adhesion: mobilization and homing.

The CXCL12/CXCR4 complex is the target on which the HSC mobilizer AMD 3100-Plerixafor is currently used for the collection of hematopoietic stem cells for transplantation purposes. (Figure 4.8).

Studies on murine models suggest that prostaglandin E2 (PGE2), produced by osteoblasts, also has a role in the regulation of HSCs, because it determines an increase in splenic derivation colonies after murine marrow transplantation in irradiated receivers. Another factor that could have a role in the regulation of HSCs is Wnt, which is believed to act by activating beta-catenins, the coding gene of which is considered an oncogene and is hyper-expressed in some types of neoplasms. Activation of the signal linked to Wnt results in increased self-renewal of the stem cells and a hyperexpression of the alpha- and beta-catenine with expansion of the HSC pool in long-term colonies. Conversely, to confirm the role of Wnt, its inhibition leads to a defect in recovery of haematopoiesis after bone marrow transplantation. A complete review of the factors regulating the state of quiescence/proliferation and recruitment/mobilization was recently proposed by de Kruijf and collaborators in 2019.

4.6 Haematopoietic Stem Cell Transplantation

Transplantation of HSCs (HSCT) is usually related to stem cells directly from the bone marrow. These HSCs can be directly harvested from the bone marrow, or can be collected from the peripheral blood (peripheral blood stem cells, or PBSC) after temporary mobilization with chemotherapy, or G-CSF, or a CXCR4 inhibitor (plerixafor). Alternatively, HSCs can be obtained from the placental blood by harvesting the cells of the cord blood (CB) that is cut after the delivery of a newborn.

The different types of transplant that will be described here include: autologous HSCT, where the HSCs are from the same patient who will receive the transplant after high-dose chemotherapy; allogeneic HSCT, where the HSCs come from a related or unrelated donor (fully or partially HLA compatible with the patient); syngeneic HSCT, where the HSCs are from an identical twin of the patient. This latter case is considered very similar to an autologous transplant. The indications for HSCT range from many types of blood cancer, to severe non-malignant congenital or acquired haematologic diseases, or in some cases to selected solid tumours or autoimmune diseases.

For clinical purposes, HSCs are identified by flow cytometry based on the expression of the CD34 antigen. The number of HSCs that a patient needs to receive in order to reconstitute his/her haematopoiesis after a chemotherapy/radiotherapy conditioning regimen is $\geq 2 \times 10^6$ CD34$^+$ cells/kg of the recipient. This number applies to transplants utilizing PBSCs, whereas in bone marrow transplants the standard minimum cell dose is 2×10^8 total nucleated cells/kg. In cord blood transplants lower numbers of HSCs are usually obtained due to the limited volume of cord blood units, and the minimum dose is lower than in PBSC or bone marrow transplants. However, CB transplants are utilized mostly in children because of low body weight. In adult patients, instead, two CB units (from different donors, and even partially incompatible to each other) can be combined together to increase the total number of HSCs. In fact, because of the immature immune development of CB T cells, CB HSC transplants can be safely performed in HLA incompatible recipients. When no HLA matched donor can be identified, the options available to many patients are an incompatible CB transplant, or a transplant from a half-HLA compatible related donor (haploidentical transplant).

Before the HSCs are transplanted, the patient usually receives a conditioning regimen with chemotherapy/radiotherapy that can last 2-6 days (based on the protocol selected) prior to transplant. Right after this,

HSCs are infused into the PB via a central venous catheter. Depending on the dose intensity of the conditioning regimen, the patient will have a profound pancytopenia that can last for up to 2-3 weeks after transplant (myeloablative transplant), or less (reduced intensity or non-myeloablative transplants). The engraftment of the HSCs is defined clinically by reaching a sustained number of circulating neutrophils $\geq 0.5 \times 10^9$/L and platelets $\geq 20 \times 10^9$/L in the peripheral blood.

4.6.1 Autologous HSCT

An autologous HSCT is performed mostly in patients with malignancies that can benefit from a very high dose of chemotherapy aimed at curing the cancer, or at least at prolonging survival, that otherwise would not be possible with a standard dose of chemotherapy. In fact, the dose of chemotherapy utilized in many haematologic malignancies is limited mostly by the toxic effect on the bone marrow, which needs to recover and produce new blood cells after each cycle of treatment. In several blood malignancies, such as multiple myeloma or relapsed lymphomas, it has been shown that higher doses of chemotherapy followed by autologous HSCT result in a significantly better outcome. These diseases represent the major indications for autologous HSCT, although it can also be utilized in selected cases of acute leukaemia or solid tumours. Progress in supportive care therapies, for examples new antimicrobials, and particularly new immunotherapy agents, such as monoclonal antibodies targeting cancer cells, have improved the clinical success of autologous HSCT even in elderly patients. In fact, currently there is no chronological age limit to receive an autologous HSCT and patients up to 80 years old have been transplanted if in overall good condition.

4.6.2 Allogeneic HSCT

The main indications of allogeneic HSCT are blood cancers, such as acute or chronic leukaemias, myelodysplastic syndromes, mye-

lofibrosis, lymphomas relapsed after chemotherapy; or non-malignant disorders, such as congenital immunodeficiencies (paediatric), or haemoglobinopathies (particularly homozygous forms of beta-thalassaemia major or sickle cell anaemia), or acquired aplastic anaemias. The goal of allogeneic HSCT in malignant diseases is both to reduce the tumour burden in the bone marrow with chemotherapy, and more importantly to replace the immune system of the patient in order for the donor T cells to have a direct effect against the cancer ('graft-versus tumour' effect). In non-malignant diseases, instead, the main purpose is to replace the non-functioning bone marrow with healthy marrow.

In order to perform an allogeneic HSCT, the donor and the patient need to be tested for HLA compatibility. HLA typing is done by molecular techniques to identify the DNA sequences of HLA genes. Molecular typing at high resolution is utilized in unrelated donor or haploidentical donor typing to characterize the HLA molecules and their antigen-binding sites, which define multiple subtypes of each HLA antigen. Low resolution molecular typing is instead sufficient to test sibling donors since it detects the HLA antigen (coming from the same parent for both) but not the specific HLA proteins (specific alleles).

In this type of transplant, HSCs have been historically transplanted from a related or unrelated donor molecularly compatible at HLA class I: A, B, C, and class II: DRB1, DQB1 loci; or mismatched at 1 antigen or allele level. Alternatively, as discussed above, CB units can be transplanted if the recipient is 1- or even 2-antigen mismatched. While this has been very useful, especially in the paediatric population, in the adult setting there have been higher rates of rejection, delayed time to achieve the engraftment, and high costs to the hospital to obtain cord blood units from international CB banks. Another option to transplant incompatible HSCs from adult donors has been utilized in dedicated transplant centres since the mid-1990s. It consists of transplanting highly purified HSCs (CD34$^+$ cell selection), thus depleting almost completely the T cells from the graft prior to transplant. In this way, the graft will not cause GVHD since there are no immune effectors transplanted into the incompatible recipient. The difficulties associated with this procedure have been mostly related to very prolonged time to reach a T cell immune reconstitution that resulted in high rates of lethal infections. Over the last decade, however, the use of HSCs from half compatible related donors (haploidentical) has become more common. This option, that with standard protocols of post-transplant immunosuppression therapies would cause a lethal acute graft-versus-host disease (aGVHD), is now possible after the discovery made at Johns Hopkins University over a decade ago. Researchers from this university demonstrated that haploidentical donor-derived T cells expand *in vivo* in response to the incompatible recipient's antigens, peaking on days 3 and 4 post transplant. Based on this observation, they showed that, by suppressing this T cell clone with high-dose cyclophosphamide administered to the patient on day 3 and day 4 post-transplant, they could eliminate the risk of GVHD. Multiple studies have suggested that the outcome of standard matched HSCT is now comparable to that achieved in haploidentical transplants with high-dose post-transplant cyclophosphamide (HD-PTCy). Importantly, with the introduction of haploidentical HSCT it has been estimated that approximately 95% of the patients may find a donor.

4.6.3 Myeloablative (MAC), Reduced Intensity (RIC), or Non-Myeloablative (NMA) Conditioning Regimens

Allogeneic HSCT is now offered to patients of almost any age, since the chemotherapy/radiation therapy utilized prior to the infusion of the cells, called 'conditioning regimen', can be reduced according to the patient's age or comorbidities in order to reduce the organ toxicity and the time of severe neutropenia (with high risk of infection).

The standard HSCT that has been performed routinely for over thirty years includes myeloablative doses of chemotherapy/radiation (Myeloablative Conditioning, or MAC). Historically it has been based on the combination of 10-12 Gy of total body irradiation (TBI) and cyclophosphamide as a way of depleting the bone marrow and immunosuppressing the recipient's immune system. Alternatively to the TBI, an alkylating agent such as busulfan was introduced to reduce the tumour burden and deplete cells in the marrow, in combination with cyclophosphamide as a strong immunosuppressive agent. In the last decade, a combination of busulfan with fludarabine (a purine analogue) has been widely utilized as a typical MAC.

Over the last two decades, however, the dogma that the conditioning regimen was required to empty the bone marrow prior to the transplant has been proven wrong. In fact, low doses of chemotherapy/radiation can be successfully utilized in HSCT, as long as the immune system of the recipient is suppressed. It has been demonstrated, therefore, that an immune space and not a physical one is necessary to allow donor stem cell engraftment. This concept shift has since then translated into at least two major advances in the field. The first has been that patients with non-malignant diseases in need of HSCT (examples: congenital haematological disorders or aplastic anaemia) can be successfully cured without being exposed to the risks of high doses of chemotherapy/radiation; the second is that elderly patients with severe haematologic malignancies (often more common in patients > 60 years old) can be transplanted safely with reduced-intensity conditioning regimens, thus limiting transplant-related mortality. It should be clear that the main "weapon" that an allogenic HSCT utilizes is always the donor immune system that can elicit an alloreactive response against the patient's residual cancer cells ('graft-versus-tumour' effect), or suppress the recipient immune cells to facilitate the establishment of donor stem cell engraftment in non-malignant diseases.

Therefore, in addition to the MAC described above, and still utilized in patients <60 years old with acute or chronic leukaemias, or myelodysplastic syndrome, other types of transplants associated with lower toxicities may be performed using a reduced-intensity conditioning (RIC), or a non-myeloablative (NMA) chemo/radiation. A RIC transplant is usually performed in patients > 60 years old or younger but with comorbidities preventing them from receiving high-dose chemo/radiation. Common indications are acute leukaemias in remission after induction chemotherapy, or refractory/relapsed lymphomas, or chronic myeloid neoplasms at diagnosis, such as intermediate/high risk myelodysplastic syndromes or primary myelofibrosis, or chronic myeloid leukaemia in chronic/accelerated phase resistant to or intolerant of tyrosine kinase inhibitors. Many regimens with different degrees of low intensity have been utilized for this type of transplant. The combination of the purine analogue fludarabine with low-dose alkylating agents, such as busulfan or melphalan, remains the most common RIC strategy worldwide. Importantly, despite the fact that patients receive a lower dose of chemo/radiation therapy compared to MAC regimens, RIC regimens still have an anti-tumour activity and cause a post-transplant pancytopenia, although not as prolonged as in MAC transplants (Figure 4.9).

A completely different approach is, instead, an HSCT prepared with an NMA conditioning regimen. Because the doses of chemotherapy and/or radiation therapy in an NMA regimen are very low, an NMA HSCT has a low risk of transplant-related morbidity and mortality even in elderly patients who otherwise would not be eligible for transplant. Of the two anticancer activities that a standard HSCT delivers, i.e. the cytoxicity through chemo/radiation therapy and the graft-versus-tumour through the donor immune system, NMA HSCT uses only the second one. The advantage, as previously described, is that blood cancer patients with advanced age can be transplanted. In these patients, however, limiting the anticancer cytotoxicity of the conditioning regimen increases the risk of cancer relapse post-transplant, especially in patients with malignancies with cytogentic, molecular or immunophenotypic high risk profiles. NMA can instead be very helpful for young patients with non-malignant diseases, such as aplastic anaemia, congenital bone marrow failures, or haemoglobinopathies (such as: thalassaemia major, sickle cell disease), or congenital dyserythropoietic anaemia. It is worth noting that haploidentical transplants have been developed and are largely performed worldwide using an NMA regimen, which means that an increasing number of patients who,

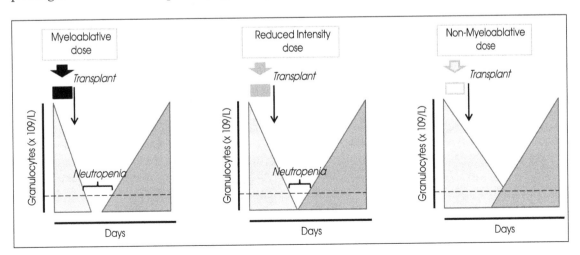

Figure 4.9. Myeloablation and haematopoietic recovery in Myeloablative, Reduced Intensity, or Non-Myeloablative transplant.

until five years ago were not considered eligible candidates for HSCT, have now a chance of cure with limited transplant toxicity.

4.6.4 Graft-versus-Host Disease (GVHD)

The immune recognition of tumour-associated antigens of the patient (host) by T lymphocytes from the donor's graft is the rationale for any allogeneic HSCT in patients with haematologic malignancies. Tumour cells may also express minor HLA antigens, that are expressed in normal cells of the recipient, and be targeted by donor T cell alloreactivity. Although some of these minor HLA antigens are known, many others still remain undiscovered, and in any case their expression does not represent an exclusion in the donor selection. In fact, the ability of donor T cells to attack tumour cells in the recipient will depend on the recognition of either tumour-specific antigens or of minor HLA anti-

gens expressed on the surface of malignant cells. The lack of any HLA difference, as in the case of a stem cell transplant from an identical twin (comparable to autologous stem cells) is devoid of an immune anti-host effect and therefore not utilized in patients with blood malignancies. However, since minor antigens are expressed on normal tissues of the host, different organs of the recipient can also be the target of a donor immune allorecognition. When this reaction of the donor against the host causes damage in one or more organs, the patient develops a syndrome called acute graft-versus-host disease (GVHD) (Figure 4.10).

The pathophysiology of acute GVHD is multifactorial. The conditioning chemo-radiotherapy administered to the patient before the transplant plays an initial role by increasing the activation and antigen presentation of the host antigens from damaged by antigen presenting

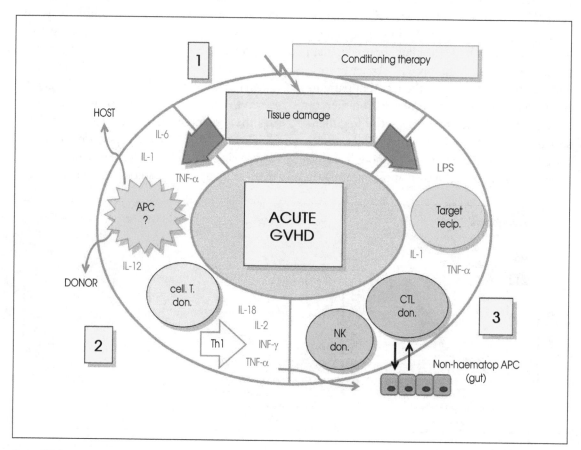

Figure 4.10. Immunological mechanisms in acute GVHD.

cells (APC) in lymphoid organs as well as in multiple organs, such as the skin, liver or gastrointestinal tract. The donor T cells and APCs transplanted with the graft then rapidly proliferate and release a variety of cytokines that will drive the differentiation of multiple subsets of effector NK and T cells, such as T-helper or T-cytotoxic 1 and 2 (Th1/Tc1 and Th2/Tc2), or Th17, and of professional APCs. Interestingly, in the last years it has been demonstrated that also cells that do not belong to the immune system, especially Paneth cells in the GI tract, and products of the microbiome can play a relevant role in triggering acute GVHD. Finally, effector T cells that have been activated against host antigens and have differentiated into cytotoxic T cells will cause cellular cytolysis in host organs, resulting in apoptotic cell death in acute GVHD. In chronic GVHD, the release of Th1 and Th2 cytokines, as well as of TGFb, can trigger the additional activation of donor B cells with antibody-mediated cell damage, and increase the development of fibrotic tissue in the host organs.

With the standard immunosuppression prophylactic treatment with calcineurin inhibitors (cyclosporin-A or tacrolimus) administered to patients starting from day -1, the incidence of GVHD depends on the degree of HLA compatibility between donor and recipient and increases by 5-10% for each mismatched HLA antigen. Until recently, only 1 antigen mismatched donors were commonly utilized. The development of haploidentical transplants (described above) with infusion of a high dose of cyclophosphamide on day +3 and +4 post-transplant, has allowed 5-6 HLA antigen mismatched transplants without increasing the risk of GVHD. The age of the patient, as well as that of the donor, can also influence the probability of GVHD, especially in the case of an older donor. After HSCT, the immunosuppressive therapy can usually be tapered and stopped within one year post transplant, unless the patient still requires this treatment to avoid GVHD. The risk of severe and sometime lethal acute GVHD of the intestine, causing massive bleeding, or of the liver, ultimately resulting in liver failure, has decreased compared to the past, but is still estimated to affect some patients (<10%). Severe chronic GVHD, instead, is often limiting the quality of life of a subset of patients who need to continue immunosuppressive therapies for many years, or for life. In a small fraction of these patients, whose lungs are affected by GVHD (causing a syndrome called *bronchiolitis obliterans*), unfortunately GVHD may result in progressive respiratory failure, and few of these patients are candidates for a lung transplant.

The treatment of acute or chronic GVHD is based on potent immunosuppressive strategies (such as high-dose corticosteroids, mycofenolic acid, rapamycin, anti-lymphocyte antibodies, extracorporeal photopheresis, rituximab). Nevertheless, its efficacy is limited to only approximately 50% of the patients with advanced-stage acute GVHD or refractory chronic GVHD. In the last few years, a new category of molecules blocking the Jak signalling triggered by pro-inflammatory cytokines have demonstrated encouraging results both in patients with acute and chronic GVHD who failed standard treatments.

Recommended reading and references

1. Lemoli RM et al. *Hematopoietic stem cell mobilization*. Haematologica 2008 Mar;93(3):321-324.

2. Anna Marciniak-Czochra, et al. *Modeling of replicative senescence in hematopoietic development*. Aging, August 2009, Vol.1 No.8.

3. Martinez-Agosto JA et al. *The hematopoietic stem cell and its niche: a comparative view*. Genes & Development 2007 21:3044–3060.

4. Frisch BJ et al. *Hematopoietic niche and bone meet*. Curr Opin Support Palliat Care 2008 September 2(3): 211–217.

5. Zon LI. *Intrinsic and extrinsic control of haematopoietic stem-cell self-renewal*. Nature 2008 453, 306-313.

6. Lapid K. et al. *Egress and Mobilization of Hematopoietic Stem and Progenitor Cells: A Dynamic Multi-facet Process*. Stembook.org 2012.

7. de Kruijf EFM. et al. *Cytokine-induced hematopoietic stem and progenitor cell mobilization: unraveling interactions between stem cells and their niche.* Ann N Y Acad Sci. 2019 Apr 21.

8. Beres AJ & Drobynski WR. *The role of regulatory T cells in the biology of graf tversus host disease.* Frontiers In Immunology 2013 Jun 24;4:163; 1-9.

9. Uy GL, et al. *Plerixafor, a CXCR4 antagonist for the mobilization of hematopoietic stem cells.* Expert Opin Biol Ther (2008) 8(11); 1797-1804.

10. Copley MR et al. *Developmental changes in hematopoietic stem cell properties.* Exp Mol Med 2013 Nov 15;45:e55.

11. Orkin SH et al. *Hematopoiesis: an evolving paradigm for stem cell biology.* Cell 2008 Feb 22;132(4):631-644.

12. Gyurkocza B et al. *Conditioning regimens for hematopoietic cell transplantation: one size does not fit all.* Blood. 2014 Jul 17;124(3):344-353.

13. Patel P et al. *Linear accelerator-based total marrow irradiation (TMI) myeloablative fludarabine/ busulfan conditioning in allogeneic stem cell transplantation for high risk hematologic malignancies: a Phase I study.* Biol Blood Marrow Transplant 2014 Dec;20(12):2034-2041.

14. Rondelli D et al. *Results of Phase II clinical trial MPD-RC 101: Allogeneic hematopoeitic stem cell transplantation conditioned with fludarabine/ melphalan in patients with myelofibrosis.* Blood 2014 Aug 14;124(7):1183-1191.

15. Saraf SL et al. *Nonmyeloablative Stem Cell Transplantation with Alemtuzumab/Low-Dose Irradiation to Cure and Improve the Quality of Life of Adults with Sickle Cell Disease.* Biol Blood Marrow Transplant 2015 Sep 5. pii: S1083-8791(15)00597-2.

16. Ferrara JL et al. *Graft-versus-host disease.* Lancet 2009 May 2;373(9674):1550-1561.

17. Blazar BR et al. *Advances in graft-versus-host disease biology and therapy.* Nat Rev Immunol 2012 May 11;12(6):443-458.

Stem cells of the vascular system

5

Gianandrea Pasquinelli   Sabrina Valente

5.1 Embryological origin of the vascular system

The vascular system is fundamental for embryogenesis and adult tissue homeostasis; any alteration of the vascular system can result in human vascular diseases, such as atherosclerosis and related clinical consequences, i.e. myocardial infarction, ischaemic stroke, peripheral arterial obstructive disease, cancer[1] and subarachnoid haemorrhage[2].

The embryological origin of the vascular system is still a source of debate in the scientific community. The most accredited vision involves the formation of vessels from mesodermal precursors through two fundamental biological processes, vasculogenesis and angiogenesis.

Vasculogenesis represents the earliest process of vascular development; it consists in the *ex novo* formation of blood vessels starting from vascular endothelial cell precursors or angioblasts. In the first days of embryonic life, vasculogenesis originates from lateral and posterior mesodermal cells that migrate in the yolk sac and form the so-called blood islands; according to this model, the yolk sac mesoderm is populated by bipotent stem cells termed haemangioblasts able to give rise to both haematopoietic precursors, or haematopoietic stem cells, and to endothelial precursors, or angioblasts. The proliferating haemangioblasts produce solid cell clusters called blood islands; in these primitive structures, the innermost cells develop into haematopoietic cells whilst the outermost cell population flattens and differentiates into angioblasts. The subsequent fusion and remodelling of the haemoangiopoietic islands leads to the formation of the primitive vascular plexus (Figure 5.1).

However, this model does not provide an explanation of why the formation of the primitive vascular plexus precedes the appearance of the first blood cells; therefore, some researchers consider that vascular origin is partly due to another mesodermal precursor located on the floor of the embryonic dorsal aorta; this precursor, a subset of endothelial cells with specific morphology and gene expression profile, gives rise to the haemogenic endothelium lining the dorsal aorta and subsequently to the haematopoietic lineage. Haemogenic endothelial cell specification is regulated by multiple

---

[1]   Tumour cells grow by promoting tumour angiogenesis; therefore, one of the main objectives of cancer research is the development of therapies able to specifically inhibit tumour angiogenesis.

[2]   Aneurysm rupture due to abnormal development of some cerebral vessels is the origin of this fearsome cerebral complication.

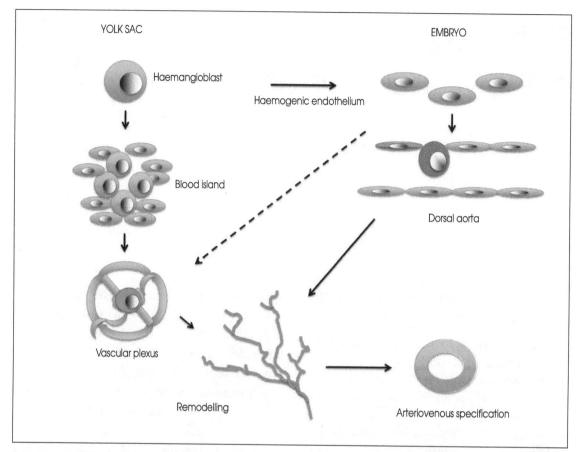

YOLK SAC

EMBRYO

Haemangioblast

Haemogenic endothelium

Blood island

Dorsal aorta

Vascular plexus

Remodelling

Arteriovenous specification

Figure 5.1. Schematic representation of endotheliogenesis starting from mesodermal progenitors in embryonic life.

molecular factors, including retinoic acid[3] signalling, Runx1[4], Notch and c-kit. Once established, the emerging vascular system is expanded and remodelled through the formation of new blood vessels from pre-existing vessels by sprouting or splitting; this process,

known as **angiogenesis,** is a complex biological phenomenon made up by distinct morphogenic phases including vessel destabilization, matrix and basement membrane remodelling, oriented migration of endothelial cells, vessel expansion by budding and branching, and their subdivision or distribution ("sprouting angiogenesis"). New vessels are also formed through "splitting angiogenesis"; in this process, the opposite endothelial cells extend from the vascular wall to the vascular lumen, making contact with each other and reorganizing themselves to form two vessels (Figure 5.2).

The subsequent development is represented by vascular specifications in arteries, veins and lymphatic vessels; this process is mainly governed by genetic mechanisms as reported in the following section.

[3] Retinoic acid (RA) derives from retinol or Vitamin A and its signalling is involved in the fate of the haemogenic endotelial cells within the yolk sac and the embryonic aorta-gonad-mesonephros. In particular it regulates HSC differentiation or self-renewal maintenance.

[4] Runx1, also known as AML1, is a transcriptional factor of the core binding factor family; during the haematopoietic system development, it induces the formation of haematopoietic stem cells, including their progenitors, through the suppression of endothelial differentiation.

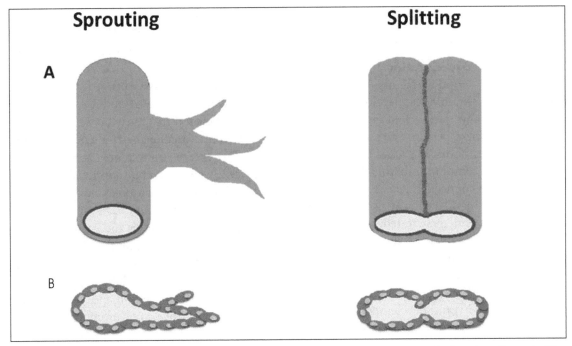

Figure 5.2. Schematic representation of different types of angiogenesis. Longitudinal (A) and transverse (B) view of sprouting and splitting angiogenesis.

In the adult organism, as well as in pathological conditions, the development of new vessels can also be achieved through a process known as arteriogenesis; it is the downstream formation of collaterals from mature interconnecting arteries as a result of a vascular obstruction to maintain blood supply and to perfuse an ischaemic tissue. This process is governed by physical and molecular mechanisms caused by significant variations of endovascular **shear stress**[5].

In response to shear stress alteration, there are distinct molecular processes that lead to endothelial activation, inflammatory cell recruitment, smooth muscle cell proliferation, migration and phenotypic changes and finally extracellular matrix remodelling.

The lymphatic vascular system is formed and grows after the vascular system through a process named lymphangiogenesis; during embryonic development, a subpopulation of venous endothelial cells (VEC) localized into the dorsolateral wall of the cardinal veins acquires lymphatic skills and subsequently the specification in **lymphatic endothelial progenitors**. Under specific stimuli, these progenitors bud from the cardinal vein and migrate into the mesenchyme of the surrounding tissues; in this area, they differentiate into lymphatic endothelial cells (LEC) and form intermediate structures or primitive lymphatic sacs before forming the entire lymphatic network.

---

[5] Shear stress corresponds to the friction of blood on the vascular walls. Under normal conditions, the shear stress is laminar and uniform leading to up-regulation of genes with antioxidant, antithrombotic and anti-adhesive properties that perform vascular protection activities. In pathological conditions, the shear stress is non-laminar or turbulent causing a down-regulation of these protective genes and the endothelium results less protected from atherogenic agents when it is subjected to a slow and turbulent flow.

5.2 Transcriptional control of vascular specification

5.2.1 Endothelial specification

Several transcription factors involved in the regulation of endothelial development and differentiation have been identified in recent years; most of them perform similar functions in haematopoiesis. This is possible as the two systems share a common embryological origin; as seen, the interconnection between haematopoiesis and the vascular system also persists in the adult body as demonstrated by the existence of CD14+ endothelial cell progenitors.

Tal1 is a transcriptional factor required for blood and endothelial separation; it is early expressed by endothelial and haematopoietic cells during embryonic development; loss of Tal1 causes damage to vasculogenesis without effects on endothelial fate.

In the family of **GATA** zinc finger transcription factors, **GATA2** is the most expressed by endothelium; **GATA2** is important for the regulation of haematopoiesis and specific endothelium genes; it is thought to be involved in haemangioblast specification in fact, studies performed on embryonic stem cells showed that **GATA2** is indispensable for the development of ancestral cells with a haemangioblast-like phenotype (flk-1+/Tal1+).

Several transcriptional factors of the **Forkhead box family (Fox)** are expressed in endothelial cells and their precursors. Among these, some members of the **FoxC** family are crucial for correct vascular morphogenesis; moreover, FoxC1 and FoxC2 play an essential role in the determination of arteries and lymphatic vessels. Other studies suggest that FoxC1 and FoxC2 are involved in the Notch signalling pathway regulating the Hey2 target gene expression.

Zinc finger proteins of the **Kruppel-like family (KLF)** represent a large family of transcriptional factors involved in different aspects of gene expression regulation, such as differentiation, embryogenesis and tumour development. In the endothelium, these proteins are exclusively expressed after the onset of endothelial specification.

The **Ets family** is made up of several subfamilies of transcriptional factors involved in the endothelial cell fate; one of their main features is that they are MAPK / ERK substrate. **Ets Fli-1 transcription factor** is early expressed by endothelial and haematopoietic precursors even if its destruction does not lead to important vasculogenesis alterations, while it has a negative impact on haematopoiesis. **Ets Etv2** is a crucial transcriptional factor for endothelial and haematopoietic differentiation; loss of Ets Etv2 function has dramatic consequences on vasculogenesis and haematopoiesis; in addition to its detention in the early stages of vascular development, Etv2 functions as activator of numerous endothelial genes, such as flk1, Tal1, Mef2c, Pecam and Tie2, directly or by binding with specific promoters.

Although several transcription factors are present, none of these is selectively expressed by the endothelium or endothelial progenitor cells, suggesting that the endothelial gene expression is synergically regulated by a range of transcriptional factors; this idea is supported by the existence of various endothelial gene promoters with many transcription factor binding sites. Based on this evidence, it is possible to suppose that endothelial fate is guided by multiple acceptor sites linked to their factors; in this context and as suggested by different authors, **GATA2, Fli-1 and Tal1 form a self-amplifying gene regulatory network** essential for endothelial and haematopoietic gene expression (Figure 5.3).

5.2.2 Arteriovenous specification

Arteriovenous cell differentiation is molecularly controlled by the receptor tyrosine kinase of the **Ephrin (Eph)** family. Specifically during the vascular plexus development, EphrinB2 is early expressed by arterial endothelial cells, while its receptor EphB4 labels venous endothelial cells; the lack of EphrinB2 causes defective vascular remodelling.

Several transcription factors and signalling pathways induce arteriovenous specification; among these, **Notch signalling** and

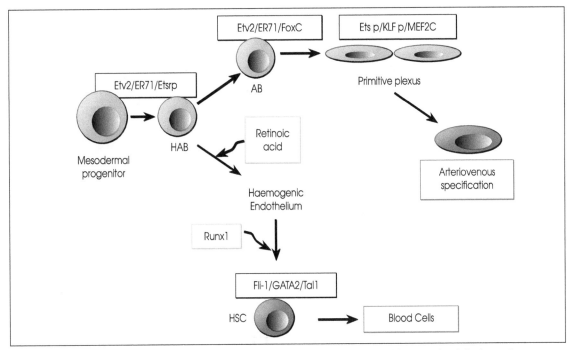

Figure 5.3. Transcriptional control of vasculogenesis. AB: angioblast; HAB: haemangioblast; HSC: haematopoietic stem cell.

COUP-TFII represent the main regulators of endothelial cell fate that cover arterial, venous and lymphatic vessels. In the arterial endothelium, one of Notch's functions is to repress the potential venous destiny; after interaction with its ligand, the Notch receptor undergoes a proteolytic cleavage freeing the cytoplasmic domain (Notch intracellular domain, NICD); **NICD** translocates into the nucleus and promotes the expression of target genes, including **Hey1** and **Hey2**, that are responsible for arterial specification. Venous specification seems to be promoted by COUP-TFII, a nuclear receptor encoded by the Nr2f2 gene, that could correspond to the endogenous ligand of retinoic acid. COUP-TFII performs its function by repressing the signalling pathway controlled by Notch; the COUP-TFII expression is specifically restricted to the venous endothelium and lymphatics (Figure 5.4).

5.2.3 Lymphatic specification

The specification of lymphatic endothelial cell progenitors begins after arteriovenous differentiation; it is promoted by Prox1, Sox18 and COUP-TFII transcription factors expressed by a subpopulation of VECs residing in the cardinal veins. In addition to these regulator factors, other molecules have been identified as controllers of the later stages of differentiation, lymphatic sac formation and lymphatic identity maintenance. These determinants of lymphatic specification are illustrated in Figure 5.4.

The **Prox1** transcriptional factor represents the main regulator of lymphatic fate. It is expressed by a subpopulation of VECs that acquires lymphatic competences, the so-called LEC progenitors (VEC Prox1); its loss causes a failure in LEC differentiation and consequently a lack of lymphatic system development. Studies performed on mice revealed that, in embryonic life, Prox1 is crucial in the commitment of VECs to the lymphatic phenotype while, in the adult stage, it is essential for maintaining LEC identity. Furthermore, an interesting aspect is that most VEC Prox1 give rise to lymphatic vessels, while a small part remains in the cardinal vein to form the lymphovenous valves.

Sox18 is a transcription factor of the SoxF family acting in the early stages of lymphatic

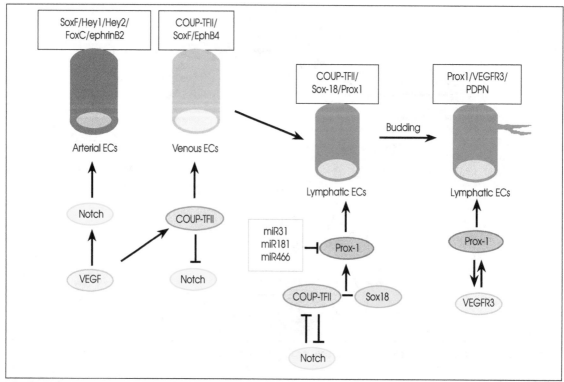

Figure 5.4. Molecular control of arteriovenous and lymphatic specification. ECs: endothelial cells.

system development. Sox18 is expressed in the VEC subpopulation before the Prox1 factor. Further, Sox18 cooperating with COUP-TFII induces Prox1 expression in the VEC population starting the specification of LEC progenitors; in fact, studies conducted on mice embryos mutated for the Sox18 gene, the Prox1 inactivation in the VEC population results in a block of lymphatic vascular specification. Furthermore, Sox18 activity is strictly limited to development without any involvement in the expansion and maturation of the lymphatic plexus contrary to Prox1 activity.

COUP-TFII, the nuclear receptor of the hormone receptor superfamily, is involved with early and late lymphangiogenesis processes. The cooperative work between COUP-TFII and Sox18 is potentially involved in Prox1 activation; moreover, studies demonstrate that COUP-TFII is able to directly interact with Prox1 in LEC progenitors and this cooperation is useful for controlling LEC identity. The absence of COUP-TFII expression produces

alterations in LEC progenitor differentiation, while the inactivation of its functions implicates a numerical reduction of LECs.

Recent findings report that the Notch signalling pathway is involved in lymphatic vascular system development. The Notch signal represses Prox1 and COUP-TFII expression causing a block in both the specification and branching of LEC progenitors; studies on *in vivo* embryonic lymphangiogenesis suggest that the Notch down-regulation results in the production of a growing number of LEC progenitors.

Recently, various studies have reported the potential role of microRNAs[6] as regulators of LEC identity through control of Prox1 mRNA and proteins. **MiR-31** exerts its

---

[6]   MicroRNA or miR are small endogenous molecules of non-coding RNA with a single filament and formed by 20-22 nucleotides; they are active in the transcriptional and post-transcriptional regulation of gene expression.

function on *in vitro* lymphatic-specific commitment by negatively modulating the Prox1 transcription. **MiR-181** is a negative regulator of lymphatic differentiation; higher miR-181 levels in embryonic LECs result in an inhibition of Prox1 gene and protein expression. In a human corneal injury, **miR-466** has been seen to be able to repress Prox1 expression causing a lymphangiogenesis failure.

Following LEC specification, these progenitors leave the cardinal veins and bud into the dorso-lateral surrounding mesenchyme through the **VEGF-C / VEGFR-3 signalling pathway** including VEGF-C, its receptors, VEGFR-3 (Flt4) and Neuropilin 2 (Nrp-2), and the secreted factor CCBE1. In experimental models, a VEGF-C overexpression or down-regulation causes pathological states; VEGFR-3 is important for LEC progenitor budding. Regarding Nrp-2, it works together with VEGFR-3 for the correct LEC sprouting. Furthermore, it has been suggested that the increase of interstitial fluid flux could result in a VEGFR-3 increment that, in turn, seems to induce the LEC proliferation. The CCBE1 functional inactivation blocks the LEC progenitors from budding, keeping them in the cardinal vein with the consequent absence of lymphatic development.

The LECs' sprouting/budding into the surrounding mesenchyme is also promoted by variations of the **Podoplanin** (PDPN) marker; it is exclusively expressed by Prox1⁺ LEC progenitors after the complete abandonment of embryonic vein endothelium permitting to discriminate the Prox1⁺ LEC progenitors of the cardinal veins from Prox1⁺/PDPN⁺ LECs involved in lymphatic sac formation.

5.3 Molecular control of angiogenesis

Angiogenesis is promoted by signals and growth factors present in the extracellular microenvironment; among these, the most important are the hypoxic signal and that mediated by VEGF-A. Vascular cells possess specific sensors for responding to oxygen variations by modulating hypoxia-inducing transcriptional factors of the HIF family.

HIF-1 is an heterodimer formed by two subunits, α and β; under normoxic conditions, HIF α is hydroxylated by HIF prolyl-hydroxylase enzyme and subsequently degraded by proteasome; in hypoxic conditions, it is not hydroxylased, it accumulates in the cytoplasm, binds the HIF β forming a heterodimer that acts as a nuclear transcriptional factor. In hypoxia environments, HIF-1 promotes critical genes for cell survival like those encoding glycolytic enzymes for favouring ATP synthesis independently by oxygen availability and VEGF for promoting angiogenesis.

VEGF-A[7] plays an important role in angiogenesis by inducing endothelial cell commitment; during this process, the vascular peduncle is formed by endothelial cells endowed with a distinct phenotype, functions and gene expression; the cells located into the apex of the peduncle ("tip endothelial cells") drive the migratory process. Tip cells are characterized by an elongated shape and develop long filopodi that overexpress KDR, Fli1 and other receptors, thus functioning as sensors of the surrounding environment. Under VEGF induction, tip cells modify their gene expression overexpressing greater levels of PDGFb, Dil4, Unc5b, Kdr, and Flt4 genes than other surrounding endothelial cells; the cells at the base of the peduncle ("stalk endothelial cells") are highly proliferating under VEGF-A stimulus and contain few filopodi (Figure 5.5).

Neo-formed vessels can stabilize or regress; among the factors involved, the Notch signalling pathway plays a fundamental role in new vessel stabilization through **Nrarp,** one of its target genes; **Notch** signalling promotes the expression of basement membrane components, such as Collagen IV and Laminin, at the level of the peduncular endothelium; moreover, it acts on the peduncle cell proliferation in syn-

---

[7] VEGF-A promotes differentiation, proliferation, migration, junction formation and inhibits apoptosis.

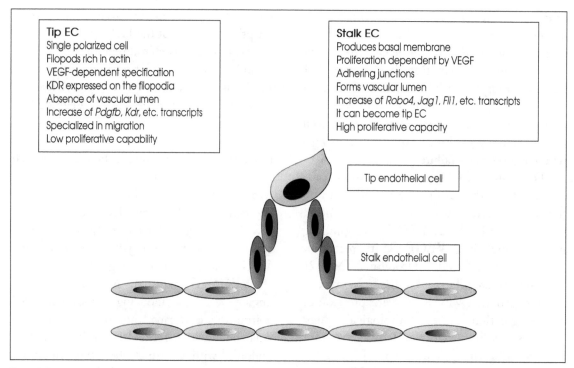

Figure 5.5. Angiogenesis mechanisms. Phenotypic and molecular differences of vascular peduncular endothelial cells.

ergism with **Wnt** signalling. Nrarp destruction causes the destabilization of new vessels due to junctional apparatus alterations followed by low peduncle cell proliferation and vascular peduncle regression which becomes a sort of tube without endothelium and is delimited by the lamina of the basal membrane.

5.4 Structure of the adult vascular system

5.4.1 Vascular system

In the vascular system we can recognize substantially three types of vessels: arteries, veins and capillaries; the latter are microvessels, part of so-called microcirculation.

The **arteries** distribute blood containing nutrients, oxygen, water and hormones from the cardiac ventricular chambers to the peripheral tissues; altogether in the arteries there are three distinct layers, termed tunics: the inner layer (tunica intima), consisting of a single continuous sheet of endothelial cells resting on the basement membrane; tunica intima is also characterized by a thin band of poorly cellu-

larized subendothelial connective matrix. The middle layer (tunica media) is separated from the intima by the internal elastic lamina; here there are multiple layers of contractile smooth muscle cells which are immersed in a stroma rich in elastic lamellae. The outer layer (tunica adventitia), separated from the media by the external elastic lamina, consists of connective tissue with fibroblasts, adipocytes, microvessels (vasa vasorum), and nerve fibres.

Based on their architecture, diameter and function, the arteries are distinguished in elastic and muscular arteries. Elastic arteries are characterized by a high calibre, a richness in elastic tissue and a low capacity to contract; this class of arteries includes the aorta, the proximal tract of the aortic collaterals and the pulmonary artery; the tunica media is composed of lamellar units consisting of incomplete elastic laminae that compartmentalize the smooth muscle cells. Functionally, this neat elastic structure allows the vessels to dilate during cardiac systole and to return the accumulated energy in the form of kinetic energy, with an elastic return during diastole which promotes an effective propulsion of the heart wave.

Medium-calibre arteries are called muscular arteries; they have lumen comprised between 5 and 2.5 mm, a thin intima, a well developed internal elastic lamina and a media constituted by concentric layers of smooth muscle cells with sparse elastic tissue; the greater amount of smooth muscle cells combined with fewer elastic laminae results in less elasticity but a better ability to constrict and dilate. This class includes the arteries of the limbs and those of the internal organs, e.g. the femoral, brachial, and coronary arteries; these vessels ensure peripheral distribution of blood.

The **veins** carry blood from the capillaries and then from the peripheral tissues to the heart; compared to the arteries, they have a simplified architecture and show a greater development of the adventitia; in the limbs, the veins present an additional layer of smooth muscle cells arranged longitudinally, and, at more or less constant intervals, flaps or semilunar valves that prevent the retrograde flow of blood resulting from the compressive effect exerted by the muscular masses.

The microcirculation includes small-calibre vessels, such as capillaries, arterioles, and venules. The post-capillary venules vary in diameter between 10 and 35 µm, while the venules, with a larger diameter, up to 100 µm, have a structure not very different from that of the arterioles from which they are distinguished by the elongated or branched form, the extremely thin wall, the absence of the internal elastic lamina and only a few smooth muscle cell layers. The small arteries have a diameter of less than 1 mm and are structurally similar to the medium-sized muscle arteries. Arterioles have a calibre of less than 300 µm and are constituted by an endothelial lining, by a few concentric layers of smooth muscle cells, while the adventitia is poorly defined, fading with the surrounding connective tissue; these arterial vessels have the task of distributing the blood flow in the capillary circulation and regulating the peripheral resistance and, therefore,

blood pressure. The **capillaries**, with a diameter of less than 20 µm, represent the site where the diffusion of gases and nutrients takes place. The capillary wall consists of endothelial cells resting on a basal membrane and a thin external layer of pericytes, mesenchymal cells characterized by contractile activity and by cytoplasmic prolongations through which they surround the capillary tube; the pericytes, whose function is still not completely defined, are surrounded by a basal membrane that continues, merging, with that of the surrounding endothelium. They are supposed to be the precursors of tissue-specific mesenchymal stem cells.

5.4.2 Lymphatics

Closely related to the vascular system, the lymphatic system specifically performs the functions listed in Box 5.1.

BOX 5.1. Functions of the lymphatic system.

Transport of immune cells to the lymph nodes
Maintenance of interstitial fluid homeostasis
Absorption of particular lipoproteins called chylomicrons through intestinal microvilli

---

Changes in the development or function of the lymphatic vasculature are associated with various pathological conditions, syndromes or diseases, such as lymphoedema, obesity, hypertension, inflammatory diseases and metastatic tumour dissemination.

The lymphatic system is present in all mammals but not in all organs; in fact, it is absent in the brain and in the retina due to the poor permeability of their barriers; they are also absent in the pancreatic islands, in the bone, in the cartilage, in the placenta, in the epidermis, in the teeth, in the hair, in the nails, in the thymus and in the cornea. The first description of the lymphatics dates back to Aristotle and Hippocrates and the first formal description is found in *De lactibus sive lacteis venis* by Gaspare Aselli. The human lymphatic system develops after the vascular system, between the 6th and 7th week of embryo life.

It is formed by a system of vessels that runs parallel to the arteries and veins, forming a second circulation system in which the lymph flows; this is a transparent or milky liquid containing proteins, white blood cells, macromolecules and lipids. Lymph circulation is supported by the contraction of smooth muscle cells and by muscular masses, the heartbeat, the pulsation of arteries, and the respiratory and peristaltic movements. Anatomically, the lymphatic system is made up of a hierarchical network of vessels terminating in blind-ended lymphatic capillaries in the peripheral tissues, which drain the lymph into increasingly larger collecting vessels, the pre-collecting vessels and collecting vessels (pre-lymph and post-lymph nodes), which in turn converge into the two large lymphatic vessels of the body called the thoracic duct and the right lymphatic duct; these finally drain the lymph into the venous circulation through the venae cavae. The lymph nodes of the humoral and cell-mediated immune response are located along the course of the collecting vessels; in addition, other lymphoid organs are present, such as the thymus, spleen and bone marrow with highly specialized functions. Lymphatic capillaries have a thin wall composed of a single layer of lymphatic endothelial cells (LEC) without smooth muscle cell (SMC) / pericyte coverage, and an intermittent or absent basement membrane. LECs are interconnected by discontinuous intercellular junctions; the thickness of the capillaries ranges from 50 to 100 nm, reaching 6 μm in the nuclear region of the LECs. LECs have an oak-leaf morphology, with poor cytoplasm and numerous longitudinally oriented cytoplasmic filaments implicated in contractile function. Lymphatic capillaries are externally anchored to the collagen and elastin fibres of the surrounding matrix through filaments of Emilin-1 and fibrillin. As the interstitial pressure increases, the anchoring filaments stretch the LECs which, by opening the intercellular junctions up to several micrometres, allow the fluids accumulated in the gap to pass through their lumen. Contrary to lymphatic capillaries,

the larger lymphatic vessels have a peri-endothelial layer of smooth muscle cells; the continuous basal membrane and LECs are joined by intercellular junctions similar to hinges that prevent the lymph from leaking out of the lumen. There are also luminal valves that prevent the retrograde flow of the lymph and force it to move unidirectionally.

5.5 The endothelial cell

5.5.1 Morphology

The endothelial cell internally covers all vascular vessels and represents the interface between the vascular wall and the circulating blood; the endothelial cell performs multiple functions relevant to fundamental biological processes, such as vessel tone control, nutrient traffic and delivery to cells and tissues, the maintenance of blood fluidity, the regulation of permeability and the formation of new vessels (angiogenesis). The morphological and functional integrity of the endothelium is therefore essential for the maintenance of vascular wall homeostasis. The endothelial cell is an elongated and flat cell, of variable thickness between 0.1 and 1 μm, of an average diameter of 10-15 μm and of variable length from 25 to 50 μm. In a healthy vessel, the endothelial cells are oriented along the direction of blood flow (Figure 5.6A); however, the morphology varies according to the anatomical site (arteries, veins, microcirculation), and environmental conditions (dynamic adaptation that also involves different phenotypic expressions). For example, in the regions of bifurcations, endothelial cells tend to assume a polygonal shape; in these areas we also observe a greater adhesion of blood mononuclear cells. In the areas of vortex flow, the endothelium presents anisocytosis (heterogeneous forms and sizes) and altered orientation, often with bizarre morphologies (Figure 5.6B). The cell surface is predominantly smooth with delicate filopodia; in addition to the common organelles, the endothelium presents a well-developed cytoskeleton; the non-contractile cytoskele-

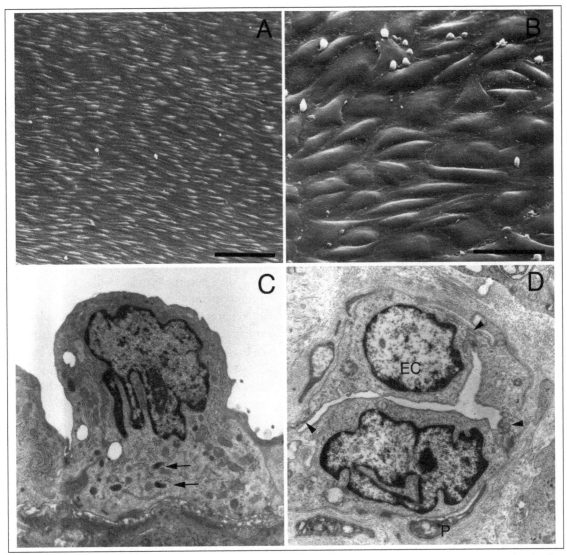

Figure 5.6. Endothelial cell morphological characteristics. A) In the normal vascular wall, endothelial cells are aligned along the direction of blood flow. SEM. Bar = 100um. B) In the areas of vortex flow, endothelial cells show heterogeneous forms and sizes and altered orientation. SEM. Bar = 50um. C) In the cytoplasm of endothelial cells, there are many bar-shaped, electron-dense Weibel-Palade bodies (arrows). TEM. Original magnification x6000. D) Endothelial cells (EC) are joined by numerous junctional complexes (arrowheads); ECs are surrounded by pericytes (P). TEM. Original magnification x4600.

ton is represented by cytoplasmic intermediate filaments (10 nm in diameter) consisting mainly of vimentin. Endothelial cells also have the ability to express intermediate filaments of simple epithelia, such as cytokeratins (Cks) 8 and 18; this happens during fetal life, while in adults the expression of Cks occurs in stressful or pathological conditions. The contractile cytoskeleton is represented by thin contractile filaments (6-8 nm) of actin and myosin. Actin filaments are observed in the subplasmalemmal

position, in correspondence with junctions or grouped with type II myosin to form transversely striated filamentary bundles, known as stress fibres; these latter are a functional cell adaptation to cell adhesion and locomotion. One unique feature of the endothelium is the presence of the Weibel-Palade bodies (rod-shaped microtubulated bodies), which are seen only ultrastructurally (Figure 5.6C). They are ovoid or bar-shaped, moderately electron dense, cytoplasmic granules; they are bounded by a membrane and contain a parallel array of microtubules embedded in the electron dense matrix. The Weibel-Palade bodies contain the von Willebrand factor (vWF), a protein that stabilizes the circulating factor VIII, and which is essential for the adhesion of platelets to the subendothelial collagen matrix in case of endothelial damage. Another distinctive feature of the endothelium is the presence of numerous 70 nm-sized pinocytosis vesicles; they allow the bidirectional transport of water soluble small molecules (transcytosis). The vesicles are observed mainly near the plasma membrane from which they originate by invagination or fusion. In some cases, the vesicles can merge to form transendothelial channels; this latter situation is typical of the liver, endocrine, and kidney endothelia. A more complex and specific transport system is that which allows the internalization of more complex metabolites, such as low-density lipoproteins (LDL); these are internalized at the level of specific plasma membrane domains (coated pits). Once they are bound to the specific receptor, LDLs are internalized into small coated vesicles, which have a peculiar lumpy morphology.

Endothelial cells are connected to each other by junctional complexes (Figure 5.6D) that can be of three types: occludent junctions (tight junctions), intermediate or adherent junctions (adherens junctions), communicating junctions (gap junctions). These latter are seen exclusively in the arterial endothelium, where they allow the electrical and metabolic coupling between cells. There are no typical epithelial junctions, desmosomes. Junctional complexes are characterized by the proteins that make up the structure. The tight and adherent junctions perform numerous functions: they help maintain cell shape and allow cell stabilization, they control and regulate permeability to water and solutes in the intercellular spaces. They are also able to respond to haemodynamic changes and to chemical factors delivering nuclear signals.

The tight junctions prevent the free passage of the water-soluble molecules along the intercellular space. In this type of junctions, the intercellular space becomes almost virtual in correspondence of a branching network of sealing strands composed of bulding proteins. By means of the freeze-etching technique, the membranes appear to be covered by a series of branched projections and protuberances; the protrusions are portions of the main integral membrane proteins involved in the formation of the junctions: occludins, claudins, and Junction Adhesion Molecules (JAM), which protrude on the outer face of the membranes and are joined together by non-covalent bonds. These proteins form a belt around the cell that prevents the passage of integral membrane proteins; thus the membrane is divided into two or more specific, functionally distinct domains. Other proteins involved in the cytoplasmic side are the proteins of Zonula Occludens (ZO proteins), cingulin and ZONAB. Under the electron microscope, the tight junctions have a three-layer laminar structure: the two outermost layers are represented by the innermost phospholipid sheets of the membranes involved in the junction, while the innermost one is given by the fusion of the two external phospholipid layers of the membranes. Consequently, the cell membrane as a whole, at the tight junction, takes on a pentalaminar aspect as three electron-dense bands are intercalated to two electron-lucent bands.

Adherens junctions are extremely dynamic multiprotein complexes that mediate, in all cells, adhesion between identical cell types (homotypic adhesion). They maintain the architectural integrity of the tissues and provide mechanical support to the cells, constituting a device through which the applied forces are broken down into many directions; moreover, they are involved in the maintenance of tissue homeostasis and in the control of permeability. Recently it has been hypothesized that these junctions can act as cellular sensors able to mediate the inhibition of proliferation, promote cell survival and modulate the shape and polarity of cells. Adhesion is made possible thanks to the presence of adhesion proteins, the

VE- and N-cadherins; cadherins, of which at least 80 members are known in mammals, are integral proteins that have a domain outside the cell that, through calcium ions, interacts with the homologous domain of another cadherin present in the adjacent cell. VE-cadherin is mainly expressed in endothelia; in the cytoplasmic side, VE-cadherin is bound by adaptive proteins to actin microfilaments which run parallel in a subplasmalemmal position. Vinculin, α-catenin, and α-actinin are some adaptive proteins. VE-cadherin then binds directly to β-catenin, to p120ctn (γ-catenin) and to placoglobin; β-catenin and p120ctn can also act as transcription factors. Under the electron microscope the adherens junctions appear as discrete areas of symmetrical thickening of the plasma membranes delimiting an intercellular space of about 15-25 nm.

5.5.2 Heterogeneity

It is well known that the major vascular diseases affect specific areas and structures of the vascular system; atherosclerosis is a disease of medium- and large-calibre arteries, whereas vasculitis generally affects small- to medium-calibre arteries. Veins are not affected by atherosclerosis, unless they are used as a graft in the arterial district. Thrombosis takes on different clinical and pathological features depending on whether the vessel involved is arterial or venous. This diversity depends on multiple causes that also include the embryological, morphological, phenotypic and functional heterogeneity of the cells that make up the vascular wall.

The endothelial cells covering the capillaries of some organs or tissues have a specific morphology; for example, the endothelium that lines the retinal and cerebral vessels is of the continuous type and has numerous tight junctions to guarantee the correct function of the blood-brain barrier. The endothelial cells covering the sinusoids of the bone marrow, liver and spleen are discontinuous to facilitate cellular traffic between the two vascular and tissue sides. The endothelium that covers the capillaries of the endocrine glands, kidney and intestinal villi is fenestrated to promote permeability, filtration and absorption.

5.5.3 Functions

In physiological conditions, the endothelium, through a subtle and delicate balance between factors most often characterized by opposing actions, ensures the maintenance of blood fluidity, of normal vessel tone, of parietal tone and therefore, ultimately, of the patency of vessels and tissue homeostasis.

Schematically, endothelial integrity is necessary for the normal function of haemostasis; in fact, endothelial injury results in (i) the exposure of the subendothelial matrix to the circulating platelets which adhere to the collagen and then aggregate and (ii) the release of the tissue factor (TF) which triggers the activation of the coagulation factors. If not balanced by reparative phenomena, endothelial damage starts a series of cellular and molecular responses that are the basis of atherosclerosis. As summarized in Table 5.1, endothelial cells have a very complex secretoma; they in fact synthesize and release molecules with multiple functions: endothelial cells produce molecules that facilitate platelet adhesion (vWF), molecules that dissociate platelet aggregates (ADAMTS 13[8]) through vWF cleavage, molecules that inhibit platelet adhesion (prostacyclin and nitric oxide), molecules endowed with local fibrinolytic activity (tissue plasminogen activator or tPA, urokinase-type plasminogen activator or uPA and its uPAR receptor, capable of binding plasma uPA), molecules endowed with local anti-fibrinolytic activity (plasminogen activator inhibitor or PAI); the endothelium participates in the regulation of vessel tone by acting on smooth muscle cells through the release of vasodilatory substances (nitric oxide, prostacyclin and the

---

[8] ADAMTS 13 is a metalloproteinase secreted in blood that degrades large vWF multimers, decreasing their activity; its genetic deficiency is responsible for the familiar variant of thrombotic thrombocytopenic purpura.

Table 5.1. Endothelial cell secretome with specific activities.	
Haemostasis control	
Control of coagulation	Binding of antithrombin III Thrombomodulin (TM) expression and protein C activation Expression of endothelial protein C receptor (EPCR) Release of tissue factor pathway inhibitor (TFPI)
Control of platelet adhesion and activation	Production and acute release of vWF Cleavage of ULvWF by ADAMTS13 Electrical repulsion by negatively charged heparan sulfates Reduction of platelet activation by release of NO and PGI_2/PGE2 Surface expression of ectonucleotidases
Fibrinolysis	Synthesis and acute release of t-PA Induction of PAI-1 u-PA/UPAR and MT1-MMP
Platelet disintegration	Thrombin-cleaved ADAMTS18 (C-terminal fragment)
Vascular tone control	
Vasodilators	NO PGI_2 EDHF
Vasoconstrictors	TXA_2 ET-1 ACE
Lipid Metabolism	Lipoprotein – lipase LDL receptor
	IL-1, 6, 8 MCP CAMs E-selectin
Growth and survival control	PDGF EDGF FGF IGF TGF-β CSFs

Abbreviations: vWF von Willebrand factor, ULvWF ultra-large VWF, ADAMTS13 a disintegrin and metalloproteinase with a thrombospondin type 1 motif, member 13, NO nitric oxide, PGI_2 prostacyclin, PGE2 prostaglandin E2, t-PA tissue-type plasminogen activator, PAI-1 plasminogen activator inhibitor-1, u-PA urokinase-type plasminogen activator, UPAR u-PA receptor, MT1-MMP membrane-type matrix metalloproteinase-1, C-terminal carboxy-terminal, EDHF endothelium derived hyperpolarizing factor, TXA_2 thromboxane, ET-1 endothelin-1, ACE angiotensin converting enzyme, LDL low density lipoprotein, IL interleukin, MCP monocyte chemoattractant protein, CAMs cell adhesion molecules, PDGF platelet derived growth factor, EDGF endothelial derived growth factor, FGF fibroblast growth factor, IGF insulin-like growth factor, TGF-b transforming growth factor β, CSFs colony stimulating factors.

elusive endothelium-derived hyperpolarizing factor (EDHF)[9] and vasoconstrictive molecules (endothelin [ET], especially ET-1 and Platelet-Activating Factor [PAF]); they modulate cell proliferation and inflammatory processes by actively participating in the maintenance of vessel geometry through the synthesis of cytokines (interleukin-1 [IL-1], IL-5, IL-6, IL-8, IL-11, IL-15), growth factors (colony-stimulating factor [CSF], granulocyte-CSF [G-CSF], macrophage CSF [M-CSF] and granulocyte-mac-

[9] Experimentally, when the two well-known endothelial vasodilators, nitric oxide and prostacyclin, are inhibited there is still another factor causing the small arteries to dilate; this factor was called EDHF. To date, no chemical factor responsible for the EDHF-induced vasodilation has been identified. Therefore the identity of EDHF is still debated. Among the vasodilator mechanisms that were associated with EDHF, there are the epoxyeicosatrienoic acids, the K ions, a sulphur signal,

C natriuretic peptide, electric signals through gap junctions.

rophage CSF [GM-CSF]), and chemokines (monocyte chemotactic protein-1 [MCP-1], RANTES, and growth-related oncogene protein-α [GRO-α]). The endothelial cells also express complex activity on the cell membrane, such as procoagulant activity (TF or tissue thromboplastin, which activates the coagulation Factor VII which in turn results, downstream, in the activation of the Factors X of Stuart and IX of Christmas; Thrombin receptor or Protease-Activated Receptor-1 [PAR1]; Fibrin and Fibrinogen Degradation Factors receptors), and anticoagulants (heparan-sulfate, antithrombin III, trombomodulin, etc.); the endothelium expresses on the surface molecules that mediate the adhesion of the mononuclear blood cells through interaction between complementary molecules present on the surface of the single cells involved. The most characterized molecules are selectin E (CD62E) and ICAM-1 (inter-cellular adhesion molecule-1, CD54) which mediate the adhesion of polymorphonuclear and mono-lymphocytes, in an IL-1 and TNFα dependent manner.

5.5.4 Phenotypic markers

Endothelial cells can be identified by flow cytometer, immunofluorescent and immunohistochemical techniques using monoclonal or, more occasionally, polyclonal antibodies, specifically directed against antigenic determinants typical of molecules expressed by the normal or dysfunctional endothelium. In some cases, alternative markers, lectins, or ligands (LDL) of specific membrane receptors may be used.

Table 5.2 lists the main vascular endothelial phenotypic markers.

The identification of specific molecules able to control the lymphangiogenesis (development and growth of lymphatic vessels) or markers exclusively express by LECs has made possible to distinguish the lymphatic endothelium by vascular endothelium.

Table 5.3 shows the phenotypic markers of lymphatic endothelial cells.

5.6 Circulating endothelial progenitors of the adult

The discovery of persistence in the adult organism of endothelial progenitors is one of the most important research findings in recent years. In fact, it has always been considered that in the adult the formation of new vessels occurred exclusively from pre-existent vessels through the processes of angiogenesis and arterogenesis; the possibility of *de novo* formation of vessels starting from the differentiation of vascular progenitors, or vasculogenesis, was considered exclusive to embryonic life. In 1997 Asahara et al. harvested a subclass of CD34+ haematopoietic stem cells from the mononuclear blood fraction capable of differentiating into mature endothelial cells when cultured on fibronectin-coated plates in the presence of angiopoietic factors; these cells, called **endothelial progenitor cells** (EPC), derive from bone marrow angioblasts and can be characterized on the basis of the phenotype as CD133+, CD34+, KDR+ cells. EPCs also have the ability, like mature endothelial cells, to incorporate acetylated LDL and to selectively bind to the **Ulex Europaeus** lectin (Figure 5.7). They also have the ability to expand clonally, possess a good proliferative capacity, and are able, under appropriate induction, to express mature endothelium molecules.

However, subsequent studies on experimental models have shown a certain heterogeneity of isolated populations; in fact, while some EPCs are able to incorporate into new vascular structures, others contribute to vasculogenesis exclusively through their secretory ability that, in any case, is essential in supporting *in vivo* the formation of the new vessels.

Accordingly, the group of Yoder et al. was able to isolate from the mononuclear blood fraction a subtype of EPCs characterized by the expression of CD14, a monocytic marker. This progenitor (CD14+ EPC) is derived from CD14+ circulating cells and co-expresses endothelial markers, such as CD31, CD105, CD144, vWF, nitric oxide endothelial synthase

Table 5.2. Main markers used to identify vascular endothelial cells on a molecular basis.

CD31 (PECAM-1). Adhesion and signalling molecule located at specific membrane functional domains.

CD34. Surface molecule expressed by endothelial progenitors, mature endothelial cells, mesenchymal stromal cells; CD34 is an adhesion molecule that mediates cell-to-cell adhesion even though little is known about its exact function.

CD54 (ICAM-1). Adhesion molecule (inter-cellular adhesion molecule 1); mediates the adhesion between endothelium and leucocytes.

CD105 (Endoglin). Surface molecule expressed by endothelial cells and mesenchymal stromal cells; it is a good marker of angiogenesis; it is part of the TGF β receptor complex.

CD146. It is also known as the melanoma cell adhesion molecule (MCAM); it is the receptor for laminin α 4, a matrix molecule that is broadly expressed within the vascular wall.

Selectin E (CD62E). Molecule that mediates the adhesion of leukocytes; it is expressed following activation of the endothelium.

KDR (VEGFR-2). Tyrosine kinase receptor of VEGF (vascular endothelial growth factor receptor); it is expressed early by endothelial precursors; it is essential for the differentiation of precursors into endothelial cells.

Flt-1 (VEGFR-1). Also known as Fms-related tyrosine kinase 1 (vascular endothelial growth factor / vascular permeability factor receptor); it is a tyrosine kinase receptor with high affinity for VEGF.

ICAM-2. Molecule expressed in junctions (inter-cellular adhesion molecule 2); restricted expression to endothelial cells and megakaryocytes.

EPCR (Endothelial protein C receptor or CD201). Glycosylated type I transmembrane protein; primarily expressed in the endothelial cells of the veins and arteries of the heart and lungs.

ESAM (Endothelial cell-selective adhesion molecule). Membrane protein selectively present on endothelial tight junctions.

ac-LDL. Low-density acetylated lipoprotein conjugated with a fluorescent probe (Alexa 488). The ac-LDL is bound by a specific receptor present in the endothelial cell.

Nestin. Intermediates of type VI filaments, under the transcriptional control of WT-1, originally described in nerve cells and stem cells of the sub-ventricular zone; it is expressed in the endothelial cells of the vasa vasorum and in the course of normal, pathological and tumour neoangiogenesis.

Nucleolin. Membrane marker; expressed in the course of tumour angiogenesis.

TEM 1, 5, 7, 8. These proteins belonging to the tumour endothelial marker group are mainly expressed in the course of tumour angiogenesis.

Ulex europeaus. The lectin Ulex europeaus agglutinin of type I is selectively bound to the residues of L-fucose present in some glycoproteins of the plasma endothelial membrane.

VCAM-1 (CD106). Vascular cell adhesion molecule-1; mediates the adhesion between endothelium and leucocytes.

VE-cadherin (CD144). Cadherin expressed in adherent endothelial junctions.

vWF (von Willebrand factor). Cytoplasmic marker of mature endothelium and megakaryocytes.

WT-1 (Wilms' Tumour-1). Transcriptional factor expressed during tumour angiogenesis.

Tie-2. Tyrosine kinase receptor of angiopoietic factor angiopoietin.

Table 5.3. Main markers used to identify lymphatic endothelial cells on a molecular basis.

LYVE-1 (Lymphatic Vessel Endothelial Hyaluronan (HA) Receptor-1). Transmembrane glycoprotein expressed both on the luminal and abluminal surfaces of the lymphatic endothelium.

Podoplanin. Mucin-type transmembrane glycoprotein expressed exclusively by lymphatic endothelial cells of the lymphatic capillaries; regulates the development of the lymphatic system.

Prox-1 (Prospero homeobox protein 1). Nuclear transcription factor expressed by the progenitors of lymphatic endothelial cells; it is fundamental in the specification of lymphatic endothelial cells and in maintaining their identity.

VEGF-C. VEGFR-3 ligand (vascular endothelial growth factor receptor-3) involved in embryonic lymphatic development and tumour lymphangiogenesis.

VEGF-D. VEGFR-3 ligand (vascular endothelial growth factor receptor-3) involved in lymphatic maturation and differentiation in adults and in tumour lymphangiogenesis.

Flt-4 (VEGF-R3). Tyrosine kinase receptor of VEGF (vascular endothelial growth factor receptor); it is expressed by the lymphatic endothelial cells that line the internal surface of the lymphatic vessels. It is implicated in lymphangiogenesis.

5'-nucleotidase (CD73) Enzyme used to study the distribution and structure of lymphatic vessels.

(eNOS), Tie-2 (angiopoietin receptor), as well as myeloid markers, such as CD1a, CD14 and CD45. In culture, these progenitors form colonies giving origin to spindle cells with hybrid myeloid and endothelial cell properties; these progenitors have the capacity to release angiopoietic molecules functional to angiogenesis (Figure 5.7).

In view of these observations, some researchers have come to consider EPCs as a highly heterogeneous population and, because published studies cannot be easily compared, this has significantly hampered scientific advances in the field and clinical translation.

5.6.1 Methods of EPC isolation

Isolation of human EPCs can be performed using at least 3 distinct approaches; the EPCs that are obtained, however, have different morphological, phenotypical and functional characteristics that are the reason for the ambiguities, also definitional, still present in the specific literature.

Selection for adhesion on fibronectin. With this method the mononuclear cells of the blood are grown on plates covered with fibronectin; the cells that adhere after a few days, show the ability to internalize acetylated LDL and to selectively bind to the Ulex Europaeus lectin. This method is criticized by several authors because fibronectin is also used to induce monocyte differentiation in macrophages; since a subpopulation of monocytes / macrophages may express endothelial line markers, EPCs isolated by this method may be the expression of a macrophage population with endothelial-like phenotype.

Positive selection by specific antibodies. It is the method originally used by Asahara et al. EPCs can be separated from the other components of the mononuclear fraction of

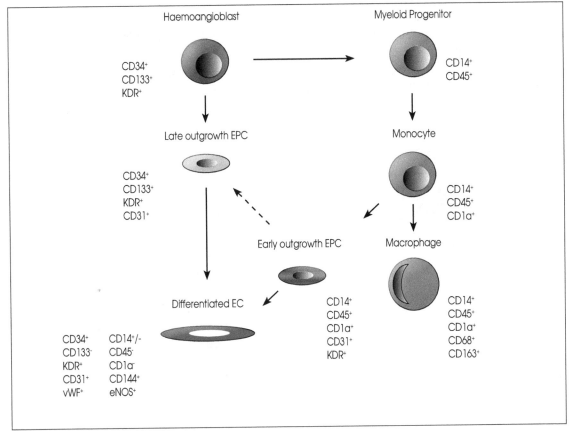

Figure 5.7. Schematic representation of presumed dual origin of circulating EPCs in adult life.

the blood by positive selection with monoclonal antibodies directed against CD34 or KDR; the separation takes place using FACS (fluorescence activated cell sorting) or by an immunomagnetic method. The isolated cells are subsequently grown in plates coated with fibronectin. Adherent cells have spindle morphology and express endothelial cell markers; at confluence they have "cobblestone" morphology. In experimental models of limb ischaemia, these EPCs demonstrated the ability to incorporate into neo-vascular structures in the ischaemic tissues. Because CD34+ KDR+ cells may also identify circulating mature endothelial cells released or detached from the intima, some research groups have included CD133 as an additional EPC marker.

Clonogenic assays. EPCs can be isolated by two types of clonogenic assays (Figure 5.8).

In the method of Hill et al., the mononuclear fraction is made to adhere to fibronectin; after 48 hours, the cells that did not adhere to the substrate are replated on fibronectin; after 5 days, cell colonies are generated with a peripheral population of expanding spindle cells. EPCs isolated by this method (colony forming unit-endothelial progenitor cells,

CFU - Hill EPCs) express both endothelial and myeloid lineage markers and are positive for CD45 hemopoietic marker; they also have the ability to differentiate into macrophages, do not form capillary structures in *in vitro* assays of angiogenesis, show low proliferative propensity and are not able to give rise to secondary colonies. These EPCs are also defined as "early outgrowth EPCs". Other synonyms are: circulating angiogenic cells (CACs), early EPCs, pro-angiogenic haematopoietic cells, haematopoietic EPCs, small EPCs, myeloid EPCs.

In the method proposed by Ingram and Yoder (endothelial colony forming cell, ECFC), the mononuclear fraction is seeded on plates coated with type I collagen and grown with endothelial growth medium (EGM-2 medium); non-adherent cells are eliminated daily and adherent cells are grown exclusively. After 14-21 days, cell colonies that express exclusively endothelial markers are generated. These EPCs, which do not express CD45 or other myeloid markers, have the ability to form secondary and tertiary colonies, to form capillary-like structures *in vitro* and, when inoculated in experimental models of ischaemia, they show the ability to incorporate into

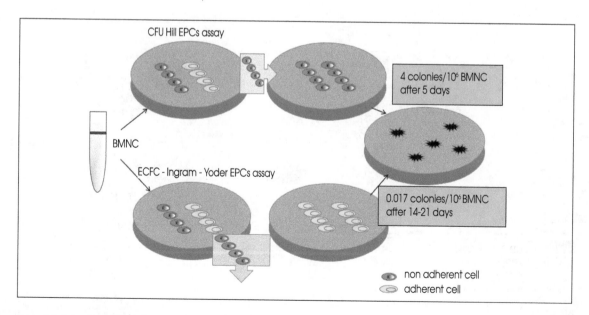

Figure 5.8. Common methods for isolating circulating EPCs. CFU - Hill EPCs and ECFC - Ingram - Yoder EPCs. BMNC: blood mononuclear cells; CFU-EC: colony forming unit-endothelial cells; ECFC: endothelial colony forming cells.

new vascular structures. These "late outgrowth EPCs" show great survival capacity, give rise to cells with cobblestone morphology, and show an almost indefinite proliferative potential, a sign of a high capacity for renewal; these EPCs are probably the endothelial progenitors that are more closer to the angioblasts. Other synonyms are: outgrowth endothelial cells, endothelial outgrowth cells, blood outgrowth endothelial cells, large EPCs, non haematopoietic EPCs.

5.6.2 Updated EPC terminology

The current EPC terminology provided by an expert group distinguishes two types of EPCs whose characteristics are listed in Table 5.4. It is recommended to use only this type of terminology and definition.

Table 5.4. Current EPC terminology and characteristics.
Myeloid Angiogenic Cells (MACs)
CD45+ CD14+ CD31+   CD146- CD34-   Conditioned media enhance endothelial capillary network formation *in vitro* and *in vivo*   Paracrine secretory activity stimulating angiogenesis
Endothelial Colony Forming Cells (ECFCs)
CD31+ CD105+ CD146+   CD45- CD14-   Intrinsic tube forming capacity *in vitro* and *in vivo*   Incorporation into new blood vessels

5.7 Resident Vascular Progenitors and Stem Cells

5.7.1 The stem cell niche of the vascular wall

In 1978, Schofield introduced the concept of a stem cell niche, defining it as a circumscribed tissue area in which stem cells maintain their potential indefinitely, thanks to a network of interactions with non-staminal resident cells, extracellular matrix components and soluble chemical compounds. The presence of tissue damage results in the rapid onset of physical and chemical signals, essential for modifying the gene expression of stem cells, inducing them to differentiate into cells functional

to tissue repair or repopulation. Ultimately, the niche saves stem cells from depletion and maintains them healthy, while protecting the host from over-exuberant or aberrant stem cell proliferation.

In the vascular wall one vasculogenic niche is located at the border between the tunica media and the adventitia; here immunohistochemical studies performed on elastic and muscular arteries have identified a phenotypic cell complexity consistent with the niche function hypothesized for this area of the vascular wall. Other elements to support this hypothesis are: the strategic arrangement at the border with the most represented portion, the tunica media, of the vascular wall; the close relationship with the vasa vasorum vascular plexus; the proximity to a typical mesoderm tissue, the adipose tissue that is abundant in the adventitia; the resistance to protracted hypoxic stress as documented with organ culture studies; the angiogenic capacity demonstrated by the "ring assay" technique; the presence of cells expressing CD117[10], a marker of stem cells and haematopoietic progenitors.

The vasa vasorum present in the adventitia of the larger vessels are capillary calibre vessels responsible for the transport of oxygen and nutrients to the deeper layers of the vascular wall and the removal of waste products from them. In normal human arteries, "hot spots" strongly expressing the stem cell markers nestin and Wilms Tumour 1 (WT-1) were identified in the vasa vasorum; these areas are candidates to represent a source of endothelial, smooth muscle and haematopoietic cells, thus contributing to the normal and pathological vascular remodelling.

It is also very likely that a further niche with dynamical characteristics will be located

---

[10] Mast/stem cell growth factor receptor (SCFR), also known as CD117, is a receptor tyrosine kinase protein that in humans is encoded by the KIT gene. Haematopoietic stem cells (HSC), multipotent progenitors (MPP), and common myeloid progenitors (CMP) express high levels of CD117.

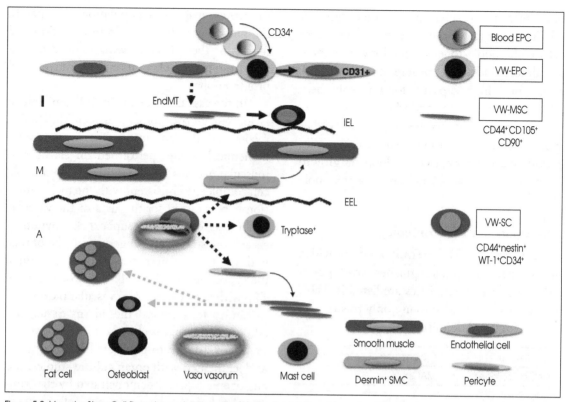

Figure 5.9. Vascular Stem Cell Domains and differentiation potential. I: intima, M: media, A: adventitia. IEL: internal elastic lamina; EEL: external elastic lamina. EndMT: endothelial-mesenchymal transition; EPC: endothelial progenitor cell; MSC: mesenchimal stromal (stem) cell; SC: stem cell; VW: vascular wall.

in the intima layer. The intimal niche, being in direct contact with the blood flow, needs to respond quickly and effectively to the continuous chemical and physical changes to which it is subjected. These characteristics could make it coincide with the recent acquisition of the concept of endothelial-mesenchymal transition, which will be briefly mentioned in a paragraph below.

A schematic representation of vascular wall domains is reported in Figure 5.9.

5.7.2 Progenitors and stem cells

Cells with characteristics similar to EPCs (CD133⁺, CD34⁺, KDR⁺) were isolated from skeletal muscle, the spleen, the liver, adipose tissue and the vascular walls.

In humans, a population of EPCs able to effectively promote angiogenesis has been documented in embryonic and fetal aortas, as well as in adult internal thoracic arteries; these

studies have provided the first evidence that EPCs reside in the vascular wall (**Vascular Wall-Endothelial Progenitor Cells**), where it is plausible that, in synergy with blood EPCs, they preside over the homeostatic control of the vascular system.

Subsequent studies performed on the elastic arteries (aorta, proximal tract of the common carotid and anonymous artery), muscular arteries (femoral arteries) and veins (saphenous vein) of healthy adult subjects (multi-organ donors and venous stripping) have also demonstrated the presence of **Mesenchymal Stromal (Stem) Cells** (MSC) characterized by morphology, phenotype and functional properties superimposable to that of MSCs derived from the bone marrow and placental membranes. MSCs resident in the vascular wall (Vascular Wall-Mesenchymal Stromal (Stem) Cells or VW-MSCs) express the typical mesengenic phenotypic constellation,

CD29, CD44, CD73, CD90, CD105, CD166, and are negative for the haematopoietic markers CD133, CD34, CD14 and CD45. Like their bone marrow counterpart, these cells are multipotent, as they can be induced to differentiate towards specific mesengenic lines, such as bone, cartilage and adipose tissue; coherently with their vascular localization, VW-MSCs are able to differentiate into endothelial cells and smooth muscle cells.

Multipotent Stem Cells of the Vascular Wall. Recently, a population of VW-MSCs residing in the wall of human elastic arteries has been isolated from adult cadavers (Donation after Circulatory Death); these cells were able to withstand prolonged ischaemic insults, surviving in the vascular tissues explanted after 48 hours from circulatory death and cryo-preserved in liquid nitrogen for more than 5 years, without losing their staminality. These multipotent adult VW-MSCs are rapidly expanding, clonogenic cells, endowed with immunomodulatory ability and capable of originating mesodermal and vascular tissues.

5.7.3 The role of stem cells in human vascular disease

Recently it has been hypothesized that several human vascular diseases can be induced or enhanced by a malfunction of the vascular stem cells: the circulating EPCs are dysfunctional in diabetes; bone marrow derived progenitors partecipate in arterial restenosis[11]; in abdominal aortic aneurysms[12] (AAA) the VW-MSCs develop a pro-inflammatory phenotype participating in the pathological vascular remodelling through a high production and release of proteolytic enzymes - the metalloproteases - and a hypomodulation of the inflammatory wall processes.

5.8 Smooth muscle cells

Smooth muscle cells (SMC) are located in the tunica media of arteries and veins, are the major cell components of the vascular wall and are essential for the proper functioning of the vascular system; in fact, their synchronous contraction and subsequent relaxation make it possible to modulate the wall thickness and the lumen diameter, adapting it to the needs of the blood flow, while supporting blood pressure.

SMCs are responsible for the synthesis of the components of the extracellular matrix (collagens, elastic tissue, proteoglycans and other proteins). They are able to change

---

[11] Restenosis is a concentric pathological thickening of the arterial intima, expression of a maladaptation of the same to a protracted inflammatory insult, for example the placement of a bare-metal stent.

[12] Abdominal aortic aneurysm (AAA) is a focal dilatation > 3 cm of the abdominal aorta; generally asymptomatic, it affects mainly the male sex in adulthood (> 50 years).

BOX 2. Characteristics of SMCs.

Morphotype	Shape	Ultrastructural Characteristics	Immunophenotype	Useful features to distinguish the two morphotypes
Contractile smooth muscle cell	Spindle-shaped, elongated, bipolar	Thin actin filaments (6 nm); dense bodies; subplasmalemmal dense plaques; basal lamina; vesicles of pinocytosis; few organelles	ASMA$^+$ SM-MHC$^+$ calponin$^+$ desmin$^+$	smoothelin H-caldesmon
Synthetic smooth muscle cell	Epithelioid, rhomboidal, multiple extensions	Rough endoplasmic reticulum; mitochondria; poorly developed contractile apparatus	ASMA$^{+/-}$ SM-MHC$^{+/-}$ calponin$^{+/-}$ desmin$^{+/-}$	CRBP-1

Abbreviations. ASMA: α smooth muscle actin; SM-MHC: heavy myosin smooth muscle chain; CRBP-1: cell-retinol binding protein; + expressed, +/- hypo-expressed.

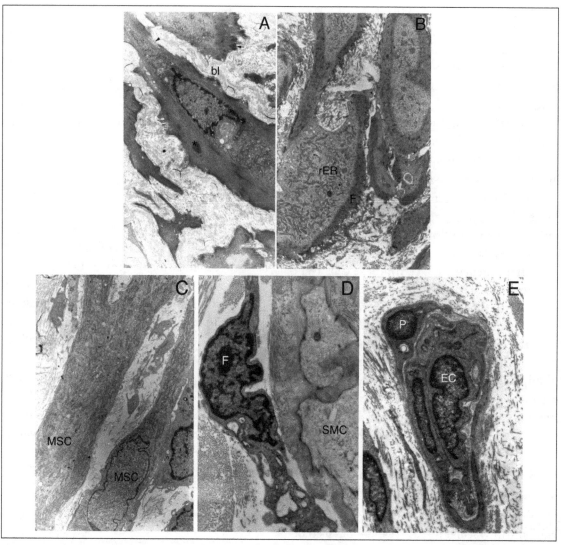

Figure 5.10. Mesenchymal cells of the arterial wall. A) Contractile SMC (SMC). The cell is spindle-shaped; thin actin filaments with dense bodies (asterisk) predominates in the cytoplasm; subplasmalemmal dense plaques are seen in correspondence with the plasma membrane (arrow); vesicles of pinocytosis (arrowhead) and a basal lamina (bl) are also evident. TEM. Original magnification x 4600. B) Synthetic SMC. The cell is epithelioid; multiple cisternae of rough endoplasmic reticulum (rER) predominates in the cytoplasm; the contractile filaments are present at the cell periphery exclusively (F). TEM. Original magnification x 3600. C, D, E) Other vascular wall cytotypes. C) MSCs are characterized by wide cytoplasm, absence of contractile filaments, richness in organelles. TEM. Original magnification x 2800. D) Fibroblasts (F) are thin bipolar cells with scarce cytoplasm and sparse rough endoplasmic reticulum cisternae. TEM. Original magnification x 13000. E) Pericytes (P) are mural cells of capillaries sharing the basal lamina with endothelial cells (EC). TEM. Original magnification x 4600.

the phenotype in a reversible manner, oscillating between a contractile and a synthetic morphotype, both characterized by specific morphology, immunophenotype, proliferative capacity and migration. In the normal arteries of the adult subjects the prevailing phenotype is the contractile phenotype, whereas in the reactive, reparative and pathological processes (atherosclerosis) the phenotype most represented is the synthetic one. The main characteristics of the smooth muscle morphotypes are summarized in Box 5.2. The basic ultrastructural characteristics are illustrated in Figure 5.10 A, B.

5.8.1 Embryological heterogeneity

SMCs show a heterogeneity that partly reflects their different embryological origin; for example, the SMCs of the ascending aorta and of the aortic arch derive from the neural crest, those of the thoracic and abdominal aorta from the mesoderm of the somites, and those of the coronary arteries from the proepicardium.

5.8.2 Phenotypic heterogeneity

In the aorta there are also distinct phenotypic populations coexisting in the same portion of the vessel. On the basis of the expression of cytoskeletal filaments, three type of SMCs have been described: V-type SMCs that express only the intermediate vimentin filament, VAD-type with complete phenotype (vimentin, ASMA and desmin), and VD-type positive to vimentin and desmin.

5.8.3 Smooth Muscle Cell progenitors

The possibility that SMCs originate in adults from circulating progenitors of bone marrow derivation or from precursors residing in the arterial wall has been hypothesized but not sufficiently demonstrated. The fact remains that, since SMCs are the main vascular cell component, an adequate renewal of these cells is necessary to guarantee and maintain vascular homeostasis during life time. In the arterogenesis processes we have previously considered, smooth muscle cells must replicate and migrate to guarantee the effective generation of collaterals after the obstruction; furthermore, at the base of the most important vascular pathological processes, a consistent numerical increase of SMCs is observed with consequent concentric (restenosis) or eccentric (atherosclerosis) pathological thickening of the intima. The mechanisms that induce the onset of these changes in the intima of the adult are still much debated and SMC progenitors are definitely involved.

These progenitors have immunophenotypic characteristics similar to those described in the sections where endothelial cell progenitors and/or MSCs are discussed. The main phenotypic modulators of smooth muscle cells are reported in Box 5.3.

BOX 3. Phenotypic modulators of smooth muscle cells.	
	Action
PDGF	Promotes the synthetic phenotype, proliferation and migration of SMCs
TGFβ	Promotes the contractile phenotype and promotes cell migration
Retinoic acid	Mainly promotes the contractile phenotype, mainly acting on the SMCs derived from the neural crest
Nitric Oxide (shear stress)	Promotes the synthetic phenotype
Mechanical stress	Promotes the contractile phenotype

5.9 Other vascular cytotypes

While SMCs with a contractile phenotype have well-defined and recognizable morphological and immunophenotypical properties, the synthetic morphotype, also described in the context of reactive or pathological conditions, shows wide overlaps with **myofibroblasts**. These, in fact, are cells with a hybrid phenotype, which share, exactly like the synthetic morphotype of the SMCs, properties of fibroblasts, the rough endoplasmic reticulum and SMCs, the contractile filaments; just as synthetic muscle cells manifest themselves only in pathological contexts, so myofibroblasts are observed only in reparative processes. The origin of both, from resident cells (through phenotypic modulation, phenotypic switch, dedifferentiation, transition) or from circulating progenitors (through differentiation), is still debated.

In addition to SMCs and MSCs (Figure 5.10C) other mesenchymal cells are observed within the vascular wall. **Fibroblasts** are present in the adventitia (Figure 5.10D); these are bipolar cells whose identification is generally made by exclusion (negativity for all the specific markers of other cell lines, positivity for vimentin, FSP-1 [Fibroblast-Specific Protein 1] and FSA [Fibroblast Surface Antigen]) or by ultrastructural documentation of rough endoplasmic reticulum cisternae, intermediate filaments and absence of basal lamina.

Telocytes are perivascular stromal cells of the microcirculation that express CD34 and present fibroblast-like morphology and dendritic extensions; they have the capacity to give rise to ASMA positive cells during the reparative processes.

The periendothelial **pericytes** of the capillaries (Figure 5.10E) are considered by most authors the true tissue precursors of the MSCs; pericytes, especially in pathological contexts, take on different morphotypes, and express NG2, desmin and PDGFR-β molecules.

5.10 Endothelial-mesenchymal transition

Under the stimulus of TGF-β 1 and of BMP2 and BMP4 (bone morphogenetic proteins), endothelial cells may undergo a phenotypic switch that its named, by analogy with the epithelial-mesenchymal transition, **endothelial-mesenchymal transition** (EndMT). In this process the endothelial cells lose adhesion to and contact with the contiguous cells (the transcription factors **Slug, Snail, Twist, ZEB-1** as well as **MMP-9** are implicated in the loss of contact), assume a spindle cell morphology, and acquire mobility and the ability to invade the surrounding stroma; these events are preceded and accompanied by a series of phenotypic modulations that include the down regulation of the most characteristic endothelial markers (CD31, vWF, Tie1 and Tie2, VE cadherin) and the parallel expression of mesenchymal proteins (vimentin, ASMA, FSP-1, fibronectin, metalloproteinases MMP2 and MMP9); the described transition could lead to the formation of tissue MSCs capable then of starting the usual mesengenic differentiation programs (Figure 5.9).

5.11 Vascular stem cells derived from reprogramming techniques

Induced pluripotent stem cells (iPS cells) are embryonic stem cells - similar to those obtained from adult somatic cells (fibroblasts) - in which the expression of some transgenes is forced (Oct3/4, Sox2, Klf4, c-Myc, Nanog, Lin28) that are critical for the maintenance of stemness. Initially, the stem cell genes were introduced stably into the host genome by using retrovirus as a vector (lentivirus). More recently, alternative methods have been proposed that avoid genomic integration and use viral vectors (adenoviruses), plasmids, purified recombinant proteins or small single chain RNA sequences (microRNA). The iPS generated, which have characteristics that can be superimposed to those of embryonic stem cells, have in turn been induced to successfully differentiate in the endothelial and SMC lineages.

Another possibility of generating vascular cells useful for regenerative medicine programs is given by the possibility of reprogramming adult somatic cells directly, giving rise to another differentiated adult line (switch of direct destiny) without going through the generation of complete iPS cells. The technique that is being developed involves the formation of partially induced pluripotent stem cells (PiPS) and their endothelial commissioning with culture media enriched with VEGF and SETSIP (SET Translocation (Myeloid Leukemia-Associated) (SET) Similar Protein).

5.12 Multivesicular bodies, exosomes and nanotubes

Stem cells use different mechanisms to propagate and exchange information and to sense changes in the microenvironment; all these mechanisms are necessary to guarantee orderly development and tissue homeostasis in multicellular organisms and to coordinate the harmonic functioning of the cells that make up the different tissue units. The main and best

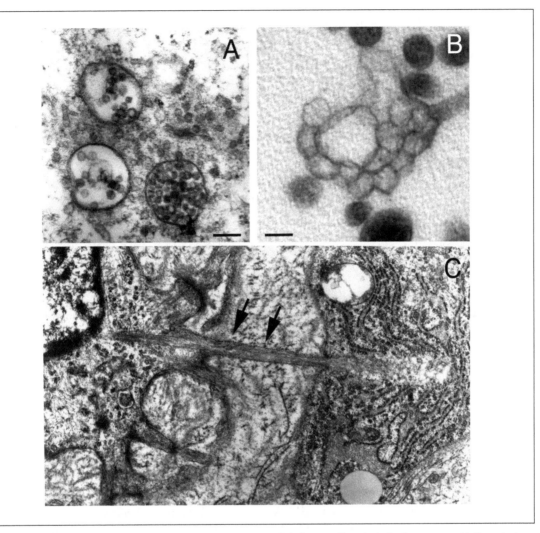

Figure 5.11. Mechanisms of communication of the functional vascular unit. A) Three multivescicular bodies are present in the cytoplasm of an MSC; each body contains multiple copies of 50 nm spherical vesicles (exosomes) ready to be discharged into the extracellular environment. TEM. Scale bar = 150 nm. B) Exosomes in the extracellular space. TEM. Scale bar = 50 nm. C) An exceptionally rare image of a nanotube; they are long and thin cell tubes (arrows) containing filamentous actin, allowing the direct transfer of cytoplasmic molecules and mitochondria between the connected cells. TEM. Original magnification x10000.

known intercellular communication mechanisms are reported in Box 5.4.

In addition to these well-known mechanisms, *in vitro* and *in vivo* research supports the role of **extracellular vesicles** in intercellular communication to exchange biological information between cells. Among the different micro-vesicles identified, delete exosomes are the most studied; they originate from the fusion of the multivescicular bodies (Figure 5.11A) with the plasma membrane; dur-

ing this process, a small part of the cytoplasm remains trapped in the vesicle. Exosomes (Figure 5.11B) are biologically active, spherical particles of 40-100 nm in diameter that are released into the extracellular environment by numerous cytotypes both in normal and pathological conditions. They are isolated from the supernatant of cell cultures grown in serum-free media by ultracentrifugation and are identified through combined Western Blot and immunoelectron microscopy techniques;

BOX 4. Main communication pathways used by stem cells		
Type of communication	Mechanism	Signals transferred
Direct Cell Contact	Gap junctions	Inorganic ions and small cytoplasmic molecules
Remote communication with target cell groups	Endocrine communication through synthesis and release of chemical messengers	Peptide hormones, steroids and amino acid derivatives
Short-range communication with homogeneous groups of target cells	Paracrine communication after synthesis and release of chemical messengers	Peptide and amino acid hormones
Self-directed communication	Autocrine communication after synthesis and release of chemical messengers	Peptide or amino acid hormones
Contact with the extracellular environment	Integrins; membrane glycoproteins that bind extracellular matrix proteins (fibronectin, vitronectin, fibrinogen, etc.)	Adapt the cellular metabolism to the characteristics of the extracellular environment by modulating the activities of kinases, such as FAK (focal adhesion kinase) and the Src kinase

they have been isolated in blood, urine, breast milk, saliva, amniotic fluid, cerebrospinal fluid and bile. Exosomes contain numerous proteins involved in the biogenesis of multivesicular bodies (Tsg 101 and Alix), in fusion and transport (Rab11, Rab7, Rab2 and Annexins), heat shock proteins (Hsc 70 and Hsc 90) and membrane proteins, such as integrins and tetraspanins (CD 9, CD63, CD81 and CD82); they also contain lipids (cholesterol and sphingomyelin), genetic material (mRNA, miR, repeated sequences, structural RNA, tRNA fragments and small interfering RNA) reflecting the protein and molecular profile of the cell that originated them.

Recently, a new cell communication mechanism has been identified based on cellular projections made up of **nanotubes** (tunneling nanotubes); these are thin membranous channels that allow the direct transfer of cytoplasmic molecules and organelles, such as mitochondria between signaling and target cells. These nanotubes (Figure 5.11C) are extremely long and thin cytoplasmic protrusions, 50-200nm in diameter, containing filamentous actin (F-actin) and able to connect distant cells without tightening contact with the substrate. Since their discovery, similar structures have been identified in numerous cytotypes, revealing a high heterogeneity in terms of morphol-

ogy, size and structure. A detailed morphological study performed on VW-MSCs showed a complex network of microtubular projections (MTPs, 700 nm in diameter), serpentiform, constituted by actin microfilaments and with characteristic bulgings due to the presence of mitochondria. Nanotubular projections (NTPs, 100 nm in diameter) originated directly from the cell body, linear with occasional bifurcations. Lastly smaller projections (50 nm in diameter) completely detached from the cell body and associated with exosomal vesicles probably due to the fragmentation of the projections are also seen.

The VW-MSCs use this articulated network both to recognize and make contact with target cells located at considerable distances but also to transfer information and cytoplasmic organelles to the same.

Recommended reading and references

1. Asahara T, et al. *Isolation of putative progenitor endothelial cells for angiogenesis.* Science 1997; 275:964-967.

2. De Val S, et al. *Transcriptional control of endothelial cell development.* Developmental Cell 2009; 16:180-195.

3. Hill JM, et al. *Circulating endothelial progenitor cells, vascular function, and cardiovascular risk.* N.Engl J Med 2003; 348:593-600.

4. Marcelo KL, et al. *Regulation of endothelial cell differentiation and specification.* Circ Res 2013; 112:1272-1287.

5. Pacilli A and Pasquinelli G. *Vascular wall resident progenitor cells.* A review. Exp Cell Res 2009; 315:901-914.

6. Pasquinelli G, et al. *Thoracic aortas from multiorgan donors are suitable for obtaining resident angiogenic mesenchymal stromal cells.* Stem Cells 2007; 25:1627-1634.

7. Rafii S, et al. *Therapeutic stem and progenitor cell transplantation for organ vascularization and regeneration.* Nat Med 2003; 9:702-712.

8. Rudini N, et al. *Adherens junctions.* Curr Biol 2008; 18:R1080-2.

9. Schofield R. *The relationship between the pleen colony-forming cell and the haemopoietic stem cell.* Blood Cells 1978; 4:7:25.

10. Sumpio BE, et al. *Cells in focus: endothelial cell.* Int J Biochem Cell Biol 2002; 34:1508-1512.

11. Cines DB, et al. *Endothelial Cells in Physiology and in the Pathophysiology of Vascular Disorders.* Blood 1998; 91(10):3527-3561.

12. Renser SSM, et al. *Regulation and characteristics of vascular smooth muscle cell phenotypic diversity.* Neth Heart J 2007; 15:100-8.

13. Yoder MC, et al. *Redifining endothelial progenitor cells via clonal analysis and hematopoietic stem / progenitor cell principals.* Blood 2007; 109:1801-1809.

14. Zengin E, et al. *Vascular wall resident progenitor cells: a source for postnatal vasculogenesis.* Development 2006; 133:1543-1551.

15. Sinha S, et al. *Embryonic origins of human vascular smooth muscle cells: implications for in vitro modeling and clinical application.* Cell Mol Life Sci2014; 71:2271-2288.

16. Medici D, et al. *Endothelial–mesenchymal transition and its contribution to the emergence of stem cell phenotype.* Semin Cancer Biol 2012; 22:379-384.

17. Yang Y, et al. *Development of the mammalian lymphatic vasculature.* J Clin Invest 2014; 124(3):888-97.

18. Valente S, et al. *Human cadaver multipotent stromal/stem cells isolated from arteries stored in liquid nitrogen for 5 years.* Stem Cell Res Ther 2014; 5(1):8.

19. Ciavarella C, et al. *Human Vascular Wall Mesenchymal Stromal Cells Contribute to Abdominal Aortic Aneurysm Pathogenesis Through an Impaired Immunomodulatory Activity and Increased Levels of Matrix Metalloproteinase-9.* Circ J. 2015;79(7): 1460-9.

20. Valente S, et al. *Exploring the Human Mesenchymal Stem Cell Tubule Communication Network through Electron Microscopy.* Ultrastruct Pathol 2014; 30:1-7.

21. Pasquinelli G and Valente S. *Ultrastructural assessment of the differentiation potential of human multipotent mesenchymal stromal cells.* Ultrastruct Pathol 2013; 37(5):318-27.

22. Vasuri F, et al. *Nestin and WT1 expression in small-sized vasa vasorum from human normal arteries.* Histol Histopathol 2012; 27(9):1195-202.

23. Pasquinelli G, et al. *Multidistrict human mesenchymal vascular cells: pluripotency and stemness characteristics.* Cytotherapy 2010;12(3):275-87.

24. Medina RJ, et al. *Endothelial Progenitors: A Consensus Statement on Nomenclature.* Stem Cells Transl Med. 2017;6(5):1316-1320.

25. Simons M, Raposo G. *Exosomes – vesicular carriers for intercellular communication.* Curr Opin Cell Biol. 2009;21(4):575-81.

Cardiogenesis

6

Carlo Ventura   Claudia Cavallini
Elena Olivi   Riccardo Tassinari

6.1 Introduction

Cardiogenesis is a complex biological process, finely orchestrated by several factors, that occurs in the early stages of embryogenesis. A detailed understanding of this process is required to address the application of stem cells in the cardiovascular field. The heart is the first functional organ in embryos, and, in the human species, it starts to beat on day 22, while blood is circulating by day 24. The functional heart is composed of diverse cell lineages, including atrial and ventricular cardiomyocytes, cells of the cardiac conduction system (CS), endocardial cells, endothelial cells (EC), connective tissue, vascular smooth muscle cells (SMC).

In the course of heart organogenesis, three different sources of precursor cells may be identified: cardiogenic mesoderm cells (CMC), proepicardium (PE) and cardiac neural crest cells (CNCC). During gastrulation, the mesodermal tissues, from which the heart will arise, become evident. Firstly, in the midline longitudinal axis of the embryonic plate we find the primitive streak, with, at its cranial end, the primitive knot (or primitive node), i.e. the gastrulation organizer. Cardiogenic mesoderm cells migrate away from the primitive streak laterally and cranially, and form two groups of mesodermal cells located bilaterally in the anterior lateral plate mesoderm, the so-called splanchnic mesoderm. At 3 weeks in the human embryo, the cardiac crescent coalesces along the midline giving rise to the first heart field (FHF). At 4 weeks, the linear heart tube derived from FHF starts beating and undergoes rightward looping while rapidly growing. The linear heart tube increases in size through two mechanisms: cell proliferation and enrollment of new cells derived from the pharyngeal mesoderm. These supplementary cells form the second heart field (SHF) and principally contribute to the right ventricle, a large portion of the atria, and the outflow tract (OFT) myocardium, while the FHF gives rise to part of the left ventricle. The wall of the adult heart consists of three cell layers: the outer epicardium, the middle myocardium, and the inner endocardium. Cells derived from the FHF and SHF form only two of them: the endocardium and the myocardium. The epicardium, comprised of cardiac fibroblasts and cells of the coronary vasculature, is not present in the tubular heart stage and arises later from the proepicardium (PE). The PE appears from the coelomic mesenchyme of the septum transversum at day 21 and forms as a multicellular protrusion, containing hyaluronic acid and a small amount of fibronectin, of the pericardial serosa. When the proepicardium differentiates into the epicardium, mesenchymal cells migrate to the subendocardial area, and form fibroblasts, secreting extracellular matrix (ECM). Moreover, these mesenchymal cells form the heart valves and play an active role in the formation of the fibrous heart skeleton, which ensures insulation of the atrial and ventricular myocardium. At day 32, the human heart appears fully septated into the four chambers, and connected to the pulmonary trunk and the aorta. The last step in heart development involves CNC cells. CNCCs are extra-cardiac cells, in particular a subpopulation of the cranial neural crest cells, that invade the arterial pole of the nascent heart and contribute to the cardiac outflow tract. A subset of the CNCCs induces the septation of the OFT into the arterial and pulmonary trunks. CNCCs differentiate into ectomesenchyme and aortic smooth muscle cells, but their principal role seems to provide proper signals for developmental processes (Figure 6.1).

As we can see, different cells are involved in different times of heart development, and, clearly, a very large number of pathways is activated at different stages.

6.1.1 Molecular basis of cardiac specification

The possible use of stem cells for the functional repair of damaged or diseased organs has given fresh impetus to embryogenesis studies. Indeed, the molecular pathways involved in heart organogenesis are now investigated in-depth, in order to better understand the signals required in cardiac specification and differentiation. The complexity of the cardiovascular specification process makes it difficult to completely resolve the intricate puzzle. Moreover, we can assume that differentiation

is driven by chemical and physical stimuli. For example, it is well known that different loading status can dramatically affect expression patterns in the adult heart. We can expect the same impact on embryonic heart cells, considering the extremely different mechanical loading conditions between the fetal heart districts. The following sections describe the genes, pathways and molecules involved in heart development, but they certainly cannot be exhaustive. The aim of this chapter is to elucidate some mechanisms, opening our eyes to this intricate but very interesting maze of cardiac specification.

Mesoderm induction is the first event in cardiogenesis, and it is driven by a few genes: bone morphogenetic protein (BMP), Nodal, Wnt/β-catenin, and fibroblast growth factor (FGF). Mesodermal induction starts with the activation of noncanonical Wnt signalling and the simultaneous inhibition of the canonical pathway, that promote the expression of T-box transcription factor Brachyury/T (Bry). Bry+ cells enter through the PE and contribute to the heart's development in two different times. At first, a population positive to Bry as well as to Fetal Liver Kinase 1 (Flk-1), a receptor for vascular endothelial growth factor (VEGF), differentiates in vasculature elements, beginning the vascular organization process. These Bry+/Flk-1+ cells, called haemangioblasts, are precursors of blood lineage and endothelial

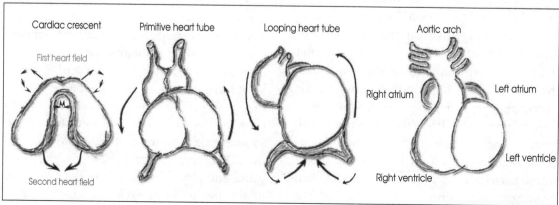

Figure 6.1. Heart organogenesis.

lineage cells. Shortly after, a second population, until then Bry⁺/Flk-1⁻, starts to express Flk-1 and constitutes the pool of cardiovascular progenitors. The subsequent down-regulation of Bry and up-regulation of T-box transcription factor Eomesodermin (Eomes), that induces the mesoderm posterior 1 (Mesp1) gene, give impetus to the formation of the FHF as well as the SHF, both of them considered as cardiogenic mesoderm. Mesp1 knock-down leads to an anomalous morphogenesis, suggesting its central role during gastrulation and in the specification of mesodermal cell lineages, as well as in mesodermal cell migration from the primitive streak to generate a single heart tube.

Cells in the FHF are characterized by a more anterior position with respect to SHF cells, and, on account of this, they are more exposed to signals from the underlying endoderm, BMP and FGF in particular, resulting in the onset of cardiac differentiation. These signals activate TBX5, a key regulator of cell fate. TBX5, once activated, induces several genes, including those codifying for Natriuretic Peptide A, the gap junction protein Connexin 40, GATA4 and NKX2.5. This event represses the haemangiogenic gene program, concomitantly driving up-regulation of other cardiac-specific genes that include Hand1, Mef2c, and myosin light chain-2v. Mutation in one of these genes leads to severe cardiac defects, ranging from functional defects to embryonic lethality. At the end of the differentiation program, FHF cells give rise to the left ventricular (LV) free wall, part of the septum, and a portion of the atria.

Commitment of SHF cells is delayed in comparison with the FHF ones and, during FHF differentiation, SHF progenitors remain in a proliferative state longer. Progenitor cells in the SHF support rapid growth of the heart, giving rise to the right ventricle, part of the septum, the outflow tract (OFT) myocardium at the arterial pole of the heart, and the atrial myocardium at the venous pole. FGF, sonic hedgehog and canonical WNT/β-catenin promote proliferation and differentiation in cardiomyocytes, endothelial cells, and smooth muscle cells. The master gene of SHF is ISL1, which is also transiently expressed in FHF that, together with GATA4, induces MEF2c. NKX2.5 is mandatory for ventricular cardiomyocyte differentiation, repressing ISL1 and turning proliferation in differentiation, while HAND2 plays a main role in right ventricle development.

As mentioned above, the FHF and SHF give rise to the heart tube, consisting of only two layers: the endocardium and the myocardium. Epicardium formation begins with proepicardium determination, driven by interaction between BMP and FGF signalling. The proepicardium is a transient structure derived from the proliferation of coelomic cells located on the pericardial side of the septum transversum or in the limit between the sinus venosus and the liver, and generates the coronary vasculature and cardiac fibroblasts. Determination of epicardial lineage and separation from myocardium differentiation is mediated by the opposite effect of FGF and BMP signalling. FGF induces propericardial fate via Mek1/2 (MAPK kinases) activation, while the BMP signal inhibits the Mek1/2 pathway, promoting myocardial fate. Tbx18 and Wt1 are earlier markers of PE. Wt1, through the regulation of Snail, a cadherin-repressor protein, promotes epithelial to mesenchymal transition (EMT). Snail is the most relevant transcriptional agent of EMT in the epicardium, repressing adhesion molecules, such as E-cadherin, largely expressed in epithelial cells, and promoting expression of the mesenchymal markers vimentin and N-cadherin. Cell lineage derived from EMT is composed of fibroblasts and cells of the coronary vasculature, which are known as epicardium-derived cells (EPDC).

Certainly EPDCs contribute to cardiac fibroblasts and vascular smooth muscle cellular pools, but it is not clear if they give rise to endothelial cells and cardiomyocytes. Molecules involved in EPDC differentiation are FGF, Notch and Retinoic Acid (RA). Probably the most important process that occurs in the epicardium, mediated by epicardial cells, is the secretion of paracrine factors that support myocardial growth. Retinoic acid, for example, is produced by subepicardial endothelial cells, and is a strong inductor of myocyte proliferation. RA activates a signal cascade that induces erythropoietin, which, in turn, activates IGF-2, another proliferative factor. FGF is essential for proper myocardial formation: depletion of the epicardially expressed FGF results in reduced cardiomyocyte proliferation and, eventually, embryonic lethality. The central role of the epicardium in heart development is emphasized by the discovery of many other secreted factors, in addition to FGF and RA, such as Hedgehog and CXCL12. Notch signalling is involved in several steps of EPDC differentiation, is specifically required for cardiac smooth muscle cell (cSMC) differentiation, and is widely expressed in the proepicardium and in EPDCs.

CNCCs, a population of cranial neural crest cells, are the third type of cardiac progenitor cells, arising from ectoderm at the lateral edge of the neural plate, whose main role is to provide developmental signals to differentiating cardiac cells. However, they give a direct cellular contribution to the heart valves and to all parasympathetic innervation. Signals involved in CNC progenitor induction are BMP, TGF-β, FGF, Wnt/ β-catenin and RA, all of which promote an epithelial to mesenchymal transformation (EMT), with a subsequent delamination and cell migration from the neural crest to the rising heart. Chemoattractive factors guide cells to OFT cushions, through semaphorin receptors plexin and neuropilin. Once they have reached in the embryonic heart, CNCCs differentiate into pericytes and smooth muscle cells, and concur in septation of the OFT into pulmonary and aortic components. Interestingly, the larger part of CNCCs undergoes apoptosis during the remodelling of the aortic arch arteries, and this process is deeply associated with TGF-β signalling. Different factors act on CNCC migration and development, many of which are not directly secreted by these cells, but by those of neighbouring areas. For instance, mutation in Tbx1,

that is not expressed in CNCCs, but found in tissue of the pharyngeal arches adjacent to CNCCs, determines defects in the development of the aortic arch arteries. In the same way, transcription factors Foxc1 and Foxc2 and Endothelin-1 are expressed in the endothelial tissues surrounding CNCCs but not in CNCCs, and are essential for proper OFT and arch artery morphogenesis.

The prominent role of a varying number of Transcription Factors (TFs) in regulating cardiac progenitor differentiation and proliferation seems, therefore, clear. Only deep understanding of TF networks will be able to increase the yield of cardiac differentiation in desired therapeutic stem cell types. Cellular reprogramming, recently finalized through induced pluripotent stem cells, has shown how a right combination of TFs can completely reverse the state of a differentiated cell, converting adult cells in progenitors, with a directed trans-lineage reprogramming. Only a few factors seem necessary to directly reprogram a cardiac fibroblast to a competent cardiomyocyte, for instance the combination of Gata4, Tbx5, and Mef2c. Not only are TFs necessary in cardiac development, but other players could be specific miRNAs, shown to play key roles in cardiac development. MicroRNAs (miRNAs) are single-stranded, non-coding RNA molecules that can negatively affect gene expression at the post-transcriptional level, either by driving mRNA degradation or by preventing protein translation. In the developing heart, for example, miR-1 and miR-133 families are expressed and regulated by serum response factor (SRF) and MEF2; their knock-out causes severe cardiac defects that lead to embryonic or perinatal lethality. Epigenetic manipulation of the cellular genome to obtain cardiomyocytes from stem cells, enhancing direct conversion of one cell type to another, represents a great hope in regenerative medicine, which would avoid genetic engineering of stem cells.

Even though a great deal still remains to be done to elucidate fetal specification of cardiomyocytes, much less is known about their post-natal maturation. This issue is of crucial importance, especially because a large number of the few engrafted stem cells fail to completely differentiate in human hearts, leading to ventricular arrhythmias. Principally, there are three hallmarks of complete cardiomyocyte differentiation: hypertrophic growth, enlarging the adult cardiomyocyte 30-40-fold, leading to the formation of large rod-shaped cells forming a length-to-width ratio of 7–9.5, higher myofibrillar density with increased sarcomere prominence, and formation of specialized organelles, such as T-tubules. CM maturity is characterized also by polyploidy, visible in 25% of adult cells. After birth, alterations in metabolism take over: a more oxidative energetic profile emerges, switching from embryonic glycolysis to adult fatty acid β-oxidation. It is clear that the complete cardiac development still has not been deeply understood, and further efforts are required.

Although our discussion has been limited to cardiac specification, we should remember that, at the end of the cardiogenic processes, the mature heart is composed of different cell types. Contractility is ensured by cardiomyocytes, accounting for approximately 25–35% of all cells, while fibroblasts and endothelial cells assure scaffolding and blood supply, respectively. Recently, thanks to studies performed with genetic tracers and flow cytometry techniques, it was demonstrated that fibroblasts comprise a relatively minor cell population, while endothelial cells seem to be the most represented cell type.

Given the difficulty to differentiate stem cells in cardiomyocytes, the near totality of efforts are intended to boost stem cell transdifferentiation. We should remember, though, that all cellular components in the heart interact with each other, affecting the regenerative potential of stem cells.

6.2 Stem cells and the heart

Cardiovascular diseases (CVDs) are the major cause of death in Western countries, accounting for more than 3.9 million deaths a year in Europe (over 1.8 million deaths in the European Union) and 836,546 deaths in the US, remaining the most common cause of death.

Myocardial infarction (MI) occurs when a portion of the heart is deprived of oxygen due to blockage of a coronary artery. Because of permanent loss of cardiomyocytes due to necrotic or apoptotic phenomena resulting from MI, the heart becomes functionally impaired. Indeed, myocardial contractile cells are replaced with scar tissue, principally composed of fibroblasts and their activated form, myofibroblasts. Fibroblasts mediate acute wound healing and the subsequent tissue remodelling, preserving the heart from myocardial rupture. Scar formation results from fibroblast proliferation and migration in the injured area, but also from the remodelling of the extracellular matrix. However, even though scar formation is necessary, it leads to loss of muscular power and increases the possibility of heart failure in the months following the acute event. Existing therapeutic options are based on strategies that limit scar formation and adverse remodelling, but loss of functional tissue is currently not resolved. In this context, many efforts have been made to identify regenerative strategies to restore cardiac contractility after myocardial infarction. Implementations in clinical practice improve symptoms and decelerate adverse cardiac remodelling, but they fail to prevent an irreversible loss of cardiac tissue. The discovery of stem cells has given new hope, and new opportunities have been envisaged. Different strategies have been proposed and many clinical trials have been conducted, but, unfortunately, results still remain controversial.

Many issues shall need to be considered to achieve the goal of regenerating a damaged heart through replacement of functional cardiomyocytes that should be fully integrated in the diseased organ. The first question which springs to mind concerns the type of cells to be transplanted. But afterwards, we have to consider in which way stem cells could be administered and at what time surgical procedures should be performed following an acute event. As described below, different cell types and different pathways are involved in cardiac specification, and each type of fully differentiated cells has specific features and plays a specific role in heart physiology. Addressing stem cells towards defined fate is a key issue we need to consider, to avoid dramatic mistakes with severe consequences on patients' health.

For medical purposes, the stem cells taken into account are (1) embryonic stem cells (ESC), (2) fetal tissue-derived stem cells (obtained from the placenta, the amniotic fluid, as well as the umbilical cord) (3) stem cells derived from different locations in the adult organism (bone marrow, adipose tissue, dental pulp) or (4) genetically reprogrammed cells derived from fully differentiated organs (e.g. iPSCs).

6.2.1. Embryonic Stem Cells (ESC)

Obviously, ESCs are the most plastic not genetically modified available cells. Stem cell plasticity is defined as the ability to differentiate in different cell types of the human body, and can be modest or pronounced, as in ESCs. Potentially, ESCs could differentiate quite easily in cardiac progenitor cells, obtaining a large yield with a high purity of differentiated cells. Two main culture techniques could be employed to obtain cardiomyogenic differentiation: 3D culture in cellular aggregates called embryoid bodies (EB) or classical monolayer culture on a plastic substrate. Spontaneous differentiation of ESCs in cardiac progenitors is extremely inefficient, in both methods: for instance, only about 8% of total embryoid bodies contain a contracting area. Various strategies to force *in vitro* differentiation have been developed, in order to manipulate signalling pathways, including specific media, some of which are commercially available. Cardiogenic media contain key drivers of *in vivo* cardiogenesis, such as Activin A and BMP4. Cardiac progenitors derived from ESCs have been tested in various animal models, with variable results, and some of them appear excit-

ing. Unfortunately, a real clinical use of these cells is very improbable, for various unrelated problems. Embryonic stem cells derive from inner cell mass of a human blastocyst, generated to this end, and obviously, due to their origin, legal and ethical debates have arisen about embryonic stem cells, and they seem hard to resolve. Furthermore, ESCs are prone to malignant transformation and teratoma formation. Despite these critical issues, a clinical trial of human ESC-derived cardiac progenitor cells, embedded into a fibrin scaffold, was performed in France (ESCORT), demonstrating the technical safety and feasibility of cellular transplant, from amplification of the pluripotent ESCs to surgical epicardial delivery. Improvement of patient clinical pictures has not been demonstrated, and additional data should be necessary.

6.2.2. Induced Pluripotent Stem Cells (iPSC)

IPSCs, at first obtained from adult mouse fibroblasts by gene transfer of Oct4, Sox2, c-Myc and Klf4 by Yamanaka from Kyoto University, are now an established technology also for human derived cells (Figure 6.2).

IPSC features are similar to those of ESCs, also in cardiac differentiation potential. Human iPSCs are able to generate functional

Figure 6.2. Epifluorescence microphotograph of Induced Pluripotent Stem Cells (IPSC) after 3 weeks of culture in stemness maintaining medium. The expression of OCT4 (typical nuclear stem marker, red channel) and TRA-1-60 (pluripotency marker, green channel) show almost 100% cells positivity. Objective 20x, scale bar 100µm..

cardiac progenitors, and there are various differentiation techniques, capable of producing nodal, atrial and ventricular-type cardiac cells. The spontaneous differentiation of iPSCs into different cell phenotypes can be driven and forced using specific media and protocols (Figure 6.3, 6.4, 6.5, 6.6, 6.7).

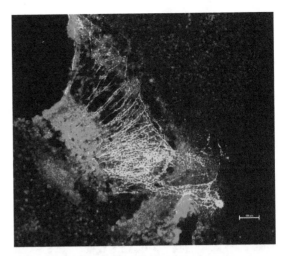

Figure 6.5. .Zoom of Fig. 6.4. Objective 20x.

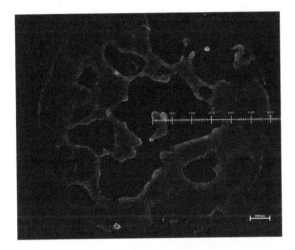

Figure 6.3. Whole coverslip (1.2 cm diameter) epifluorescence microphotograph of confluent Induced Pluripotent Stem Cells (IPSC) after 3 weeks of culture in non-specific differentiating medium. The expression of OCT4 (green channel) show the stem profile of non-differentiating cells: this ability is maintained by a small amount of cells located near the edges of cell islets. Objective 4x.

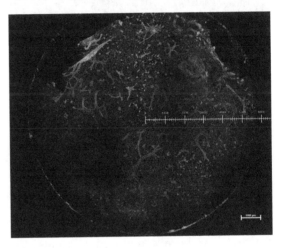

Figure 6.6. Whole coverslip (1.2 cm diameter) epifluorescence microphotograph of confluent Induced Pluripotent Stem Cell (IPSC) after 3 weeks of culture in cardiac driving medium. The expression of Troponin T (red channel) and Connexin 43 (green channel) shows the "superstructure" that spans millimetres of cardiac fibre involving thousands of cells. Objective 4x.

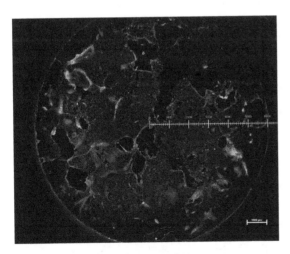

Figure 6.4. Whole coverslip (1.2 cm diameter) epifluorescence microphotograph of confluent Induced Pluripotent Stem Cells (IPSC) after 3 weeks of culture in non-specific differentiating medium. The spontaneous expression of Neural Growth Factor Receptor (red channel) and β-III-Tubulin (green channel) shows the "superstructure" that spans millimetres of neural-like structure involving hundreds of cells. Objective 4x.

Just like ESC-derived cardiomyocytes, iPSC-derived cardiac cells were transplanted into hearts in animal models of myocardial infarction. *In vivo* studies demonstrated a positive impact of implanted iPSCs on cardiac function, in term of successful engraftment, improvement of myocardial metabolism and left ventricular function, decrease of fibrosis and reduction of infarct size. No clinical trials have been performed in cardiac repair for humans, due to issues concerning the unknown side effects of gene-modified cells; additional

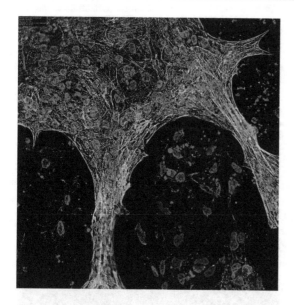

Figure 6.7. Epifluorescence deconvolved microphotograph of Induced Pluripotent Stem Cells (IPSC) cell culture after 3 weeks of culture in cardiac driving medium. The expression of Troponin I (red channel) and α-Sarcomeric Actinin (green channel) show the intricate structure in single cells and inside cells coupled and linked together to form a unique cardiac beating fibre. Z-lines and defined sarcomere structure are clearly visible. Objective 20x, scale bar 100μm.

animal studies are recommended to ensure the efficacy but especially the safety, of iPSCs. Despite this, iPSCs are very appealing in clinical research due to their developmental potential, and have been announced as a powerful tool to study diseases. IPSCs derived from dermal fibroblasts obtained from patients can be induced *in vitro* to differentiate in functional cardiomyocytes, in order to test not only clinical drugs, but also to identify specific features of patient syndrome and disease phenotype.

6.2.3 Adult stem cells

Not only do adult stem cells have a reduced self-renewal potential compared to iPSCs or ESCs, but their ability to differentiate in different cell types, through transdifferentiation, is also less pronounced. However, adult stem cells possess some characteristics that make them appealing for clinical uses: first and foremost the possibility of autologous origin, that prevents rejection after transplantation. Moreover, adult stem cell sources are increasing in

number, and sample collection appears safer and easier than in the past. Adult stem cells, already used in clinical studies, will be discussed below.

6.2.4 Bone marrow-derived cells

Bone marrow is composed of a very heterogeneous cellular component, made up of differentiated cells, such as lymphocytes, monocytes, osteoclasts, osteoblasts and many others, and a certain amount of undifferentiated cells. These stem cells, fractionally small and largely varied, can be obtained with gradient centrifugation of whole bone marrow, and reside in a pool referred to as bone marrow mononuclear cells (BMMNC). In broad terms, this pool should be divided in Haematopoietic Stem Cells (HSC), comprising haemangioblasts and endothelial progenitor cells (EPC), and non-haematopoietic mesenchymal precursors that give rise to mesenchymal (stromal) stem cells (MSC). The specific properties of both types of stem cells have been extensively explained elsewhere in this book; here we explain more specifically their applications in cardiac regenerative medicine. *In vivo*, undifferentiated BMMNCs do not contribute to cardiac lineage cells, but many *in vitro* studies have attempted to force their differentiation capability. HSCs are able to differentiate in many cell phenotypes, including neurons, hepatocytes, skeletal muscle cells, but whether they are able to transdifferentiate in cardiomyocytes remains controversial. On the contrary, specific *in vitro* treatments induce MSCs to differentiate in cardiac progenitor cells, by providing some regulatory factors, including 5-Azacytidine, miRNAs, cytokines, physical microenvironment, Caveolin-1, VR-1 and many others. The mechanisms of MSC differentiation in cardiomyocytes are not yet fully elucidated, and this is a major issue for their use in clinical application. 5-Azacytidine promotes differentiation via random demethylation of DNA, but its carcinogenicity has precluded clinical applications. Epigenetic modifications have an important role in MSC differentiation into cardiomyocytes. In the first decade of the 21st century, we demonstrated that a mixed ester of hyaluronan with butyric and retinoic acid (HBR) can act as cardiogenic/vasculogenic agent in human mesenchymal stem cells, increasing *in vitro* the transcription of the cardiac lineage-promoting genes GATA-4 and Nkx-2.5. Unexpectedly, HBR remarkably enhanced vascular endothelial growth factor (VEGF), KDR, and hepatocyte growth factor (HGF) gene expression and the secretion of the endothelial angiogenic, mitogenic, and antiapoptotic factors VEGF and HGF, priming stem cell differentiation cells. Butyric moiety of the mixed ester mediates epigenetic changes in MSCs, being a well-known histone deacetylase (HDAC) inhibitor. Chromatin remodelling can largely affect transcription factor accessibility, to target cis-acting regulatory sites, promoting differentiation. Retinoic acid, also present in HBR, plays a crucial role in mammalian vascular development and enhances angiogenesis. Many cytokines affect cell growth and differentiation. Plenty of efforts have been made to force MSC differentiation with growth factors, such as epidermal growth factor (EGF), platelet-derived growth factor (PDGF), fibroblast growth factor (FGF), nerve growth factor (NGF), insulin-like growth factor (IGF), basic fibroblast growth factor (bFGF), etc. For instance, it has been demonstrated that TGF-β1 promoted cardiomyogenic differentiation of rat bone marrow-derived MSCs, and transplantation of TGF-β1-treated MSCs improved heart function after MI in an animal model. Many other protocols have been developed, also with combination of different cytokines and drugs. Nevertheless, there is not a fully understanding of cytokine signalling pathways and their complex biological effects, but this point is essential for future clinical applications. An innovative strategy to induce differentiation is based on microRNAs (miRNAs). miRNAs are a class of noncoding RNAs of about 22 nucleotides, that perform their function as negative regulators of gene expression by binding to the 3' UTR of mRNAs. Recently, many studies have demonstrated how miRNAs can modulate MSC differentiation, but little is known about their potential to give rise to cardiovascular lineage. Different miRNAs exerting influence on cardiomyocyte differentiation have been identified: up-regulation of miR-1a could promote the differentiation of BMSCs into myocardial cells, but in contrast miR-124 is significantly down-regulated during this process, and its overexpression had an inhibitory effect. Furthermore, miRNAs are crucial players in many cardiovascular disorders, such as stroke, hypertension, atrial fibrillation, but the underlying mechanisms remain partially unclear. For instance, miR-22 may inhibit fibrosis thought suppression of TGF-β receptor I (Tβ RI) in fibroblasts, preventing their conversion to myofibroblasts; by contrast, miR-34a heightens the progression of cardiac fibrosis, directly targeting Smad4. miR-133 holds a place of honour among promising therapeutic miRNAs. Currently, miR-133, in animal models of cardiac diseases, is able to freeze cardiac remodelling, arresting cardiac hypertrophy and cardiac fibrosis. Moreover, miR-133 acts on stem cells, facilitating the reprogramming of cardiac fibroblasts in cardiomyocytes, as well as improving MSC survival in ischaemic microenvironments and preventing cardiac progenitor cell apoptosis. Other studies should be performed to confirm the safety and efficacy of miRNAs in clinical practice, even though we are close to the employment of miRNAs in therapy. Clearly, other differentiating strategies shall be taken into account, including protein expression modulation, and many studies are still ongoing.

6.2.5 Bone marrow-derived stem cells in clinical studies

Due to prior experience in bone marrow transplantation, many hospitals proceed with trials using bone marrow-derived (mesenchymal) stem cells. Unfortunately, the first generation of clinical trials were approved and conducted on the wave of promising *in vivo* results, but lacked trustworthy knowledge about the real mechanisms that control tissue regeneration. Early clinical trials had poor results, with minimal, inconsistent and transient improvement in the clinical condition of treated patients. Certainly, cell transplantation has proven to be a safe and feasible therapy, but this is a poor result, much weaker compared to the benefit expected. Many issues have emerged and many questions have to be resolved before proceeding.

First of all, many different protocols for stem cell isolation have been used, a situation which engenders a whole new range of related problems. In some trials BMMNCs were used (BOOST, ASTAMI, SCAMI); at other times enriched MSCs were administered (REPAIR-AMI). Also different techniques of selection were developed: gradient centrifugation and immunoselection (PreSERVE-AMI, with CD34+ cells), for example. It is clear how different antigens can identify different stem cell populations, increasing variability between trials using immunoselected cells. Moreover, in some cases, stem cells were *ex vivo* expanded, in GMP facilities that in addition apply different culture conditions, and sometimes were directly transferred after collection into patients.

6.2.6. Mesenchymal stem cells from alternative sources

Recently, alternative sources to obtain mesenchymal stem cells have been assessed. Bone marrow aspiration from the iliac crest is an invasive procedure, and it would be desirable to obtain stem cells with bloodless approaches. Various tissues have been identified as possible sources: adipose tissue, dental pulp, the foreskin, placental and fetal membrane, and many others.

Various studies have revealed the presence of pluripotent stem/progenitor cells, the so-called adipose-derived stem cells (ASCs), capable of self-renewing and differentiation into a range of mesenchymal tissues, including classical mesenchymal lineages (adipogenesis, chondrogenesis, osteogenesis).

The therapeutic potential of these stem cells is also increased when ASCs are administered within the so-called adipose-derived stromal vascular fraction (AD-SVF), rich not only in ADSCs, but also in endothelial progenitor cells, T cells, B cells, mast cells, and adipose-resident macrophages. Many isolation protocols require enzymatic digestion using collagenase, that seemed hardly necessary for efficient collection. In our experience, enzymatic digestion deeply modifies cell behaviour, altering surface proteins and consequently cellular interaction.

Enzymatic preparations, collagenase in particular, can trigger activation on human complement, inducing a sustained local inflammatory reaction. Furthermore, enzymatic methods can induce stem cell differentiation. In this context, many efforts have been made to identify new strategies which overcome enzymatic preparations, to preserve AD-SVF. We have identified an innovative system, named Lipogems, which uses mild mechanical forces to provide a non-expanded, ready-to-use fat product. The Lipogems product presented a remarkably preserved vascular stroma, whereas immunohistochemical analyses revealed that the Lipogems stromal vascular tissue included abundant cells with pericyte/hMSC identity (Figure 6.8, 6.9, 6.10).

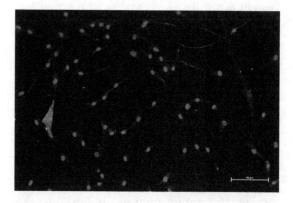

Figure 6.8. Epifluorescence microphotograph of a cell culture of Adipose Derived Stem Cells (ADSC) after 1 passage from the fresh tissue. CD31 expression (red channel) show single cell positive for vascular marker. Another endothelial marker stain, VE-Cadherin (green channel), is 100% positive, however its citoplasmatic localization show that cells are losing their vascular phenotype. Objective 20x, scale bar 100µm.

Figure 6.9. Epifluorescence and DIC (bright field) micropho-tograph of the whole adipose tissue. CD31 expression (red channel) shows the intact structure of the vessels, a necessary condition to obtain good quality stem cell culture. DAPI (blue channel) stains nuclei. Objective 10x, scale bar 100μm.

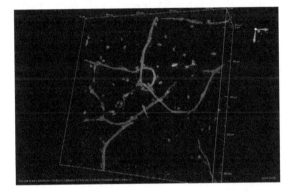

Figure 6.10. Confocal scanning 3D reconstruction of adipose tis-sue. CD31 expression (red channel) shows intact vessel net that feed adipose cells and mesenchymal niches. Membrane Deep Red marker (cyan channel) stains the cellular membrane: the adipocytes' morphological distinctive traits are clearly visible, with the nuclei in the periphery and very large monovacuolar lipid droplet surrounded by a thin layer of cytoplasm, giving the tissue a structure similar to foam. Objective 20x.

Despite promising results in animal mod-els, where ASCs were able to improve ejection fraction in experimentally induced myocardial infarction, promoting angiogenesis and low-ering fibrosis, the application of these cells in a clinical setting for cardiovascular diseases is still under discussion and evaluation. A rand-omized double-blind placebo-controlled clin-ical trial, the MystromalCell trial, has investi-gated the treatment effects of intramyocardial administration of ASCs, *ex vivo* pre-treated with VEGF-A, in patients with chronic ischaemic heart disease and refractory angina,

but with preserved left ventricle ejection frac-tion (> 40%). Even if no statistically significant differences have been observed between pla-cebo and cell-treated patients for the identi-fied primary endpoint, there was a significant increase in maximal bicycle exercise tolerance test (ETT, measured as time duration and work capacity) in patients receiving ASCs, which was not seen in the placebo group. ASCs con-tinue to be considered an attractive possibility due to their easy isolation and to their immu-nomodulatory properties.

6.2.7 Perinatal stem cells

Extraembryonic-associated tissues are a very promising source of stem cells, most of which falling within the category of mesen-chymal stem cells, due to low level of involve-ment in ethical issues, and easy collection and manipulation with no harm to the baby or mother. Perinatal stem cells exhibit greater proliferative activity than adult mesenchymal stem cells, displaying the advantage of rapid expansion and consequent downstream appli-cation. Stem cells could be isolated from dif-ferent compartments of the umbilical cord, such as the veins, the arteries, Wharton's jelly, the umbilical cord lining. Also fetal (embry-onic) membranes, that are defined as all mem-branous structures closely associated with or surrounding a developing vertebrate embryo, including the amnion, chorion, allantois, and yolk sac, are a source of mesenchymal stem cells. Many researchers are studying the pos-sible applications in regenerative medicine of these promising and non-controversial sources of stem cells, also in the cardiovascular field. Acute myocardial diseases are a matter of clinical urgency in order to prevent irreversi-ble damage. Allogeneic transplant of perinatal stem cells could definitively resolve the ques-tion of stem cell availability during acute car-diac events, nearly impossible to be guaranteed by using autologous stem cells.

A pilot study performed by Lilyanna et al. on an animal model demonstrated that cord lining-derived MSCs combined with a vascularized omental flap were able to ameliorate cardiac dysfunction by myocardial revascularization and attenuated remodelling in a rat model of chronic ischaemic heart failure, whilst another study, Kang et al., indicated how polycaprolactone nanofibres immobilized with umbilical cord-derived MSC-seeded fibronectin enhanced left ventricular ejection fraction, inhibiting ventricular remodelling, in a rat model of myocardial infarction. Human umbilical cord-derived MSCs were able to differentiate in cardiac "polymicrotissue", which could be used as a therapeutic patch in the infarct cardiac area, when stem cells are treated with a combination of growth factors, as demonstrated by Konstantinou et al. Wharton's jelly–derived mesenchymal stem cells (WJMSC) were administered by intracoronary infusion in patients with ST-elevation acute myocardial infarction, in a randomized, double-blind, controlled trial, described by Gao et al. One hundred sixteen patients were involved in this study, which reported a reduction in infarct size and improved heart function, preventing adverse remodelling after an observation period of 18 months. The real mechanism of action of WJMSCs was not fully elucidated during this trial, but certainly they exert sustained paracrine effects though secretion of antiapoptotic, angiogenic and growth factors, boosting regeneration of the myocardium and coronary vessels. In past years, we demonstrated that transplantation of HBR-preconditioned fetal membrane-derived human mesenchymal stem cells, in a rat model of myocardial infarction, was able to decrease the infarct size, enhancing capillary density and the yield of endothelial cells expressing human vWF. Unfortunately, a small number of differentiated cells was found when histological analyses were performed. We hypothesized that the beneficial effects of HBR-exposed FMhMSCs may be principally mediated by angiogenic and antiapoptotic factors, or FMhMSC differentiation into vascular cells.

Despite promising results, there is a lot of evidence that injection of MSCs into the damaged heart results in limited differentiation, with the exception of vascular lineages. The beneficial effects of perinatal stem cell injection, similarly to those shown for bone marrow stem cells, are mainly due to paracrine effects, rather than *de novo* cardiomyogenesis by the engrafted cells.

6.2.8 Endogenously derived resident cardiac stem cells

A brilliant study by Bergmann et al. analyzed cardiomyocyte renewal in humans, by exploiting the integration of ^{14}C, generated by nuclear bomb tests during the Cold War, into DNA. They demonstrated that no more than 50% of cardiomyocytes are exchanged during a lifespan, with a maximum annual turnover of 1%. These data suggest a limited, or maybe absent, chance of recovery after MI arising from cardiomyocytes. Many researchers have tried to understand if the heart can contain endogenous stem cells, able to help functional recovery after acute events. Unfortunately, enormous discrepancies exist between data from different laboratories, and sometimes these data are unreliable. A population of small cells expressing stem cell markers, such as c-kit, Sca-1 etc., was identified in the heart, leading some researchers to hypothesize the existence of a lineage commitment of resident Cardiac Stem Cells (CSC) capable of becoming cardiac progenitors and then cardiomyocytes into the heart. Supposed cardiac stem cells were isolated and *ex vivo* expanded. Moreover, several studies described how spherical aggregates of cells, named "cardiospheres", can originate from human endomyocardial biopsies grown in culture; the contained cells were called cardiosphere-derived cells (CDC). Clinical trials with both cell populations have already begun, but clinical outcomes remain unclear. At the present date, the real existence of cardiac stem cells is a very contentious issue. Using c-kit$^+$ lineage tracing mouse models, van Berlo et al., demonstrated that c-kit-labelled progenitors abundantly generate endothelial cells *in vivo*, but do not differentiate in cardiac myocytes. They concluded that small, albeit significant functional improvements in the heart function, when exogenous c-kit⁺ cells are transplanted in patients, can be due to the inability of these cells to really differentiate in functional cardiomyocytes.

6.3 Open questions about stem cell transplantation in ischaemic heart disease

To summarize, we can draw some conclusions about stem cell transplantation in regenerative medicine and performed clinical trials. The results arising from completed clinical trials are difficult to interpret, due to differences in delivered cells (mixed or enriched populations), in the amount of implanted cells, in the delivery methods, and in the injection time intervals after an acute event. Here we discuss briefly some of these open issues, each of which could be argued extensively; in the bibliography section we recommend some papers to which the reader can refer for further details.

6.3.1 Treated pathologies

Even if cell therapy has been principally tested on patients with acute myocardial infarction, some studies included patients with chronic ischaemia, as well as ischaemic and non ischaemic heart failure. These pathologies are very different, in particular concerning the local vascular, cellular, and chemical microenvironments. This heterogeneity complicates the already fragmented picture of clinical trials, and leads to an impossibility to draw exact conclusions. It would be desirable to target a sicker patient population in future design of studies. Moreover, the amount of involved patients in the different clinical trials was highly variable, ranging from a few tens to hundreds. Furthermore, co-morbidities, such as hypertension, diabetes, hyperlipidaemia, obesity, etc. could have an unpredictable effect on cell therapy, negatively affecting the effectiveness and efficiency of transplantation.

6.3.2 Mechanism of action

There is no doubt that transplanted stem cells provide a local "cell-help-cell" effect, through paracrine effect. Stem cells promote angiogenesis and vasculogenesis, acting as a biological and living factory of peptides, such as cytokines, chemokines and growth factors. Transdifferentiation into vascular phenotypes, such as endothelial and smooth muscle cells, and even more into functional cardiomyocytes is the subject of extensive discussion and remains controversial. Regardless, it is clear that transdifferentiation occurs at a functionally insignificant level, and is a highly inefficient and, to say the least, rare event. The much more accepted mechanism of action is paracrine signalling. Stem cells and, in particular, mesenchymal stem cells, through their secretome, improve neovascularization, reduce apoptosis of endogenous cells, promote recruitment of circulating stem cells, and can activate tissue intrinsic progenitor cells. The secretome is composed not only of nude proteins, but also contains micro- and nanovesicles, such as exosomes, with a specific pro-survival action. The deciphering of the composition of the MSC secretome is a key question in regenerative medicine, especially because it can influence stem cell type selection. Moreover, donor health status can deeply influence the features of the secretome, affecting its regenerative potential and, as a consequence, myocardial recovery.

6.3.3 Time, dose and way of administration

Three routes for stem cell delivery have been mainly used in clinical trials: systemic intravenous infusion, intracoronary infusion, and intramyocardial injection. Cell delivery still lacks efficiency, with less than 10% of stem cells retained after 24 hours, regardless of delivery route, usually washed out or mechanically ejected. Intravenous infusion offers, compared to the other two options, the advantage of simplicity and least invasive nature, and a decrease in risks and side effects, such as bleeding in intramyocardial injection or occlusion and embolization in intracoronary infusion. Moreover, the cell infusion procedure could be repeated several times. Unfortunately, it has been estimated that no more than 0.04% of the originally administered cells reach the infarct region, and the near totality of cells is trapped inside the lungs. This has two major consequences: firstly, the number of infused cells must be largely increased and, secondly, the effects of stem cells trapped in the lung must be evaluated, as they could promote inflammation or acute immune responses.

Direct intramyocardial injection is practicable during open-chest Coronary Artery Bypass Graft (CABG) surgery but presents a severe risk of complication and mortality, making it not easily feasible. Therefore, percutaneous catheter-based intramyocardial injection is preferred, as is transcoronary venous or transendocardial approach. Stem cells can be infused in the coronary artery thought balloon catheters, but the majority of stem cells are lost, due to washout. The merits and demerits of different routes are difficult to judge, but at present, no significant differences in outcomes with intracoronary infusion and intramyocardial injection were found. To complicate matters even further, the few retained cells do not survive for long in such an inhospitable microenvironment. A meta-analysis by Lui et at., to assess the impacts of timing on the efficacy of bone marrow stem cell transplantation, found that stem cell therapy was able to ameliorate clinical outputs only in a restricted time window, from 4 to 7 days after MI. Immediately after an acute event, the massive tissue necrosis triggers a great inflammatory response, mediated by cytokines and chemokines, with the consequent recruitment of neutrophils and macrophages. Inflammation peaks 3 days after MI, and is more or less exhausted at day 5. Probably, after these first few days, a normalization of microenvironment allows stem cell engraftment and survival. Intriguingly, endogenous circulating progenitor cells released from bone marrow peak around 7 days after MI. Later, after 1 week from MI, the scars appear consolidated, and stiffness changes (from flexible to rigid) due to myocardial remodelling: stem cell injection after this day seems to be ineffective, and regeneration seems no longer possible.

Cell dosage is another open issue, ranging from 2 million to 60 billion injected stem cells. The animal model suggests that a smaller number of selected cells is preferable to a larger number of unselected ones. Meta-analyses of different clinical trials suggest that less than 40 million cells failed to improve significantly major outcome parameters, and transplantation of at least 100 million cells was necessary to improve left ventricular ejection fraction. A real threshold between the dosage and the therapeutic effects has not yet been found.

6.3.4 Conclusion

Collectively, all the discussed questions reveal the urgency to deeply understand how stem cell transplantation could be helpful in clinical practice. Further efforts could be addressed to identifying standardized techniques. Moreover, it is now clear that individual patient characteristics, starting from specific disease to co-morbidities, age, etc. can largely influence clinical outcomes. Recently, some studies showed that the human adult heart possesses a certain potential of self-renewal, with a low but constant cardiomyocyte turnover during the lifespan. This limited capability of endogenous regeneration fails to counteract the massive loss of cardiomyocytes occurring during and after MI. Stem cells, especially through their secretome, seem to have not only a prosurvival effect on damaged tissue, but can probably accelerate cardiomyocyte turnover.

6.3.5 A different point of view

This concise chapter shows us how far we are from effective regenerative medicine with stem cells. Probably there is some fundamental bit of evidence which eludes us. Despite the importance of the efforts to understand the molecular pathways involved in cardiac differentiation, we think that a fundamental aspect is quite neglected. Cells, and consequently stem cells, live in a "physical" world that talks with them. The environment can communicate with chemical messages, but not only with them. During progenitor cell differentiation, the heart becomes a tridimensional organ that, while beating, produces a rhythmic sound. Spatial disposition and mechanical stimulation can influence developing, in combination with transcription networks and molecular signalling. In particular, physical cues activate the intracellular signalling cascade, as well as chemical stimuli. The nature of the intracellular molecular phenomena triggered by mechanical cues is still largely unclear, mainly due to the insufficient availability of differentiation and morphogenesis bio-mechanical models.

Modifications in cell shape contribute to different morphogenetic processes, and can involve individual cells, independently of neighbours, but mostly affect hundreds of neighbouring cells driving shrinkage, extension, folding and movement of tissues. In the heart cardiac progenitors migrate to form the linear heart tube, that loops around and forms the mature heart. As the heart tube starts to beat, it undergoes mechanical deformations and fluid flow, as well. Hove et al. proved that, when flow was occluded in zebrafish embryos, cardiac looping was prevented, demonstrating that, without fluid flow, the heart failed to properly develop. The significant role of fluid forces in heart morphogenesis is corroborated by *in vitro* data on mouse ESCs in which cytoskeletal arrangement and increase in cardiovascular gene expression were induced by a specific laminar shear stress (between 5 and 15 dyn/cm^2). Cycling strain generated by beating cardiomyocytes is also supposed to influence differentiation. In monolayer cell cultures of mouse ESCs, cycling stress significantly decreases the genes involved in stemness, such as Nanog, and on the other hand, increases endodermal markers. The effect of cyclic strain on hESCs is more controversial: different types of stimulation at different days seem to have opposite effects; in general, results suggest that maintenance of pluripotency is favoured by extended cyclic strain and that, on the contrary, short applications of higher magnitude induce differentiation.

Also adult stem cells respond to the physical environment altering their differentiative potential. In 2004, McBeath et al. demonstrated that cell shape, determined by using different micropaterning, can regulate hMSC lineage commitment, switching from the osteoblastic to the adipocytic phenotype, through RhoA activity and its effect on cytoskeletal tension. Intriguingly, the cocktail of differentiation factors can be entirely replaced by direct manipulation of RhoA signalling. Previous studies had already shown how Rho GTPase activity has a crucial role in determining cell fate during the differentiation decision that leads to adipocyte or myocyte precursors.

Not only mechanical forces are involved in or influence stem cell differentiation. We first demonstrated how exposure to extremely low frequency magnetic fields (ELF-MF) of mouse embryonic stem (ES) cells results in a remarkable increase in spontaneously beating cardiac myocytes. More recently, we tested an innovative technology, named Radio Electric Asymmetric Conveyer (REAC), able to generate radioelectric asymmetrically conveyed microcurrents in tissues, without depth limits, on human adipose-derived mesenchymal cells. REAC treatment was able to induce a transient overexpression of stemness genes, followed by their down-regulation, leading to a high-yield commitment towards myocardial, neuronal, and skeletal muscle differentiation.

Non-ionizing radiation (light) has many effects on biological systems, and the study of these effects is called photobiology. Different wavelength regions of radiation are absorbed differently by cells: for instance, low-level visible red to near infrared light seems to have a direct effect on mitochondria, modulating ATP synthesis and ROS generation. Clearly, many parameters influence the cellular response to photobiomodulation (PBM), such as wavelength, energy density, power density, and continuous or pulsed irradiation. Various effects on stem cells are described in literature: osteogenic and chondrogenic improvement, inhibition of proliferation, but also increase of proliferation in different cell types. Further studies must be performed to elucidate the mechanisms and implication of photobiomodulation in stem cell physiology.

Recommended reading and references

1. Dan P, Velot É, Decot V, Menu P. *The role of mechanical stimuli in the vascular differentiation of mesenchymal stem cells.* J Cell Sci. 2015 Jul 15;128(14):2415-22. doi: 10.1242/jcs.167783.

2. Galdos FX, Guo Y, Paige SL, VanDusen NJ, Wu SM, Pu WT. *Cardiac Regeneration: Lessons From Development.* Circ Res. 2017;120(6):941–959.doi: 10.1161/CIRCRESAHA.116.309040

3. Guo X, Bai Y, Zhang L, Zhang B, Zagidullin N, Carvalho K, Du Z, Cai B. *Cardiomyocyte differentiation of mesenchymal stem cells from bone marrow: new regulators and its implications.* Stem Cell Res Ther. 2018 Feb 26;9(1):44. doi:10.1186/s13287-018-0773-9.

4. Hao M, Wang R, Wang W. *Cell Therapies in Cardiomyopathy: Current Status of Clinical Trials.* Anal Cell Pathol (Amst). 2017;2017:9404057. doi:10.1155/2017/9404057.

5. Kumar A, Placone JK, Engler AJ. *Understanding the extracellular forces that determine cell fate and maintenance.* Development. 2017 Dec 1;144(23):4261-4270. doi: 10.1242/dev.158469.

6. Michler RE. *The current status of stem cell therapy in ischemic heart disease.* J Card Surg. 2018 Sep;33(9):520-531. doi: 10.1111/jocs.13789.

7. Patwari P, Lee RT. *Mechanical control of tissue morphogenesis.* Circ Res. 2008;103(3):234–243. doi:10.1161/CIRCRESAHA.108.175331.

8. Srivastava D. *Making or breaking the heart: from lineage determination to morphogenesis.* Cell. 2006 Sep 22;126(6):1037-48. doi:10.1016/j.cell.2006.09.003.

9. Ventura C, Cavallini C, Bianchi F, Cantoni S. *Stem cells and cardiovascular repair: a role for natural and synthetic molecules harboring differentiating and paracrine logics.* Cardiovasc Hematol Agents Med Chem. 2008 Jan;6(1):60-8.

10. Ventura C. *Tuning stem cell fate with physical energies.* Cytotherapy. 2013 Dec;15(12):1441-3. doi: 10.1016/j.jcyt.2013.10.001.

11. Xu H, Yi BA, Chien KR. *Shortcuts to making cardiomyocytes.* Nat Cell Biol. 2011 Mar;13(3):191-3. doi: 10.1038/ncb0311-191.

Stem cells in muscle development, diseases and regeneration

7

Maurilio Sampaolesi,
Mattia Quattrocelli,   Enrico Pozzo

The muscle is an essential tissue for motility formed by highly specialized cells, called muscular fibres. Muscles can be classified as somatic (or skeletal) and visceral based on their function. Somatic muscles - found in the body wall, appendages, and tail - orient the organism in the surrounding environment. Visceral muscles, on the other hand, help in the structural maintenance of the internal body environment by forming the wall of hollow organs and blood vessels, as well as the intrinsic muscle of ocular bulb and hair erector muscles.

From a histological standpoint, muscle tissue can be categorized into smooth, cardiac and skeletal. Smooth muscle tissue constitutes the muscular layer present in the vegetative life organs. Involuntary contractions determine variations in shape and calibre of the organs to facilitate the passage and expulsion of blood. Cardiac muscle tissue constitutes the walls of the heart and uses involuntary contractions to pump blood throughout the body. Skeletal muscle tissue forms the superficial and deep muscles: the former are inserted in the deep derma (e.g. mimetic muscles of the face in primates), while the latter are found connected to the bone extremities or the sensory organs, as well as in relation with the digestive, respiratory and urogenital tracts.

Muscle cells can perform movements by means of transforming the chemical energy of ATP into mechanical energy via the contraction of sarcomeres (i.e. the morphofunctional and contractile units of striated skeletal and cardiac muscle cells). The contraction of a sufficient number of cells causes the shortening and increase in size of the entire muscle mass: if the muscle surrounds a lumen, this gets restricted; if it is tense between two structures, as in the case of two bones, these get closer.

The process of contraction is mediated by actin and myosin proteins constituting the thin (actin) and thick (myosin) filaments of sarcomeres. At the electron microscope, the sarcomere is formed by the Z-line (i.e. actin filament insertion), M-line (i.e. myosin filament insertion), H-zone, A-band and I-band. These different areas can be distinguished from each other, since the Z-band forms the beginning and end of the sarcomere, while the M-line can be seen as a dark line running through the centre of the sarcomere. Similarly, myosin filaments can be found in the H-zone and A-band, while actin filaments can be found in the I-band and A-band. During contraction, the cell structure is maintained thanks to structural proteins, including dystrophin, sarcoglycan, troponin and tropomyosin.

Among the different types of muscle tissues, in this chapter we will mainly focus on skeletal muscles formed by individual contractile elements, known as myocytes. These cells, derived from precursors called myoblasts, take part in the differentiation process of the adult muscle and thus remain isolated in the adult muscle tissue as dormant cell types named satellite cells. Following a lesion in the muscle, the satellite cells can increase in size, divide and fuse to form new muscle fibres and contribute to tissue repair.

Skeletal muscle fibres have characteristics considerably different compared to the other types of cells (Figure 7.1).

A first and obvious difference is represented by the significantly bigger dimensions compared to the majority of the other cells of the organism. A muscle fibre of the leg, for example, can have a diameter of 100 μm and be 30-40 cm in length (equal to the entire muscle length). A second difference is that every skeletal muscle fibre contains hundreds of nuclei arranged right beneath the cellular membrane. The number of nuclei depends on the length of the fibre: there are approximately 35 for every mm of its length. Nuclei have an ovoidal or elongated shape and are arranged in the periphery of the fibre in a hypolemmal position.

7.1 Myogenesis

In this chapter we will discuss the development and maturation process of skeletal muscle tissue, known as myogenesis. Due to the high resemblance of its development with human muscle tissue, the majority of our knowledge on myogenesis derives from research on murine models. Thus, we will mainly focus on the cellular and molecular characterizations obtained in the muscle of this animal model.

7.1.1 Molecular signals of myogenesis

Myogenesis is the process of muscular regeneration mediated by the cascade expression of transcription factors regulating cellular differentiation.

Myogenesis can be subdivided in three phases (Figure 7.2).

Embryonic myogenesis (E10.5-12.5): myogenic precursors, or embryonic myoblasts, migrate from the dermomyotome to the limb buds and start differentiating in multinucleated muscle fibres known as primary fibres;

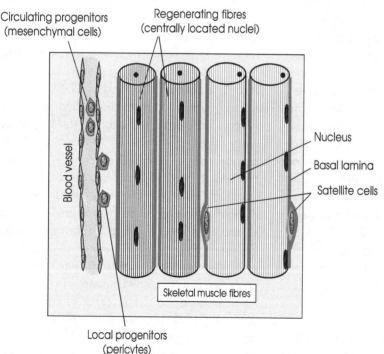

Figure 7.1 Skeletal muscle fibres and muscle progenitors

Fetal myogenesis (E14.5-17.5): fetal myoblasts fuse with each other as well as with primary fibres, giving rise to secondary fibres;

Perinatal and postnatal myogenesis: mononuclear unipotent stem cells found between the basal lamina and the plasma membrane of the fibre divide, and progenitor cells fuse with adjacent fibres to add new nuclei to growing muscle fibres. At the end of postnatal growth, these mononuclear cells, also called satellite cells, enter in a quiescent state from which, in response to specific signals, they can escape to contribute to the repair of compromised or damaged muscle tissue.

Except for some cranial and facial muscles, all skeletal muscles constituting the body of vertebrates derive from progenitors found in somites, i.e. transient mesodermal-derived units forming rostral to caudal on both sides of the neural tube in a process mediated by paraxial mesoderm segmentation (Figure 7.3).

These primitive cell masses rapidly differentiate into the ventral sclerotome and dorsal dermomyotome. While the former gives rise to vertebral and rib cartilage, the latter, considered the "fuel of myogenesis", is able to generate different types of cells, including those for skeletal muscle formation (myotome) and skin (dermatome). Normally the dermomyotome is subdivided in:

- the Epaxial domain (generates dorsal muscles), and the Hypaxial domain (generates ventral muscles).
- the activation of myogenesis is controlled by myogenic regulatory factors (MRF), i.e. helix-loop-helix transcriptional regula-

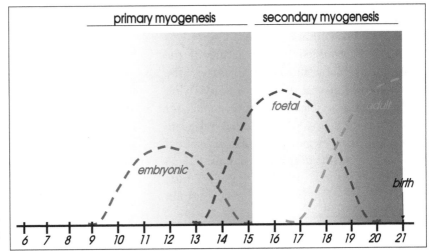

Figura 7.2 Prenatal myogenesis and the differentiation waves

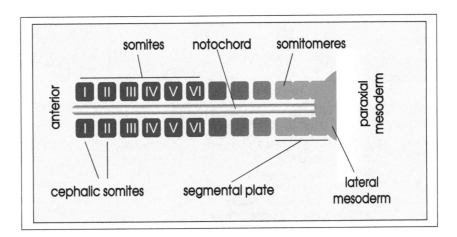

Figura 7.3 Somitogenesis

tors with preserved link domains to DNA able to promote the differentiation towards skeletal muscle. The MRFs are:

- Myogenic factor 5 (*Myf5*),
- Myogenic differentiation determinant (*MyoD1/MyoD*),
- Herculin (*Myf6/Mrf4*),
- Myogenin (*Myog*).

MRFs are activated in differentiating myoblasts and control the expression of genes required for the production of contractile proteins. These genes act downstream of transcription factors *Pax3* and *Pax7* during the different phases of embryonic and adult myogenesis. *Pax3* has a fundamental role during primary myogenesis, while *Pax7* acts mainly during the late phases of muscular formation. Initially the expression of *Pax3* is extended to the entire somite; subsequently it is limited to the dermomyotome epithelium to eventually shut off in late myogenesis.

The microenvironment needed for myogenesis is determined by the nature of the signals secreted by surrounding tissues. The notochord, the neural tube and the overlying ectoderm surface release positive signals for primary myogenesis, while the lateral plate mesoderm is a negative regulator. Epaxial muscular precursors depend on signals derived from axial structures, including the neural tube and the notochord. Hypaxial precursors, on the other hand, require signals coming from the ectoderm's surface and the adjacent lateral mesoderm plate.

In epaxial muscles, *MyoD* expression is induced in parallel by *Pax3*, *Myf5* and *Myf6*. Conversely, in hypaxial dermomyotome muscles, *Pax3* stimulates the expression of *Myf5*, which in turn activates the expression of *MyoD*. The *Wnt* pathway is involved in myogenesis induction, with the *Wnt1* signal originating from the dorsal neural tube activating *Myf5* activation, and the *Wnt7a* signal deriving from the dorsal ectoderm activating *MyoD1*. The *Hedgehog* signal, which comes from the notochord, promotes myogenesis by maintaining *Myf5* active. The gene family *Six* plays a role in myogenesis, with *Six1* and *Six4* regulating *Myf6* in epaxial dermomyotome. The same genes, together with cofactors *Eya1* and *Eya2*, induce *Pax3* in the hypaxial dermomyotome (Figure 7.4).

7.1.2 MicroRNAs and myogenesis

MicroRNAs (miRNAs) constitute a class of small ~ 22bp non-coding RNAs that are able to regulate the gene expression profile. miRNAs are transcribed starting from mono- or poly-cystronic units dispersed in the intergenic space or inside introns. Once transcribed and matured, miRNAs - connected to the *Dicer* protein complex - target one or more mRNAs,

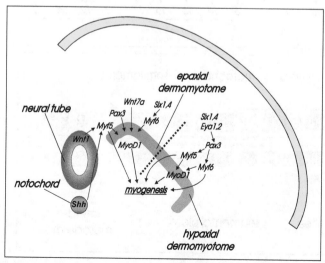

Figure 7.4   Molecular signals of embryonic myogenesis activation

usually recognizing a specific sequence at the 3' UTR. In the majority of cases, the targeted transcript is subsequently degraded or its translation into peptide is inhibited.

Evidence supporting the general impact of miRNAs on the development of skeletal muscle in vertebrates comes from transgenic mice, where a conditional allele of *Dicer* is removed during development thanks to the expression of Cre recombinase driven by the *MyoD1* promoter. In the embryos of these transgenic mice, *Dicer* expression and the miRNA activity are absent in the developing skeletal muscle starting from 9 dpc. The removal of the allele causes massive disturbances in somite development, with muscular hypoplasia and perinatal death. Interestingly, conditional knock-out of *Dicer* in adult satellite cells leads to their exit from quiescence and entrance in the cell cycle. It appears that this phenotype related to *Dicer* disruption may be mediated by miR-489, as this miRNA is highly expressed in the quiescent state and gets quickly down-regulated with *Dicer* disruption-mediated satellite cell activation. Then miR-27b-mediated reduction in Pax3 levels favours premature differentiation of the myogenic progenitor cells migrated into the limb bud. Over time, reduction in muscle mass and a mild muscle fibre atrophy in mice lacking *Dicer* is observed.

In recent literature there are reports of an opposite role of two miRNAs, i.e. miR-1 and miR-133, on myoblast differentiation. miR-1 and miR-133 are transcribed from the same bicistronic sequence. However, miR-1 represses the expression of *HDAC4*, a histone deacetylase normally involved in *Mef2* repression which, in turn, is both a transcriptional factor associated with myogenic differentiation and a potent transcriptional activator of miR-1. Thus, *Mef2* and miR-1 establish a regulatory circuit able to promote the differentiation of myoblasts. Conversely, miR-133 promotes myoblast proliferation, inhibiting the translation of *SRF4* and thus blocking myogenic differentiation.

Another fundamental miRNA for the myogenic development is miR-206 which,

unlike the aforementioned miRNAs, is specific to skeletal muscle and absent in the cardiac muscle. Recent studies have shown that miR-206 expression promotes the late stages of fibre maturation by inhibiting *Cx43*, a connexin fundamental for electric transmission in cardiomyocytes but negative for the terminal development of skeletal muscle fibres. Moreover, miR-206 also inhibits the translation of subunit p180 of DNA polymerase α, blocking the proliferation and unbalancing myoblasts towards terminal differentiation. Finally, miR-206 has been proposed as the molecular effector with which *MyoD1* inhibits genes like follistatin-like 1 (*Fstl1*) and utrophin during the early phases of fibre formation.

The aforementioned miRNAs are part of the group of so-called muscle-specific miRNAs, or myomiRs. In differentiated skeletal muscle, these miRNAs have either uniform expression throughout the muscle (miR-1 and miR-133a), or are rich in slow-twitch, type I muscles (miR-206, miR-208b and miR-499).

In the adult muscle, miRNA-mediated post-transcriptional regulation is required to maintain quiescence in satellite cells. This is accomplished by either cell cycle entry prevention via targeting *Dek* (miR-489) and/or *Cdc25/Ccnd* (miR-195/497), or by silencing of the myogenic regulatory factor *Myf5* (miR-31). Other miRNAs found in quiescence and lost upon satellite cell activation include miRNAs of the miR-127/miR-136 and miR-379/miR-410 clusters. Interestingly, myomiRs represent only 3% of miRNAs expressed in quiescent satellite cells, but as much as 74% of miRNAs expressed in differentiated cells.

Recently, miR-669a and miR-669q have been implicated in the regulation of *MyoD1* expression not only in skeletal but also in cardiac muscle, where this gene has to be constantly expressed in order to avoid the aberrant differentiation into striated fibres not electrophysiologically connected to the myocardium and thus arrhythmogenic.

Thus, during the embryonic and fetal myogenic development, a finely tuned molecular regulation is required for the activation of specific miRNAs at different moments of myogenesis in order to guarantee the correct balance between proliferation and myoblast differentiation.

7.1.3 Prenatal muscle precursors and differentiation waves

Somitogenesis in the mouse embryo starts at 8.75 days post coitum (dpc). During this phase, some precursors of the dorsal dermomyotome will give rise to mononuclear muscular cells of the primary myotome (or primary myoblasts), while other precursors will induce the growth of muscles during late embryonic, fetal and postnatal life. Thus, it appears to be evident that the diverse differentiation processes of these cells, although being in the same microenvironment, depend exclusively on the different responses to stimuli.

At 11 dpc, embryonic myoblasts invade the myotome and fuse, forming myotubes. In this first wave of myogenesis, defined as primary myogenesis, primary fibres are formed.

From 14.5 to 17.5 dpc, a second wave of myogenesis hits, defined as secondary myogenesis, where the fusion of fetal myoblasts and the generation of secondary fibres occur. At the end of this phase, satellite cells can be morphologically identified as mononucleated cells sitting between the basal lamina and the plasma membrane of the muscular fibre, i.e. the sarcolemma.

During the perinatal and postnatal period, satellite cells divide, with most of them fusing with adjacent fibres and contributing to the growth of muscular fibres and to the majority of nuclei present in mature muscles. At the end of postnatal growth, satellite cells enter in a quiescent state but can be activated in response to skeletal tissue damage or to secondary reprise of muscle growth. Moreover, non-somitic cells, including mesenchymal cells

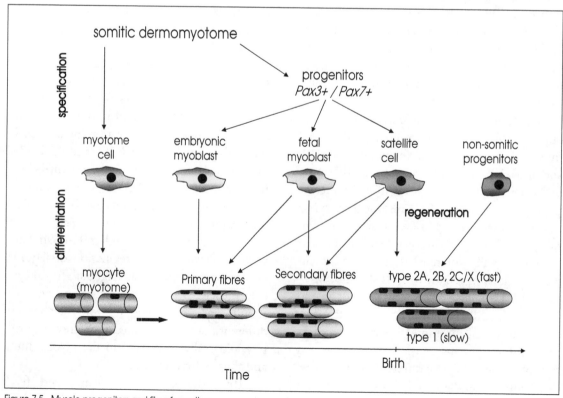

Figure 7.5 Muscle progenitors and fibre formation

and mesodermal-derived stem cells, have the capacity to participate in postnatal muscular regeneration (Figure 7.5).

7.1.4 First phase of myogenesis

The dermomyotome is the source of the primary myotome, contributing also to the formation of the derma, endothelial cells and smooth muscle. The epithelium is a central sheet surrounded by four contiguous lips towards the ventral somite. The cells that are localized in the four lips sit between the dermomyotome and sclerotome (a subcompartment of the ventral somite) and form the primary myotome. The central portion of the dermomyotome plays an important role during secondary myogenesis, followed by the dissolution of this epithelial structure.

A population of postmitotic progenitors derive from the dorso-medial portion of the anterior somite for the formation of the dermomyotome. The characteristics of the dermomyotome's initial epithelium, as well as the origin of the cell types that derive from this structure, require specific regulations for cellular adhesion; some of these cells express *N-Cadherin*, a cellular adhesion molecule, differentiating the epithelial plate in hypaxial and epaxial. During primary myogenesis, embryonic myoblasts fuse and form primary fibres. In this phase, fetal myoblasts and satellite cells remain in an undifferentiated state in the presence of Transforming Growth Factor beta (*Tgf*-β) and Bone Morphogenetic Protein 4 (*Bmp4*). Once the primary fibres have been formed, they can release mitogens that induce a new wave of proliferation in fetal myoblasts. When the central portion of the dermomyotome starts dissolving, cells divide inside of it in an apico-vasal fashion, perpendicular to the epithelial plate. The gene N-cadherin continues to be expressed in the apical portion of the epithelium by dividing cells, which are committed to contributing to the myotome growth and the progression of secondary myogenesis. If *Myf5* and *Myod1* signals are absent, primary myogenesis is altered and the early myotome is structurally damaged.

7.1.5 Second phase of myogenesis

Secondary myogenesis is characterized by cells that co-express *Pax3* and *Pax7*. In this phase, fetal myoblasts generate secondary fibres and the platelet-derived growth factor (*Pdgf*) signal maintains satellite cells in an undifferentiated state. *Pax3* is an initial regulator of myogenic cascade needed for primary myogenesis, while *Pax7* is needed for the determination and maintenance of satellite cells. The latter form the fibres during postnatal development and remain in quiescent state in the healthy adult muscle.

7.1.6 Somitogenesis

In the mouse, somitogenesis starts at around 8.75 dpc and continues until the 14th day of gestation. The important stages of this process are periodicity, epithelization, specification and differentiation.

Periodicity of somite formation

The first somites appear in the anterior part of the trunk and new somites bud at regular intervals from the rostral end of the paraxial mesoderm. Somite formation starts when paraxial mesoderm cells organize in segmental units called somitomeres. Somitomeres, once they become compact and are being held together by an epithelium, separate from the presomitic paraxial mesoderm forming distinct somites (Figure 7.3). Since the single embryos can develop at slightly different pace, the number of somites present is usually the best indicator of the grade of achieved development. The total number of somites formed in the mouse is 65 pairs, in a rostral to caudal maturation gradient.

Although the mechanisms regulating the periodicity of somite formation have not been fully elucidated, one of the key factors of this process is the *Notch* signalling pathway that drives the maturation of the somite itself.

The derivations of the somites (specification)

The somites form:

Vertebral and rib cartilage;

The muscles of the thoracic cage, limbs, abdominal wall, back and tongue;

The cutaneous derma of the back.

The determination of somite cells to their destiny occurs relatively late, after the somite has already formed. Once the somite has just separated from presomitic mesoderm, all its cells can give rise to a specific structure. The epithelial structure is maintained for approximately 10 hours, after which the medioventral cells (localized farther from the back but closer to the neural tube) undergo mitosis and move along the notochord giving rise to the sclerotome, i.e. the precursor of cartilage (chondrocytes), the vertebrae and part of the ribs. The cells of the two lateral portions of the epithelium (the closest and farthest regions from the neural tube) constitute the region that gives rise to the muscle, the myotome. The cells of the myotome divide, forming an internal layer of myoblasts. The derived double-layered structure is called dermomyotome. The myoblasts originating in the region closer to the neural tube form the epaxial muscles (deep muscles of the back), while myoblasts that originate in the distal portion of the neural tube form the hypaxial muscles of the body wall, limbs and tongue.

7.1.7 Head and trunk myogenesis

As opposed to the muscles of the trunk and the limbs that have a somitic origin, the muscles of the head derive from three distinct areas of the embryo: the occipital somites, the prechordial mesoderm head and the paraxial mesoderm head. The craniofacial skeletal muscles can be subdivided in distinct classes: extraocular, brachial, somitic axial-derived muscles and hypoglossal-derived muscles. The extraocular muscles, that permit the movement and stability of the eye, originate in the paraxial and prechordial head of the mesoderm. The brachiomeric muscle progenitors originate from the paraxial head of the mesoderm, while the muscles wrapping the cranium originate from the occipital somites. Most of the craniofacial muscle progenitors, which originate in the non-segmented mesoderm head, migrate from this site of origin as condensed premuscular cell mass, using the same strategy adopted for the generation of limb muscles.

The genetic expression pattern during the embryonic development of the muscles of the head is highly variable compared to the trunk muscles. Similarly to those of the trunk, all the muscles of the head express *MyoD1* under the initial stimulus of *Myf5*, while *Pax3*, differently from the muscles of the trunk, is not expressed; in fact, *Pax3* knockout mice do not have defects at the cranium level. Moreover, in the appropriate growth and expansion conditions *ex vivo*, cranial skeletal progenitors tend to co-express cardiac markers together with skeletal ones. This points to the fact that there are substantial differences between craniofacial and somitic-derived myogenic development (including the postnatal-associated satellite cells).

7.1.8 Adult myogenesis

The presence of a quiescent adult muscle stem cell population is vastly documented, but little is known about the relation between myogenesis in the primary myotome and the role of satellite cells in muscle tissues. In fact, the satellite cells have a somitic origin, but their relation with other myogenic precursor cells is not clear. Satellite cells derive from the hypaxial dermomyotome. Specific subpopulations of satellite cells contribute to the repair of fibres in postnatal life, in the presence of muscular damage, and express proto-oncogene Met (*Met*) and *Pax7*, although recent papers suggest that the latter is not required for the reactivation and regenerative capacity of adult myoblasts.

The division plate determines the destiny of satellite cells (Figure 7.6):

Those who present a planar division show a symmetric expression of *Myf5* and fuse with the muscle fibre, and

Those who divide along the apical-basal plate present an asymmetric expression of *Myf5*.

In this way, satellite cells can generate new muscle fibres and self-sustain themselves, giving rise to:

Myogenic progenitor cells (positive for *Myf5*), and

Satellite cells (negative for *Myf5*).

In the progenitor cells, *Pax7* regulates the expression of *Myf5*. The progenitors that have activated *Myf5* subsequently express *MyoD1*, promoting the activation of muscle-specific genes. The satellite cells in quiescent state are activated by several growth factors, including Hepatocyte growth factor (HGF), which binds and activates the tyrosine kinase receptor c-MET. HGF has a primary role in the activation of satellite cells when the muscle is compromised or damaged.

It is worth noting that genetic alterations resulting in a pathological muscular phenotype, including mutations associated with some subtypes of muscular dystrophies, interfere with the normal dynamics of activation, expansion and differentiation of resident satellite cells.

In recent years, attention has shifted to other stem cells able to reconstitute *in vivo* myofibres in the adult organism. Potential candidates for therapeutic purposes, both for acute and for chronic degenerative damage, include myoendothelial precursors, mesoangioblasts (a myogenic subpopulation of pericytes of the skeletal muscle) and the subpopulation of cir-culating mesenchymal stem cells (including the so-called side population, or the CD133+ or CD146+ population). These progenitors of unknown origin are associated or are found circulating in muscular vessels. Once isolated and reinjected in lesion conditions or in muscular inflammation, they are able to fuse and form new functional myofibres.

7.2 Skeletal muscle disorders

In this section we will consider pathologies related to: genetic defects in the normal sarcolemma (muscular dystrophies), the effects of chronic diseases (cachexia) or ageing (sarcopenia) on skeletal muscle, and uncontrolled proliferation of myogenic precursors (rhabdomyosarcoma).

Muscular Dystrophies

Skeletal muscle fibres derive from mononuclear progenitor cell fusion originating in the somites. During fetal myogenesis, the basal lamina defines the specific environment suitable to home muscle-specific satellite cells. These resident stem cells migrate to the space comprised between the basal lamina and the plasma membrane of muscular fibres, forming

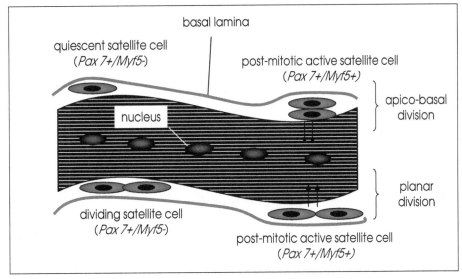

Figure 7.6 Satellite cell activation in adult myogenesis

the muscular stem cell niche. During postnatal development and growth, satellite cells slowly divide and contribute to muscle growth and regeneration. Conversely, in the adult muscle, satellite cells are normally quiescent but can re-enter mitosis following the response to acute damage or can be continuously active in chronic muscular pathologies like muscular dystrophies (MD). MDs are a heterogeneous group of genetic conditions, mainly characterized by severe and chronic muscle degeneration, that limit motility and reduce life expectancy. In affected individuals, satellite cells present the same genetic defect of muscular fibres. Thus, in a possible cell-based therapeutic protocol, satellite cells derived from the same patient must be corrected to proceed through *ex vivo* gene therapy. On the other hand, in the heterologous setting, the patient must undergo immune suppressive therapy to prevent the rejection of donor cells. Besides this characteristic, satellite cells are not able to traverse the vessel wall and thus cannot be introduced systemically and, moreover, do not migrate away from the site of intramuscular injection. Their therapeutic use would require thousands of injections to achieve a therapeutic effect in all muscles of the body and this limits enormously their clinical utility for cell-based treatment approaches.

Recently, the therapeutic potential of resident stem cells has been tested by several researchers all over the world. Thanks to their migration and regenerative capacity, skeletal muscle stem cells have shown a beneficial effect in preclinical models of muscular pathologies, and clinical trials are verifying their therapeutic potentials in patients affected by Duchenne MD, one of the worse and most frequent forms of MDs. Duchenne MD (DMD) is the most serious form and is caused by frame-shift, deletions, duplications or point mutations of the dystrophin gene, one of the largest genes in the human genome (its mRNA is 14kb long). In this type of dystrophy, the protein is totally or partially lost. A variably milder phenotype is described in Becker's dystrophy, where muta-tions in the dystrophin gene still allow myofi-bres to maintain a truncated yet partially functional protein isoform. Some recessive forms of limb girdle muscular dystrophy (LGMD type 2) are caused by mutations in α-, β-, γ- and δ-sarcoglycan genes (*Sgca*, *Sgcb*, *Sgcg* and *Sgcd*, respectively), which prevent the formation of the sarcoglycan protein complex necessary for sarcolemmal integrity.

The mobility of patients affected by DMD is progressively compromised and the outcome of the disease is still lethal, in most cases due to respiratory or cardiac failure normally in the second decade of life. To improve the overall outcome, new strategies for MD treatments are currently under investigation and can be classified into two different therapeutic approaches:

- endogenous activation of muscle precursors and
- exogenous delivery of viral vectors or stem cells.

In the first strategy, the scope is to activate endogenous cells with myogenic properties, counteracting the loss of strength / mass in the muscle fibres under chronic damage-induced inflammation. To achieve this goal, several small molecules or recombinant proteins have thus far been considered, such as IGF1, valproic acid or MagicF1.

Conversely, the exogenous delivery of viral vectors or stem cells aims at improving muscle regeneration using gene or cell therapy to provide new functional fibres to the dystrophic muscle or strenghten the existing ones. By targeting the correction of genetic defects, the goal of gene therapy is to provide the muscle with the correct gene form or alter the target gene splicing to overcome the observed pathological mutations. Cell therapy, on the other hand, is based on muscle regeneration using precursors of skeletal muscle or stem cells, with local or systemic injections.

Sarcopenia

An overall improvement in the quality of life since the 19th century has led to ageing of the world population. By 2050, the global population of seniors, aged 60 years or older, is estimated to more than double its size compared to 2015. Inevitably, the prevalence of age-related conditions, like sarcopenia and frailty, increases.

Sarcopenia is characterized by an age-induced decline in muscle mass, muscle strength and physical performance. Various factors contribute to sarcopenia, including diet, chronic illness, physical activity and physiological ageing. The accelerating decrease in muscle mass due to ageing can start as early as 35 years of age. After the age of 60, a decrease in muscle mass of 1.4% to 2.5% per year is to be expected, with a total decrease in mass of approximately 40% from adulthood to death.

In sarcopenia, muscle deconditioning involves a negative equilibrium between anabolic and catabolic factors, as well as between apoptosis and regeneration processes. For example, the main underlying causes are an imbalance in protein synthesis and limited incorporation of new nuclei by satellite cells and myogenic precursor cells in aged muscle fibres. Multiple other aspects affect sarcopenia, including fatty infiltration by fibro/adipogenic progenitors (FAP), decreased release of anabolic hormones, such as growth hormone (GH) and insulin-like growth factor 1 (IGF-1), and the presence of a baseline chronic inflammation as seen by higher levels of serum interleukin 6 (IL-6) and tumour necrosis factor α (TNF-α).

Current therapies to combat sarcopenia are limited. Exercise appears to be an excellent strategy; however it is often impeded due to lack of motivation and the presence of comorbidities, such as osteoarthritis and cardiovascular disease. Other strategies, although limited due to their side effects or limited efficacy, include hormone replacement therapies and supplementation with β-hydroxy-β-methylbutyrate (HMB) shown to reduce muscle loss.

Cachexia

Cachexia is a chronic syndrome affecting 2% of the overall patient population in the Western world and is characterized by weight loss due to reduced fat and body mass. The symptoms range from fatigue to shortness of breath and impaired exercise tolerance. It is found in association with advanced stage chronic diseases, including cancer, chronic heart failure, chronic kidney disease, chronic obstructive pulmonary disease, neurological disease and rheumatoid arthritis. Among age-related complications, cachexia and sarcopenia, besides some overlap in definition, are different clinical concepts, because only cachexia requires weight loss, whereas patients with sarcopenia may or may not have lost weight. Cachexia represents a major contributor to morbidity and mortality as it further worsens the compromised clinical picture, leading to an overall poor prognosis. Patients with cachexia have an overall marked skeletal muscle weight loss, massive myofibre degradation and cardiac dysfunction. These observed phenotypes are not only due to the disease itself but also to the treatments tackling the underlying disease, whether chemotherapy and radiotherapy in cancer patients or corticosteroids in immune suppressed patients. The multifactorial mechanisms of cancer cachexia have yet to be elucidated. However, the mediators of cancer cachexia are thought to derive from immune or tumour cells, or the targeted mesenchymal tissues undergoing wasting. Considered to be at the top of this list are the pro-inflammatory cytokines, including TNFα, IL-1, IL-4, IL-6 and IL-18. All these molecules are altered in the plasma level of patients affected by cachexia. Subjects with cachexia could extend their life expectancy by preserving fat and skeletal muscle as observed in animal models and in clinical studies. However, nutritional interventions have shown limited success in preserving fat and no effect in preserving muscle mass. While preclinical studies have shown that a derangement in the myogenic program may cause the atrophy observed in skeletal muscle, the molecular pathways leading to cachectic muscles are yet to be elucidated.

Rhabdomyosarcoma

Rhabdomyosarcoma is the most common soft tissue sarcoma in the paediatric population. It is defined as a cancer with myogenic features, due to its site of origin in the skeletal muscle as well as the expression of myogenic regulatory factors, MyoD, myogenin, desmin, and actin. According to the WHO classification of soft tissue tumours, rhabdomyosarcoma can be classified into four subtypes, i.e.:

Embryonal rhabdomyosarcoma (60% of all rhabdomyosarcomas),

Alveolar rhabdomyosarcoma (20% of all rhabdomyosarcomas),

Spindle cell/sclerosing rhabdomyosarcoma (10% of all rhabdomyosarcomas),

Pleomorphic rhabdomyosarcoma (10% of all rhabdomyosarcomas).

Embryonal rhabdomyosarcoma is the most common subtype, usually occurring within the first ten years of life. It is associated with mutations leading to tumour progression (e.g. RAS/Hedgehog mutations) and/or absence of tumour surveillance mechanism (e.g. TP53 mutations). It usually has a more favourable outcome, with 80% of patients having a localized disease at presentation for which the 5-year survival rate is 70%.

Alveolar rhabdomyosarcoma is a more aggressive disease with different age of onset (older children and adults), genetic drivers (PAX3–FOXO1 or PAX7–FOXO1 chimeric oncoproteins), translocations (t(2;13) (q35;q14) or t(1;13)(p36;q14) translocations in 80% of cases) and a higher rate of metastasis upon initial diagnosis. Thus, patients diagnosed with alveolar rhabdomyosarcoma experience a poorer clinical outcome.

Spindle cell/sclerosing rhabdomyosarcoma has recently been identified by WHO a single pathologic entity distinct from embryonal and alveolar rhabdomyosarcoma. Depending on the age of development, it can either harbour *VGLL2*-related gene fusions (congenital/infantile subset; excellent prognosis), *MYOD1* mutations (the most common abnormality; highly aggressive, poor response to combined chemo- and radiotherapy, overall unfavourable outcome) or none of the above (favourable clinical course; however, limited data to determine whether this subset differs from embryonal rhabdomyosarcoma).

Pleomorphic rhabdomyosarcoma is a very aggressive sarcoma with a high propensity for metastasis, occurring mostly in male patients around their seventh decade of life. It arises in the deep soft tissues of the extremities, and the lesions display variable myoregulatory protein expression and skeletal muscle differentiation features.

7.2.1 Animal models of skeletal muscle disorders

Different strategies are used to study skeletal muscle disorders in the preclinical setting. Although the possibility exists to study diseases in large animal models, the majority of translational studies rely on transgenic rodents. These include knockout mice for genes involved in human muscle pathologies and ageing, or syngeneic/xenograft transplants in mice to investigate muscle cachectic and neoplastic phenotypes.

Muscular Dystrophies

MDs originate from defects in the physical interactions between dystrophin-sarcoglycan complex proteins that, under normal conditions, tether actin fibres to the sarcolemma membrane. These alterations are the basis of chronic myofibre loss, progressive fibrotic infiltration and strength reduction. In the clinical evaluation of these conditions, cardiac muscle is often reported as affected and chronic dilated cardiomyopathy, scarring infiltrations, aneurysms, repeated micro-infarcts are common findings.

Several animal models have been developed to study muscular dystrophies, in particular for DMD and LGMDs. The most widespread animal model for MD is the *mdx* mouse, which bears a point mutation in the X-linked *dystrophin* gene. *Mdx* mouse phenotype mimics, at least partially, some of the features of the

DMD pathology in humans. In *mdx* mice, the effects of degeneration are less severe, mainly due to the presence of a relatively large number of revertant fibres (1-3%) and a hyper-activation of the *utrophin* gene. *Utrophin* is similar to *dystrophin* but shorter and normally localized in neuromuscular junctions. *Utrophin* upregulation in *mdx* mice could contribute to mitigating the degenerative phenotype and extend their life span similar to wild-type mice. This generates some controversies on the use of this animal for the development of novel therapeutic approaches.

Recently, it has been shown that satellite cells from *mdx* skeletal muscle are subject to premature erosion of telomeres and this molecular phenotype has been linked to limitation in their regenerative potential. Nevertheless, the presence of other myogenic progenitors, with a higher telomerase activity, might ensure a compensatory effect capable of counteracting the premature ageing of satellite cells, conferring a substantially normal life expectancy on *mdx* mice.

Mouse models for LGMD type 2 are generally mice engineered with a genetic knock-out for genes encoding sarcoglycans. The pathological phenotype of α- or β- sarcoglycan knock-out mice is rather similar to the pathological features observed in humans with cases of LGMD2D and -2E, respectively. The pathological progression encompasses chronic degeneration of skeletal muscle and, in the case of mice deficient for β-sarcoglycan dilated cardiomyopathy. In mice deficient for α-sarcoglycan, the *Sgca* gene is interrupted by a neomycin-resistance cassette, inserted between exons 1 and 9 through homologous recombination. Similarly, in β-sarcoglycan knock-out mice, the region comprising the 3-6 exons of the *Sgcb* gene was altered through insertion of a neomycin cassette to interrupt the normal reading frame. For some experimental settings, LGMD mice present a better dystrophic phenotype than *mdx* mice, due to the lack of revertant fibres, which often clouds results obtained in *mdx* mice. Another widely studied animal

model for DMD is the dystrophic dog. Indeed, the fibres of the canine musculature are larger than their murine counterpart and often better mimic the effects of human muscular dystrophy. Currently, there are at least two prominent colonies of dystrophic dogs all over the world, carrying the same mutation in different genetic backgrounds: a colony of Golden Retrievers and one of Beagles. These animals are both derived from crosses with a natural dystrophic founder, since the creation of transgenics would be unethical in these large animals. The mutation resides in intron 6 of the canine dystrophin gene, and results in aberrant splicing and premature transcription stop. Dystrophic dogs from both breeds present serious problems in motility, posture, salivation and exhibit severe scarring and chronic degeneration of muscle tissues. These characteristics, coupled with the scarcity of revertant fibres, make the canine model an excellent tool for the analysis of muscle regeneration enabled by gene and cell therapies.

Sarcopenia

Mice and rats are suitable animal models often used for studying muscle ageing. It has been shown that rodents proceed from 80% to 50% survival between 24 and 30 months of age, and this is well-documented in Fischer 344 × Brown Norway (F344BN) rats. However, up to 24 months of follow-up can be costly and time consuming. Therefore, senescence-accelerated mice (SAM) are chosen as a representative sarcopenic mouse model. This model is characterized by accelerated senescence and age-related pathologies. Out of these lineages the senescence-prone (SAMP8) model, and its normal aging control strain, the senescence-resistant (SAMR1) model, are largely used. IL-10-null mice mimic human frailty, with typical characteristics of muscle weakness, inflammation and decreased physical function anticipated at 10 months. Other transgenic mice mimicking Hutchinson-Gilford progeria syndrome including Ku80-null and Zmpste24-null mice are also considered useful animal models for sarcopenia. These accelerated ageing models have a median survival age of 123 days and develop premature sarcopenia; however, they do not always demonstrate characteristics typical of ageing.

Cachexia

Several animal models are available to study cancer cachexia, including those generated with cell lines of colon 26 adenocarcinoma (C26), Lewis lung carcinoma, Yoshida ascites hepatoma AH130, Walker 256 carcinosarcoma and MAC 16 adenocarcinoma (MAC16). However, there is no ideal animal model that perfectly resembles human cancer cachexia. Indeed, the characteristics of these animal models should be considered carefully by researchers with specific scientific questions, considering that cachexia is a multifactorial chronic disease. Recent clinical studies have also highlighted the presence of cardiac cachexia in people who have heart failure or underwent chemotherapy treatments that contribute to myocardial dysfunction in cachectic patients. Surgical models, including left arterial descending coronary artery ligation, transverse aortic constriction, calsequestrin-overexpressing mice and pharmacological induction with monocrotaline, show cardiac cachexia phenotypes.

Rhabdomyosarcoma

Rhabdomyosarcoma can arise from several developmental stages of muscle cells and can be studied by means of two different approaches. One approach employs xenograft transplantation of patient-derived cell lines in the mouse, which gives the possibility to investigate the tumour heterogeneity observed in the clinics. Conversely, the creation of rhabdomyosarcoma transgenic models with either the activation of oncogenes or the deletion of tumour suppressors gives the possibility to study the biology of the disease in an immune competent mouse. Due to the genetic heterogeneity of embryonal rhabdomyosarcoma, various pathways have been harnessed to model the disease. These include mutant Trp53, deletion of Ptch1,

HGF expression in Cdkn2a-null background, and oncogenic human KRAS. Conversely, for alveolar rhabdomyosarcoma, the expression of Pax3–FOXO1 in a Cdkn2a⁻ or Trp53-null background shows morphological and gene set enrichment analysis resemblance to the human counterpart.

7.2.2 Cell-based therapies in skeletal muscle disorders

In this section we will analyse the therapeutic strategies aimed at the use of *in vivo* cell therapy and improvements for the treatment of skeletal muscle disorders (Figure 7.7). The majority of research has been focused on MDs associated with genetic abnormalities of the dystrophin-sarcoglycan complex, such as DMD or limb girdle MD (LGMD).

Thus far, the clinical management of MDs relies on alleviation of inflammation and degeneration, including glucocorticoid steroid administration and non-invasive, positive pressure intermittent ventilation. Together with pain relief and anti-scoliosis strategies, these treatments have definitely delayed loss of ambulation, improved quality of life and increased life expectancy. However, these treatments show many side effects, such as weight gain, and, most importantly, do not have direct beneficial effects on genetic mutations and the intrinsic strength of dystrophic muscle. Cell therapy is a valuable theoretical alternative that could become clinically relevant in the future. The main aim of cell therapy is to directly regenerate the damaged muscle fibres by systemic or targeted injection of stem cells, with the goal of combatting myofibre necrosis and restoring normal muscle function. It is currently still difficult to combine transplantation efficiency and high capacity in cell properties like motility, homing, engraftment and differentiation, especially in the context of severe inflammation and degeneration within the muscle tissue. Several cell models have been tested *in vivo*, with different results. Three main classes of stem cells with myogenic potential have been considered in pre-clinical

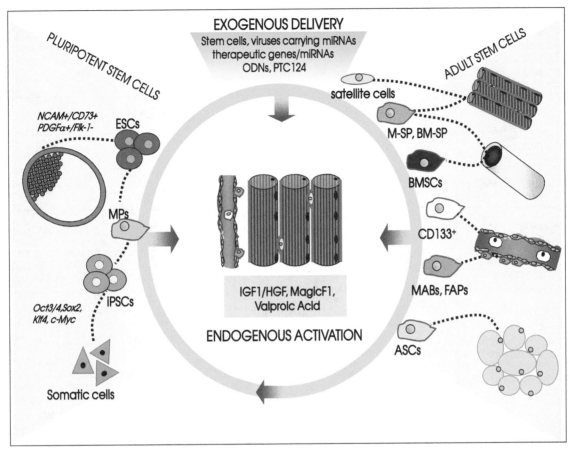

Figure 7.7 Schematic overview of the different approaches for the induction of muscle regeneration in the adult; ESCs, embryonic stem cells; iPSCs, induced pluripotent stem cells; MPs, muscle progenitors; M-SP, muscle side population (negative for lineage-specific markers, not intercalating Hoechst nuclear stain); BM-SP, bone marrow side population; BMSCs, bone marrow-derived stem cells; MABs, mesoangioblasts; FAPs, fibroadipogenic progenitors; ASCs, adipose-derived stem cells.

and clinical studies for muscular dystrophy treatment: i) embryonic stem cells (ESC) and induced pluripotent stem cells (iPSC); ii) bone marrow-derived mesenchymal cells (BMSC) and circulating progenitors; iii) local myogenic progenitors (Table 7.1)

Bone marrow-derived mesenchymal cells and circulating progenitors.

Mesenchymal stem cells have been tested in acute and chronic muscle damage, although the results are still controversial. In the case of bone marrow transplantation (BMT) in dystrophic mice, bone marrow-derived mesenchymal cells (BMSC) were shown to migrate and contribute to the formation of new $Myf5^+$ nuclei, through repeated cycles of inflamma-

tion and regeneration in the *mdx* muscle. In humans, a clinical case was reported where a young DMD patient (bearing a deletion in exon 45 of the dystrophin gene) showed nuclei of donor cells fused in 0.5% of dystrophic fibres 12 years after a BMT. Quantitative PCR assays detected a small amount of a truncated dystrophy isoform, lacking exons 44 and 45, and traces of the wild-type gene (0.0005%), although there is no direct correlation between the transplanted nuclei and the expression of the wild-type isoform. In addition, mesenchymal stem cells isolated from the synovial membrane of adult donors produced new functional myofibres without any sign of fusion, following intra-muscle transplantation in the tibi-

Table 7.1. List of main stem cell types or muscle progenitors used for the *in vivo* regeneration of skeletal muscle. ESCs, embryonic stem cells (h, human); iPSCs, induced pluripotent stem cells; BMSCs, bone marrow-derived mesenchymal stem cells; BM-SP, bone marrow side population; ASC, adipose stem cells; HSC, haematopoietic stem cells; SMP, skeletal muscle progenitors; SP, side population; MABs, mesoangioblasts.

Stem cell type	Surface markers	Animal model	Muscle damage	Administration
hBMSCs (human)	VIMENTIN+/CD44+	NMRI nu-/- / mdx mice	acute/chronic	intramuscular
BM-SP (human)	CD34-/low/CD117+/ Sca1+	Sgcd2-/- mice	chronic	intravenous
ASCs (human, mouse)	CD44+/CD90+/CD34-/ HLA-DR-/HLA-Ilow	mdx mice	acute/chronic	intramuscular
CD133+(human circulating progenitors)	CD133+/CD34+/CD45+/ CD90+	scid/mdx mice	chronic	intramuscular / intra-arterial
HSCs (dog)	CD45+	Cxmd dogs	chronic	intramuscular myoblasts
Satellite cells (human, mouse)	CD34+/Pax7+/CD31-/ Sca1-	Mdx/nu-/- mice	chronic	intramuscular
	CD34+/Integrin+ (clonal)	NOD/SCID mice	acute (resident satellite cell ablation)	intramuscular
SMPs, skeletal muscle precursors (mouse)	CD45-/Sca1-/Mac1- Cxcr4+/ 1integrin+	mdx mice	acute	intramuscular
SP muscle cells (mouse)	Sca1+/CD45+/Abcg2+	mdx5cv mice	chronic	intra-arterial
	Sca1+/Abcg2+/Syndecan4+/ Pax7+	Rosa26 / mdx mice	acute/chronic	intramuscular
MABs (mouse, dog, human)	Pdgfr +/ Pdgfr+/Ng2+/ Alp+	Sgca-/- mice / GRMD dogs/ scid/mdx mice	chronic	intra-arterial
Myo-endothelial progenitors (human)	CD56+/CD34+/CD144+	scid mice	acute	intramuscular
hESCs (human)	CD73+/CD56+	scid/beige mice	acute	intramuscular
ESCs (mouse)	Pdgfr+/Flk1- Pdgfr+/Vegfr2+	Rag2-/-c-/- / mdx mice KSN mice	acute/chronic acute	intra-arterial/intravenous/intramuscular
iPSCs (mouse)	CD56+	Sgca-/- mice	chronic	intramuscular

alis anterior muscle of *mdx* mice. These cells might also contribute to long-term re-population of the satellite cell pool and restoration of mechanical growth factor (MGF) expression in treated muscles. The myogenic potential of these cells correlated with the post-injection microenvironment, considering that, once systemically injected into dystrophic mice, they appear non-specific in all tissues.

Given the large availability at the source, human multipotent adipose tissue-derived stem cells (hASC) have been proposed as a possible alternative for muscle regeneration. The hASCs are CD44+/CD90+/CD105+, confirming their mesenchymal nature. Once injected intramuscularly into the tibialis muscle of immuno-competent and immuno-compromised *mdx* mice, hASCs fused into chimaeric myofibres, which stained positively for human dystrophin up to 6 months after transplantation. It is interesting to note, however, that there were no differences in the effects of injections between immune-competent and immune-compromised mice, and that hASCs significantly reduced the levels of necrosis in the dystrophic muscle. These results were further improved by conditioning the adipose mesenchymal in co-culture with myoblasts or by overexpressing *MyoD*.

Another very interesting example consists of a subpopulation of circulating cells, the *CD133+* haematopoietic progenitors, easily isolatable from humans and expressing early markers of muscle differentiation. Intra-arterial or intra-muscle injection of *CD133+* progenitors, isolated from the peripheral blood of DMD patients, promoted significant recovery of muscle morphology, function and expression of human dystrophin in *scid/mdx* mice.

Reports of incomplete or negligible rates of muscle regeneration by mesenchymal and haematopoietic cells have also been reported. Intravenous injection into a mouse model of LGMD2F (δ-sarcoglycan-knockout mice) from bone marrow cells produced chimaeric fibres but did not restore the expression of δ-sarcoglycan. GFP+ mesenchymal cells,

transplanted by retro-orbital injection, fused with approximately 3% of the myofibres in the *mdx* tibialis anterior, but dystrophin re-expression was negligible in GFP+ myofibres. These data were confirmed in another publication, where it was shown that more than 80% of transplanted BMSC nuclei were silenced. The nuclei incorporated in the receiving fibres did not express myogenic factors, including dystrophin, and this silenced state was maintained even in the presence of chromatin remodelling agents, such as 5'-azacitidine. It has also been shown that haematopoietic cell transplantation (HCT) does not result in any skeletal fibre regeneration or expression of any myogenic factors. However, an interesting role for HCT in muscle regeneration may result from the immune tolerance induction towards allogeneic myoblast transplantation. DMD dogs were successfully treated by combining peripheral HCT and myoblasts isolated from the same healthy donor. Injected myoblasts expressed dystrophin for 24 weeks up to 7% more than wild-type levels, without pharmacological immunosuppression. Finally, another class of multipotent progenitors isolated from the bone marrow (multipotent adult progenitor cells, MAPC) showed a good capacity for long-lasting regeneration of ischaemic limbs, thanks to an effective revascularization of the necrotic tissues.

Local myogenic progenitors

Given their natural commitment, satellite cells are easily defined as the main putative candidate for muscle regeneration in muscular dystrophies. In a study featuring individual fibre transplantation into the tibialis anterior muscles of irradiated *mdx* mice (irradiation removes the existing population of satellite cells), satellite cells from the donor fibre expanded, re-populated the endogenous pool and differentiated into functional myofibres. *Pax7+/CD34+/GFP+* satellite cells, isolated from the diaphragm of Pax3::GFP mice, were shown to be a good model for treatment of irradiated *mdx* muscles, resulting in restoration of dystrophin expression in many skeletal fibres and reconstitution of the resident satellite pool.

Intra-muscular injections, however, revealed a significant problem: satellite cells have a very low migratory capacity and a reduced capacity for integration if expanded *in vitro*, even if for a limited time. In order to test the regenerative capacity of satellite cells to a clonal level, single-cell dilutions of *CD34+/integrin α7+* satellite cells, carrying a luciferase reporter, were injected into the skeletal muscle of *NOD/SCID* mice deprived of resident cells by irradiation. *In vivo* imaging experiments have shown that a single satellite cell can reconstitute the resident satellite compartment and, in the presence of further damage, the newly formed satellite cells can quickly re-enter a new proliferative wave, generating myofibres.

Recently, interesting results have been obtained with skeletal myogenic precursors (SMP), a *CD45-/Sca1-/mac1-/Cxcr4+/β1integrin+* subpopulation of the satellite pool. Once injected into immunodeficient *mdx* muscles, SMPs contributed robustly to muscle regeneration (up to 94%), fusing with pre-existing fibres or stimulating *de novo* myogenesis. Myofibre morphology and contractile force were significantly higher in treated mice than in control animals. Furthermore, SMPs significantly contributed to the endogenous satellite cell population. However, SMPs were injected right after isolation, without *in vitro* expansion, and their migratory capacity remained limited to the areas surrounding the intra-muscular injection point. One of the greatest limitations on the use of satellite cells is likely to be their heterogeneity. The variable homing rate of the satellite cells from single myofibre transplantation could be due to functional heterogeneity of the cell pool and to their niche of origin. Satellite cell heterogeneity is still a controversial issue, widely discussed in several studies.

Other than satellite cells, subpopulation of muscle-associated progenitors has been also reported, called the muscle side population (SP), fibro/adipogenic progenitors (FAP), PW1 (Peg3) expressing interstitial cells (PIC) and mesoangioblasts (MAB). SP cells are Sca1+/CD45+ myogenic cells, capable of quickly expelling the Hoechst 33.342 dye. SP cells are associated with vasculature and are generally directed towards the haematopoietic line. In case of co-culture with myoblasts, SP cells can form myotubes *in vitro* and, if injected intra-muscularly into the tibialis anterior of SCID/bg mice, can contribute to up to 1% of regenerating fibres. Homing efficiency was increased to 5-8% through injection in the femoral artery of *mdx5cv* mice. Indeed, injected cells migrated from the vessels and homed in inflammation foci, expressing *Pax7* and desmin. Promising results were obtained with the isolation of a rare subset (0.25%) of SP cells, characterized by markers of both satellite and SP cells (Sca1+/Abcg2+/Syndecan4+/Pax7+) and positioned below the basal lamina. Once isolated from the mononuclear fraction, these cells grew in association with individual muscle fibres and robustly differentiated *in vitro*. After intra-muscular injection, in the presence of 1.2% BaCl2, these SP-satellite cells effectively competed with endogenous satellite cells in regenerating wild-type muscle. Injected cells regenerated up to 30% of fibres and, surprisingly, reconstituted up to 75% of the endogenous satellite pool. In addition, the same long-term effects were demonstrated through transplantation of *mdx4cv* dystrophic tibialis muscles, where these cells contributed to up to 70% of new myofibres. However, muscle damage induced by BaCl2 is not a commonly accepted regenerative model and this aspect must be considered when interpreting these results.

FAPs are thought to support SC differentiation and are characterized by Sca-1 and CD34 expression. They are located in the interstitium between the myofibres and are known to indirectly enhance SC differentiation; however, their fusion with damaged myofibres is controversial. Upon injury, FAPs start to proliferate under the impulse of IL-4/IL-13 expression of eosinophils, attracted by inflammatory cytokines, to be able to support myogenesis. FAPs also seem to be required for clearance of necrotic debris and in this way stimulate muscle regeneration, as well. However, with ageing or during chronic regeneration, FAPs switch to an adipogenic fate, a shift that is not so well understood.

Another stem cell population with myogenic potential is Peg3$^+$/Pax7- PICs. PICs are also located in the interstitium and can repopulate the SC pool after engraftment into damaged muscle tissue. PICs are myogenic *in vitro* by converting to a Pax7$^+$/MyoD$^+$ state. This cell population seems to share a lot of features with FAPs, for example their expression of CD34 and Sca-1 and their adaptation to an adipogenic cell fate. Therefore, these cells can be considered to be a subpopulation of FAPs.

MABs are multipotent stem cells of muscle origin associated with vessels that have been first characterized in literature and used for therapeutic approaches in chronic muscle diseases. MABs were initially isolated from the mouse fetal dorsal aorta (E9.5) and then from the adult skeletal muscles of mice, dogs and humans. MABs are CD34$^+$/Sca1$^+$/Pdgfrα$^+$/Pdgfrβ$^+$/Ng2$^+$/AP$^+$, supporting the hypothesis that they belong to a subgroup of the pericytic population. They also show high rates of *in vitro* proliferation, scant tumour-forming capacity and multipotent differentiation capacity to myogenic, osteogenic, chondrogenic and adipogenic lines, both *in vitro* and in chimaeric embryos. After intra-arterial delivery into dystrophic muscles of αsg-KO mice or Golden Retriever DMD dogs, MABs were able to regenerate up to 50% of myofibres, restoring muscle architecture, expression of sarcoglycan/dystrophin complex genes and improving electrophysiological and contractile properties. Likewise, beneficial effects were obtained with transplantation of human MABs into *mdx-scid* dystrophic mice. Recent studies have shown that Notch and Bmp signal pathways regulate the myogenic differentiation of MABs. Treatment of dystrophic dogs with MABs isolated from healthy dogs produced encouraging and long-term results in some animals subjected to immunosuppression, assessed as recovery of general motility and regeneration of entire muscles. However, in other specimens treated with autologous cells genetically treated with a reduced version of the gene (micro-dystrophin) that was effective in the *mdx* mouse, there was no substantial improvement in motor capacity. This confirms the general idea that genetic variability in major organisms, such as dogs or humans, should be seriously evaluated for effective cell therapies against degeneration caused by muscular dystrophy.

Embryonic stem cells and induced pluripotent stem cells

Embryonic stem cells (ESC) are generally considered a promising natural source of pluripotent cells for cell therapy, although the first published attempts have demonstrated rather low levels of muscle regeneration. Furthermore, the ethical questions regarding their derivation, such as blastocyst disintegration and oocyte demand, have raised concerns and *de facto* limited human ESC use for research purposes in many countries. The critical step in the use of ESCs resides in their conditioning prior to transplantation, a necessary step to increase the rate of myogenic differentiation and avoid the formation of teratomas. A heterogeneous suspension, derived from co-culture of male embryonic bodies and female dystrophic satellite cells, produced some chimaeric fibres, positive for dystrophin, in the muscles of female *mdx* mice. Promising results were obtained with human ESCs, enriched for mesenchymal precursors *in vivo*. The CD73$^+$/NCAM$^+$ fraction was able to produce myotubes *in vitro* and regenerate up to 7% of skeletal muscle tissue in immune deficient mice. Another strategy consists in deriving paraxial mesoderm progenitors during ESC differentiation. After coaxing ESCs to the myogenic lineage through *Pax3* overexpression, the PDGFRα$^+$/Flk1$^-$ subpopulation activates myogenic transcription factors *in vitro* and, when transplanted into muscles damaged with cardiotoxin or into dystrophic muscles, differentiates in dystrophin-positive myofibres. Transplanted mice showed an improvement in strength and contractility. In another study, paraxial mesoderm progenitors were isolated as PDGFRα$^+$/VEGFR2$^+$ and successfully tested in cardiotoxin-injured quadriceps muscles of immuno-deficient KSN mice. Recently, many studies have explored the possibility of *in vitro* differentiation of human ESCs under controlled conditions and through epigenetic control factors. A new source of pluripotent cells resides in the reprogramming of murine or human somatic cells through the forced expression of pluripotency factors. Murine or human induced pluripotent stem cells (iPSC) are reprogrammed from cells that are easily isolated from an adult body, such as fibroblasts, to a status similar to ESCs. This reprogramming is achieved through transient over-expression of *OCT4*, *SOX2*, *KLF4* and, although dispensable, *c-MYC*. iPSCs represent a valid and attractive alternative to ESCs, since they overcome ESC-related ethical problems, while still being pluripotent. However, there are still many reservations about iPSC safety *in vivo* . Indeed, iPSCs display an intrinsic teratogenic risk, which will most likely be overcome through better differentiation control and specific isolation of progenitors prior to *in vivo* administration. A potential tool for increasing the efficiency of iPSC myogenic differentiation and reducing secondary manipulation during maturation is the so-called "epigenetic memory". In murine and human iPSCs, the choice of donor cells confers on to the reprogrammed cells a spontaneous differentiation potential, similar to the lineage of source cells before reprogramming. An example in the myogenic field is constituted by the iPSCs generated by skeletal mesoangioblasts. These iPSCs spontaneously differentiated with higher efficiency to skeletal muscle *in vitro* and *in vivo*, as compared to iPSCs generated from isogenic non-muscle fibroblasts. Another important possibility in not only regenerative medicine but also disease modelling is the creation of iPSCs specific for certain genetic

muscle diseases. Human iPSCs (hiPSC) have been generated by patients suffering from a wide range of mendelian or complex genetic diseases, including DMD and Becker's dystrophies. These cells could represent an important step in terms of plasticity and resistance to senescence, compared to other cell lines tested to date. Moreover, DMD$^-$ or BMD$^-$specific hiPSCs bear the same genome as their human donors and therefore represent an excellent model for *in vitro* pharmacological tests. Furthermore, after appropriate protocols of genetic correction, these cells might constitute a virtually rejection-free cell line suitable for skeletal muscle regeneration *in vivo*.

Recently, iPSCs have been generated from MABs (MAB-iPSC). MAB-iPSCs reproduce unique features of pluripotent stem cells, still retaining a biased epigenetic memory towards the myogenic lineage. Interestingly, MAB-iPSC-derived mesodermal progenitors (MiP) can be used for combined treatment of both skeletal and cardiac muscles in dystrophic mice. MiPs are isolated from iPSC pre-induced to mesoderm differentiation as a specific population triple positive for common markers shared by stem cells important for skeletal muscle regeneration (CD140a, CD140b, and CD44). Notably, both MAB-MiPs and f-MiPs were able to engraft in the cardiac muscle of dystrophic mice, while only MAB-MiPs were able to functionally regenerate the skeletal muscle when injected intra-arterially in dystrophic mice. Interestingly, the boosted differentiation potential towards skeletal muscle correlated with retained signatures of DNA methylation and histone marks from parental progenies. Human MiPs have also been derived and characterized through cell therapy approaches with promising results.

7.3 Conclusions and perspectives

Skeletal muscle is an incredibly dynamic tissue and plays an important role both in the physiological and the pathological setting. It has helped humans in their evolution by providing a solid structure to rely on for bipedal movement, as well as for the social interactions with other human beings via the use of mimetic muscles. According to the current knowledge, genetic diseases as well as acquired diseases of the muscle have a detrimental effect on the human body and thus research is required to eventually improve the conditions of patients affected by these diseases.

Stem cell-mediated therapy is a promising approach for muscular dystrophies and research in this field has moved rapidly in recent years. Experiments on small and large animal models are paving the way for clinical trials, but it would be imprudent to foresee a 'cure' from these initial attempts. A clinical trial based on systemic injections of mesoangioblasts from HLA-compatible donors in DMD patients (developed by the San Raffaele Institute in Milan, Italy and the cells produced and expanded in GLP/GMP by MOLMED, Italy) proved the feasibility and safety of intra-arterial transplantation of donor mesoangioblasts in humans, although no functional improvement was observed.

Other clinical trials are based on re-introduction of non-mutated genes using adeno-associated viruses for γ-sarcoglycan or μ-dystrophin, or blockade of myostatin, a muscle growth inhibitor, through specific antibodies. Encouraging results have been obtained from clinical studies using exon-skipping technology. Specific mutated exons can be skipped during splicing through antisense oligonucleotides, in order to restore the reading frame and consequently the production of a truncated yet partially functional dystrophin isoform.

Two clinical trials investigating the effects of two different drugs, i.e. eteplirsen (AVI-4658, developed by the MDEX Consortium, United Kingdom and produced by AVI BioPharma) and Drisapersen (PRO051, developed by the University of Leiden, the Netherlands, in collaboration with Prosensa BV), were conducted on DMD patients. In both studies, biopsies showed that injection of antisense oligonucleotides to skip exon 51 in dystrophic muscles successfully induced re-expression of new dystrophin without adverse phenomena. In the evaluation of the long-term efficacy and safety of eteplirsen, at the 3-year follow-up, treated patients showed a slower rate of decline in ambulation assessed by 6-minute walk tests compared to untreated matched historical controls. Conversely, in the placebo-controlled phase 3 trial of drisapersen, a statistically significant improvement in 6-minute walk distance was observed solely in a *posthoc* analysis performed on the results obtained from a less impaired population of DMD subjects.

In the near future, it is reasonable to expect encouraging results from studies based on combination of stem cell and gene therapy. However, it is still mandatory to investigate in greater detail the biological properties of stem cells and their paracrine action for the treatment of muscle diseases, in order to increase the potential benefits of these new treatments. The scientific community largely recognizes the presence of adult stem cells in virtually all tissues, but their origin is still controversial. For instance, we and other authors have suggested that MABs are a source of somatic stem cells intrinsically present in skeletal and cardiac musculature. They are influenced by the surrounding microenvironment in maintaining their own differentiation capacity, even if this needs to be clarified in diseased tissues. It is interesting to note that other research groups have identified mesenchymal stem cells from all tissues, raising doubts about the confinement of cellular plasticity to the bone marrow. It is believed that it is possible for cells to switch from the bone marrow to the pericytic compartment, in order to adopt a specific destiny influenced by the local niche. To further clarify their origin, it is necessary to proceed with the generation of transgenic animals using gene tracers able to mark endogenous stem cells during muscle development and regeneration. Despite the fact that the clinical investigation of strategies successfully tested in animal models is still impeded by time-consuming regulatory restrictions, some clinical trials are currently underway. In addition, the actual costs of GLP/GMP technology (standardized laboratory and production procedures) applied to stem cells limit the possibility of extensive cell therapy treatments in patients with muscular dystrophy. Nevertheless, different strategies to reduce costs are currently being studied, so as to develop treatments that are available to a greater number of patients. In conclusion, preclinical and clinical studies have shown the great therapeutic potential of stem cells in degenerative muscle diseases. Yet, caution is still advised for these new therapeutic strategies, especially where iPSC-based technology is concerned. More basic and translational research is needed to better understand the origin of stem cells and their role in regenerative medicine of skeletal muscle.

Acknowledgements

Our laboratory at KU Leuven is supported by the "Opening the Future" campaign (EJJ-OPTFUT-02010), CARIPLO 2015_0634, FWO (G088715N, G060612N, G0A8813N, 1S90718N), GOA (EJJC2161-GOA/11/012), IUAP-VII/07 (EJJ-C4851-17/07-P),OT09-053(EJJC0420-OT/09/053), Project Financing Stem Cells (PFO3 10/019), and Rondoufonds voor Duchenne Onderzoek (EQQ-FODUCH-O2010). We thank Silvia Querceto, Tristan Pulinckx, the colleagues at the Human Anatomy laboratory of the University of Pavia and the colleagues at the Translational Cardiomyology laboratory of KU Leuven for their contributions.

Recommended reading and references

Molecular signals of myogenesis

1. Chang CN, Kioussi C. (2018). *Location, Location, Location: Signals in Muscle Specification*. J Dev Biol. **6**(2).
2. Quattrocelli M, Costamagna D, Giacomazzi G, Camps J, Sampaolesi M. (2014). *Notch signaling regulates myogenic regenera-*

tive capacity of murine and human mesoangioblasts. Cell Death Dis. **5**: e1448.
3. Costamagna D, Quattrocelli M, van Tienen F, Umans L, de Coo IF, Zwijsen A, Huylebroeck D, Sampaolesi M. (2016). *Smad1/5/8 are myogenic regulators of murine and human mesoangioblasts.* J Mol Cell Biol. **8**(1):73-87

MicroRNAs and myogenic development

1. Quattrocelli M, Crippa S, Montecchiani C, Camps J, Cornaglia Icaro A, Boldrin L, Morgan J, Calligaro A, Casasco A, Orlacchio A, Gijsbers R, D'Hooge J, Toelen J, Janssens S, Sampaolesi M. (2013). *Long-term miR-669a therapy alleviates chronic dilated cardiomyopathy in dystrophic mice.* J Am Heart Assoc. **2**(4): e000284.
2. Quattrocelli M, Sampaolesi M. (2015). *The mesmiRizing complexity of microRNAs for striated muscle tissue engineering.* Adv Drug Deliv Rev. **88**: 37-52.
3. Horak M, Novak J, Bienertova-Vasku J. (2016). *Muscle-specific microRNAs in skeletal muscle development.* Dev Biol. **410**(1):1-13.
4. Mok GF, Lozano-Velasco E, Münsterberg A. (2017). *MicroRNAs in skeletal muscle development.* Semin Cell Dev Biol. **72**:67-76.
5. Castel D, Baghdadi MB, Mella S, Gayraud-Morel B, Marty V, Cavaillé J, Antoniewski C, Tajbakhsh S. (2018). *Small-RNA sequencing identifies dynamic microRNA deregulation during skeletal muscle lineage progression.* Sci Rep. **8**(1):4208.

First and second phases of myogenesis

1. Buckingham M, Vincent SD. (2009) *Distinct and dynamic myogenic populations in the vertebrate embryo.* Curr Opin Genet Dev. **19**(5): 444-53.
2. Yusuf F, Brand-Saberi B. (2006). *The eventful somite: patterning, fate determination and cell division in the somite.* Anat Embryol (Berl). **211** Suppl 1: 21-30.
3. Nagandla H, Stewart MD. (2017). *Quantification of Embryonic Myofiber Development*

by Immunofluorescence. Methods Mol Biol. **1668**:167-176.

4. Bryson-Richardson RJ, Currie PD. (2008). *The genetics of vertebrate myogenesis*. Nat Rev Genet. **9**(8):632-46.

5. Buckingham M, Bajard L, Chang T, Daubas P, Hadchouel J, Meilhac S, Montarras D, Rocancourt D, Relaix F. (2003). *The formation of skeletal muscle: from somite to limb*. J Anat. **202**(1): 59-68.

6. Buckingham M, Bajard L, Daubas P, Esner M, Lagha M, Relaix F, Rocancourt D. (2006). *Myogenic progenitor cells in the mouse embryo are marked by the expression of Pax3/7 genes that regulate their survival and myogenic potential*. Anat Embryol (Berl). **211** Suppl 1: 51-6.

Somitogenesis

1. Takahashi Y, Sato Y. (2008). *Somitogenesis as a model to study the formation of morphological boundaries and cell epithelialization*. Dev Growth Differ. **50** Suppl 1: S149-55.

2. Lewis J, Hanisch A, Holder M. (2009). *Notch signaling, the segmentation clock, and the patterning of vertebrate somites*. J Biol. **8**(4): 44.

Head and trunk myogenesis

1. Shih HP, Gross MK, Kioussi C. (2008). *Muscle development: forming the head and trunk muscles*. Acta Histochem. **110**(2):97-108.

2. Sambasivan R, Kuratani S, Tajbakhsh S. (2011). *An eye on the head: the development and evolution of craniofacial muscles*. Development. **138**(12): 2401-15.

Adult myogenesis

1. Biressi S, Rando TA. (2010). *Heterogeneity in the muscle satellite cell population*. Semin Cell Dev Biol. **21**(8): 845-54.

2. Mounier R, Chrétien F, Chazaud B. (2011). *Blood vessels and the satellite cell niche*. Curr Top Dev Biol. **96**: 121-38.

3. Cassano M, Dellavalle A, Tedesco FS, Quattrocelli M, Crippa S, Ronzoni F, Sal-

vade A, Berardi E, Torrente Y, Cossu G, Sampaolesi M. (2011). *Alpha sarcoglycan is required for FGF-dependent myogenic progenitor cell proliferation in vitro and in vivo*. Development. **138**(20):4523-33.

Skeletal muscle disorders

Rhabdomyosarcoma

1. Saab R, Spunt SL, Skapek SX. (2011). *Myogenesis and rhabdomyosarcoma: the Jekyll and Hyde of skeletal muscle*. Curr Top Dev Biol. **94**:197-234.

2. Yu PY, Guttridge DC. (2018). *Dysregulated Myogenesis in Rhabdomyosarcoma*. Curr Top Dev Biol. **126**:285-297.

3. Kashi VP, Hatley ME, Galindo RL. (2015). *Probing for a deeper understanding of rhabdomyosarcoma: insights from complementary model systems*. Nat Rev Cancer. **15**(7):426-39.

Cachexia

1. Evans WJ, Morley JE, Argilés J, Bales C, Baracos V, Guttridge D, Jatoi A, Kalantar-Zadeh K, Lochs H, Mantovani G, Marks D, Mitch WE, Muscaritoli M, Najand A, Ponikowski P, Rossi Fanelli F, Schambelan M, Schols A, Schuster M, Thomas D, Wolfe R, Anker SD. (2008). *Cachexia: a new definition*. Clin Nutr. **27**(6):793-9.2.

2. Von Haehling S, Anker MS, Anker SD. (2016). *Prevalence and clinical impact of cachexia in chronic illness in Europe, USA, and Japan: facts and number update 2016*. J Cachexia Sarcopenia Muscle. **7**(5):507-509.

3. Habedank D, Ewert R, Hetzer R, Anker SD. (2009). *Reversibility of cachexia after bilateral lung transplantation*. Int J Cardiol. **133**(1):46-50.

4. Anker SD, Negassa A, Coats AJ, Afzal R, Poole-Wilson PA, Cohn JN, Yusuf S. (2003). *Prognostic importance of weight loss in chronic heart failure and the effect of treatment with angiotensin-converting-enzyme inhibitors: an observational study*. Lancet. **361**(9363):1077-83.

5. Gullett NP, Mazurak VC, Hebbar G, Ziegler TR. (2011). *Nutritional interventions for cancer-induced cachexia.* Curr Probl Cancer. **35**(2):58-90.6.

6. He WA, Berardi E, Cardillo VM, Acharyya S, Aulino P, Thomas-Ahner J, Wang J, Bloomston M, Muscarella P, Nau P, Shah N, Butchbach ME, Ladner K, Adamo S, Rudnicki MA, Keller C, Coletti D, Montanaro F, Guttridge DC. (2013). *NF-κB-mediated Pax7 dysregulation in the muscle microenvironment promotes cancer cachexia.* J Clin Invest. **123**(11):4821-35.

7. Ishida J, Saitoh M, Doehner W, von Haehling S, Anker M, Anker SD, Springer J. (2017). *Animal models of cachexia and sarcopenia in chronic illness: Cardiac function, body composition changes and therapeutic results.* Int J Cardiol. **238**:12-18.

Sarcopenia

1. United Nations, Department of Economic and Social Affairs, Population Division (2017). World Population Ageing 2017 - Highlights (ST/ESA/SER.A/397).

2. Brioche T, Pagano AF, Py G, Chopard A. (2016). *Muscle wasting and aging: Experimental models, fatty infiltrations, and prevention.* Mol Aspects Med. **50**:56–87.

3. Hager K, Machein U, Krieger S, Platt D, Seefried G, Bauer J. (1994). *Interleukin-6 and selected plasma proteins in healthy persons of different ages.* Neurobiol Aging. **15**(6):771–2.

4. Beyer I, Mets T, Bautmans I. *Chronic low-grade inflammation and age-related sarcopenia.* (2012). Curr Opin Clin Nutr Metab Care. **15**(1):12–22.

5. Sandri M, Barberi L, Bijlsma AY, Blaauw B, Dyar KA, Milan G, Mammucari C, Meskers CG, Pallafacchina G, Paoli A, Pion D, Roceri M, Romanello V, Serrano AL, Toniolo L, Larsson L, Maier AB, Muñoz-Cánoves P, Musarò A, Pende M, Reggiani C, Rizzuto R, Schiaffino S. (2013). *Signalling pathways regulating muscle mass in ageing skeletal muscle: the role of the IGF1–Akt-mTOR-FoxO pathway.* Biogerontology. **14**(3):303-23.

6. Romanick M, Thompson LV, Brown-Borg HM. (2013). *Murine models of atrophy, cachexia, and sarcopenia in skeletal muscle.* Biochim Biophys Acta. **1832**(9):1410-20

7. Di Filippo ES, Mancinelli R, Pietrangelo T, La Rovere RM, Quattrocelli M, Sampaolesi M, Fulle S. (2016). *Myomir dysregulation and reactive oxygen species in aged human satellite cells.* Biochem Biophys Res Commun. **473**(2):462-70.

8. Rotini A, Martínez-Sarrà E, Duelen R, Costamagna D, Di Filippo ES, Giacomazzi G, Grosemans H, Fulle S, Sampaolesi M. (2018). *Aging affects the in vivo regenerative potential of human mesoangioblasts.* Aging Cell. **17**(2).

Stem cells in muscular regeneration

1. Quattrocelli M, Cassano M, Crippa S, Perini I, Sampaolesi M. (2010). *Cell therapy strategies and improvements for muscular dystrophy.* Cell Death Differ. **17**(8): 1222-9.

2. Quattrocelli M, Palazzolo G, Floris G, Schöffski P, Anastasia L, Orlacchio A, Vandendriessche T, Chuah MK, Cossu G, Verfaillie C, Sampaolesi M. (2011). *Intrinsic cell memory reinforces myogenic commitment of pericyte-derived iPSCs.* J Pathol. **223**(5): 593-603.

3. Kim K, Zhao R, Doi A, Ng K, Unternaehrer J, Cahan P, Huo H, Loh YH, Aryee MJ, Lensch MW, Li H, Collins JJ, Feinberg AP, Daley GQ. (2011). *Donor cell type can influence the epigenome and differentiation potential of human induced pluripotent stem cells.* Nat Biotechnol. **29**(12): 1117-9.

4. Quattrocelli M, Palazzolo G, Perini I, Crippa S, Cassano M, Sampaolesi M. (2012). *Mouse and human mesoangioblasts: isolation and characterization from adult skeletal muscles.* Methods Mol Biol. **798**: 65-76.

5. Albini S, Coutinho P, Malecova B, Giordani L, Savchenko A, Forcales SV, Puri PL. (2013). *Epigenetic reprogramming of human embryonic stem cells into skeletal muscle cells*

and generation of contractile myospheres. Cell Rep. **3**(3): 661-70.

6. Perini I, Elia I, Lo Nigro A, Ronzoni F, Berardi E, Grosemans H, Fukada S, Sampaolesi M. (2015). *Myogenic induction of adult and pluripotent stem cells using recombinant proteins.* Biochem Biophys Res Commun. **464**(3): 755-61.

7. Costamagna D, Berardi E, Ceccarelli G, Sampaolesi M. (2015). *Adult Stem Cells and Skeletal Muscle Regeneration.* Curr Gene Ther. **15**(4): 348-6.

8. Quattrocelli M, Swinnen M, Giacomazzi G, Camps J, Barthélemy I, Ceccarelli G, Caluwé E, Grosemans H, Thorrez L, Pelizzo G, Muijtjens M, Verfaillie CM, Blot S, Janssens S, Sampaolesi M. (2015). *Mesodermal iPSC-derived progenitor cells functionally regenerate cardiac and skeletal muscle.* J Clin Invest. **125**(12):4463-82.

9. Giacomazzi G, Holvoet B, Trenson S, Caluwé E, Kravic B, Grosemans H, Cortés-Calabuig Á, Deroose CM, Huylebroeck D, Hashemolhosseini S, Janssens S, McNally E, Quattrocelli M, Sampaolesi M. (2017). *MicroRNAs promote skeletal muscle differentiation of mesodermal iPSC-derived progenitors.* Nat Commun. **8**(1):1249.

Mesenchymal stem cells: cartilage

8

Livia Roseti   Brunella Grigolo

This chapter is dedicated to our "Prof" Andrea Facchini, who passed away too early, and with whom we shared research in the field of cartilage regenerative medicine for many years.

8.1 Cartilage

Cartilage tissue constitutes the first draft of most of the skeleton during embryogenesis, which will be subsequently replaced by bone through a mineralization process, and the metaphyses during body growth (growth plates). It persists in the adult, covering bone articular surfaces and forming the intervertebral discs, the pubic symphysis, part of the ribs, and the menisci. Moreover it gives support to the respiratory tract and the auricle. Cartilage is composed of specialized cells, termed chondrocytes, and an extracellular matrix (ECM) formed by fibres embedded in an amorphous substance in the gel state. It is covered with a poorly vascularized lamina of fibrous tissue, the perichondrium. It differs from all other connective tissues as it is neither vascularized nor innervated. In the body there are three main types of cartilage: hyaline, elastic and fibrous, which differ depending on their ECM composition and, therefore, function.

8.2 Articular cartilage

Articular hyaline cartilage is a connective tissue covering the ends of long bones, without an external perichondrium. It possesses tensile strength and elasticity to guarantee an adequate and balanced distribution of pressure loads over the entire articular surface, minimizing, at the same time, the compressive forces acting on the subchondral bone (Figure 8.1). As indicated by the term hyaline, from the Latin "hyalinum", this tissue appears as translucent, opalescent and blue-white coloured. From a

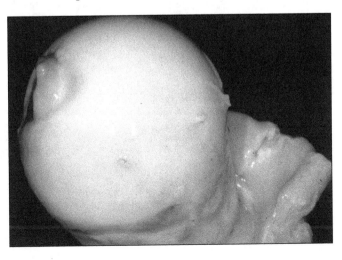

Figure 8.1. Healthy articular cartilage.

morphological point of view, two phases can be recognized:

a. a solid phase composed mainly of a network of collagen type II, glycosaminoglycans (GAGs), proteoglycans, and glycoproteins, all responsible for the overall shape of the tissue;

b. a liquid phase of water and electrolytes where all the solid components are immersed.

These two phases constitute the ECM and account for the biomechanical properties of cartilage, combining compressive stiffness, resilience, and shear resistance.

The ECM varies in terms of thickness, cell density, mechanical properties and matrix composition not only in different joints, but also within the same joint. In particular, three structurally different areas are present: a superficial zone where cells are tangentially arranged, the lacunae are close together and the matrix is scarce and mostly composed of collagens and a few proteoglycans (i.e. aggrecan); an intermediate region with rounded cells not aggregated in isogenic groups; a deep area where round or ovoid-shaped chondroblasts are distributed in isogenic groups and are embedded in an abundant matrix rich in proteoglycans. Below the deepest area there is a border zone, defined as a tide-mark, which separates cartilage from sub-chondral bone (Figure 8.2).

Chondrocytes, the only cell type of cartilage, are located in lacunae surrounded by ECM. They vary in shape and metabolic activity throughout the tissue. In particular, they tend to flatten out on the surface layer, while they are arranged in columns in the deepest area. Chondrocytes contain many mitochondria, an extended complex of Golgi, and vesicles rich in glycogen. They are indeed responsible for maintaining homeostasis through a balance of anabolic and catabolic activities. Cartilage ECM constitutes the environment where chondrocytes stay viable. It is composed mostly of water (about 70% of its total weight), collagens, proteoglycans, non-collagenous proteins and small amounts of lipids and lipoproteins. Its composition constitutes a predominantly anaerobic environment allowing intercellular interactions, nutrient transportation and catabolic product elimination by diffusion. Collagens ensure tensile strength and contribute to tissue stability by trapping proteoglycans and non-collagenous proteins.

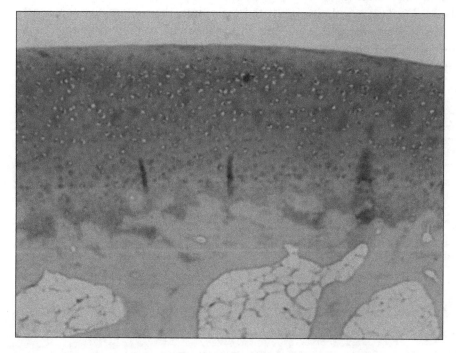

Figure 8.2. Histological image of hyaline cartilage (staining Safranin-O Fast green).

Different groups of collagen exist in cartilage: long fibre (type I, II, III, V, XI), interrupted triple helix (type IX, XII, XIV), braided (type VI) and with a laminar structure (type IV, VIII, X). Approximately 90% of the fibrils is composed of type II collagen (three polypeptide chains α1 folded in a triple helix), which is synthesized and secreted as a precursor (pro-collagen) and embedded in the matrix after removal of its ends by proteolytic enzymes. Type IX collagen is able to form bonds making the cartilaginous tissue more stable from the mechanical point of view, and more protected from enzyme action. Although present in smaller amounts (2-3%), type IX collagen plays an organizational role in the lateral growth of type II collagen by wrapping it through the globular heads and establishing contacts with type IX collagen and other components. Type X collagen is synthesized by hypertrophic chondrocytes, present in the deep layer of the cartilage matrix. The helical domain of its chains is much shorter than type II collagen. Type VI collagen is exclusively synthesized in adult cartilage; it contains short triple-helix domains and large globular domains at both ends. Its micro-fibrils seem to be present only in chondrocyte pericellular regions. As described above, besides collagens, proteoglycans (ubiquitous glycoconjugate complexes that constitute up to 35-37% of the dry weight) and glycoproteins are also prevalent in cartilage ECM. Proteoglycans, like aggrecan, are large macromolecule complexes composed of a core protein along with multiple GAG chains are attached. The most common GAGs are chondroitin sulfate and keratan sulfate. Aggrecan is in turn non-covalently attached to a central chain of hyaluronic acid (HA) that is intertwined among collagen fibres. Proteoglycans, due to their large size, occupy a lot of space in the ECM. Aggrecan represents the predominant type (90%), mostly providing cartilage with its deformation ability. Under physiological conditions, chondrocytes maintain the equilibrium between the anabolic and the catabolic processes, and thus keep the concentrations of all ECM components stable.

Catabolism is regulated by endogenous degrading enzymes, in particular by the following matrix metalloproteinases (MMP):

- MMP-1, specific for interstitial and type X collagen;
- MMP-2, specific for type VI collagen;

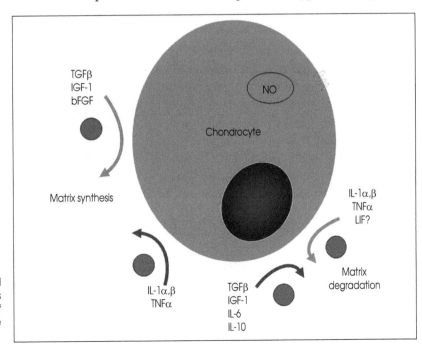

Figure 8.3. Image of the principal anabolic and catabolic factors involved in the mechanisms of synthesis and degradation of the extracellular matrix.

- MMP-3, specific for type VI, IX and XI collagen and able to split aggrecan proteic nucleus.

The activity of MMPs is under the feedback control of the tissue inhibitors of metalloproteinases (TIMP), which can easily penetrate into the cartilage matrix, thanks to their reduced molecular weight. Cartilage degradation and matrix depletion are also stimulated by a series of inflammatory mediators, mainly interleukin-1beta (IL-1β) and Tumor Necrosis Factor-alpha (TNF-α) (Figure 8.3). These two cytokines regulate the degradation pathway of proteoglycans and act as inhibitors of the anabolic processes, especially in the superficial areas of cartilage, causing a decrease in aggrecan synthesis and promoting the degradation of proteoglycans in a significant and dose-dependent manner. Other cytokines involved in cartilage homeostasis are Transforming Growth Factor-beta (TGF-β), with an *in vitro* pro-anabolic activity, interferon-gamma (INF-γ), which inhibits the transcription and synthesis of type I, II and III collagen, and Insulin-Like Growth Factor-1 (IGF-1), which plays a key role in cartilage homeostasis.

8.3 Cartilage damage

Traumas due to road or sports accidents may have a profound effect on cartilage tissue structure and function. The problem becomes more complex when we consider the higher percentage of incidence of inflammatory, rheumatic and degenerative cartilage pathologies which often occur as post-traumatic consequences and are typical of an ageing population. Traumatic lesions can be micro-traumas, and chondral or osteochondral damage. Micro-traumas can be caused by a single or repetitive trauma and are not necessarily associated with articular surface lesions.

Chondral damage is characterized by the tearing of more or less extended areas of the articular surface, without sub-chondral bone involvement. In this type of injury, chondrocytes located at the periphery of the affected area increase their mitotic activity and the synthesis of type II collagen. Osteochondral fractures cross the entire thickness of the cartilaginous tissue, up to the bone. The triggered repair response is similar to that of other tissues, given the vascularization of the affected bone area. The lesion is first perfused by blood and then filled with fibrous tissue. The cells secrete several factors, such as TGFβ, IGF-I and Platelet Derived Growth Factor (PDGF).

Mesenchymal stem cells reside within the cartilage tissue, where they can differentiate into chondroblasts and chondrocytes. It takes six to eight weeks for the repair tissue to comprise cells with chondrocyte-like morphology and an ECM characterized by proteoglycans and collagen type. This implies a consequent decrease in resistance compared to the original tissue, even if there is good functionality. The neo-formed tissue presents indeed different histological characteristics than hyaline cartilage, with the consequence of compromised joint functionality, favouring the appearance of degenerative phenomena over time (Figure 8.4).

Various therapeutic interventions have been developed to date and are still used today in the treatment of cartilage lesions. These interventions are generally aimed at inducing the migration of cells from the bone marrow and the subchondral spongiosa, in order to induce the reparative process. In general, these techniques lead to an improvement in terms of

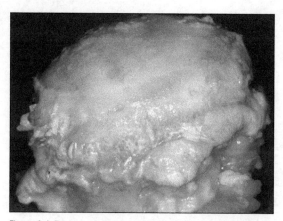

Figure 8.4. Representative image of articular cartilage of a patient affected by osteoarthritis.

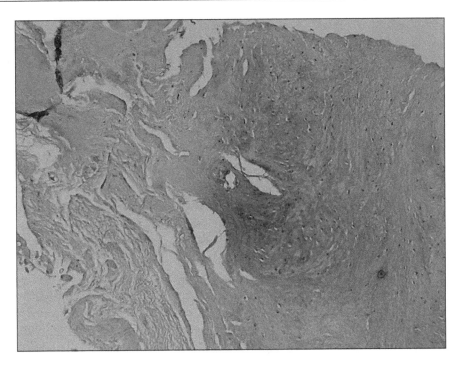

Figure 8.5. Fibrocartilage.

pain reduction and increased mobility, but the resulting fibrous tissue possesses less mechanical resistance than hyaline cartilage (Figure 8.5).

8.4 Regenerative medicine: a new frontier in the treatment of cartilage lesions

Recent advances in the fields of cell biology and biotechnology have made possible the *in vitro* reconstruction of tissues or organs. This possibility falls under the definition of "Tissue engineering", a new branch of the biomedical sciences. This technology allows the *ex vivo* expanding and subsequent seeding of autologous cells in three-dimensional biocompatible polymer matrices and final implanting of the engineered tissue in the site of the lesion for regeneration purposes. By modulating the chemical, mechanical and physical characteristics of such matrices, it is possible to regenerate different types of tissues *in vitro*. These bio-artificial structures represent the second generation of organ and tissue replacement procedures. The first generation essentially includes traditional artificial organs (kidneys, heart-lung machine, cardiac valve prostheses, cardiac pacemakers, ileo-femoral and knee joint prostheses), whose clinical alternative is the transplantation of human organs obtained from donors. Tissue engineering represents an evolution of these therapeutic interventions, allowing the association between living cell transplantation and artificial organ technology for the realization of functional structures. It involves the study of cell characteristics and functions, the structure and composition of the biomaterials, acting physical forces, and the biochemical and molecular factors inducing the regeneration process. The result of these studies is tissue-engineered products, whose purpose is to associate living and artificial structures, making physiological functions available.

In the orthopaedic field, good results have been obtained by transplanting human autologous chondrocytes or mesenchymal stem cells for the reconstruction of cartilage damaged as a result of trauma or disease (i.e. osteochondritis dissecans or chondromalacia patellae) and for the treatment of skeletal abnormalities, trauma and bone tumors.

The subject of neo-chondrogenesis arises and is therefore justified by the opportunity and challenge to restore the structural integrity and functions of the damaged tissue that should be mechanically suitable for bearing physiological loads, avoiding or reducing the arthritic evolution of the initial lesion. Hyaline cartilage is an ideal candidate for tissue engineering applications because its trophism is not dependent on blood flow, being ensured directly by the synovial fluid, innervation is not necessary and the capacity for intrinsic repair is very limited. Several surgical therapies have been developed to regenerate normal articular cartilage. They include "debridement" techniques, microfractures, arthroscopic perforations and arthroplasty abrasion, which have been shown to be effective in terms of pain reduction and increased mobility. However, the newly formed tissue displays fibro-cartilaginous features, consisting mainly of type I collagen, and lower mechanical strength compared to hyaline cartilage where the type II collagen predominates. The techniques based on perichondrium or periosteum implantation, both having chondrogenic potential, also present limits, such as, in particular, a low engraftment with the sub-chondral bone. Other types of approaches in the regeneration of articular cartilage are allogeneic osteochondral transplants which have been shown to be immunologically active, especially within the sub-chondral component.

The results obtained from the Autologous Chondrocyte Implantation (ACI) procedure certainly represent an important milestone for cartilage regenerative medicine. Small grafts of normal cartilage are removed from non-weight bearing areas of the knee. Isolated chondrocytes are cultured in monolayer and, after several weeks, harvested and prepared for re-implantation. In the operating theatre, the cartilage defect is sutured with a periosteal flap (harvested from the proximal medial tibia) under which the cell suspension is injected. The long-term follow-up histological analyses have demonstrated the high quality of the regenerated tissue, which shows characteristics very similar to hyaline cartilage. However, this approach displays several disadvantages. First of all, it requires the previous harvest of healthy cartilage, necessarily involving a two-stage surgery; secondly, the time spent in monolayer culture can cause the loss of chondrocyte phenotype which appears fibro-blastic-like cells, producing type I collagen and other molecules characteristic of fibrous

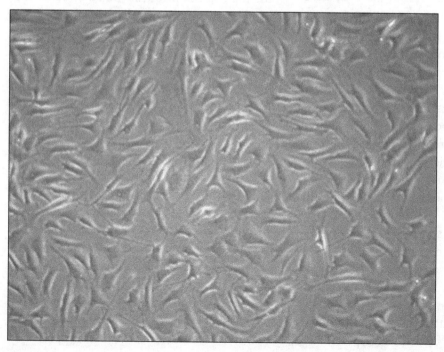

Figure 8.6. Chondrocyte-monolayer culture.

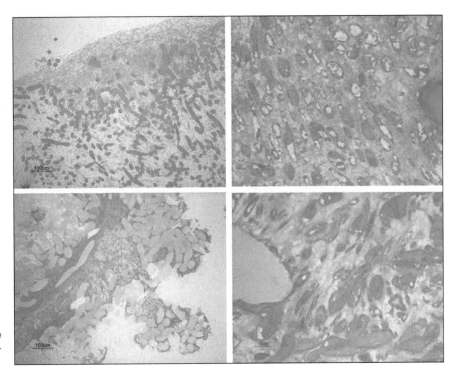

Figure 8.7. Chondrocyte (C) growth onto a hyaluronan biomaterial (S).

tissues (type I, III, V collagen and versican) (Figure 8.6). Furthermore, some doubts have been raised on the method of using the periosteum for cell fixation. In fact, it is possible that cartilage reconstruction can occur by means of mesenchymal periosteum cells rather than autologous injected chondrocytes. Besides, it has been demonstrated that chondrocytes are not always able to induce regeneration, due to their reduced number (sub-clinical dose) or poor metabolic activity. To overcome the issues describe above, the ACI procedure has been implemented by tissue engineering through the use of biomaterials. They are biological substitutes, defined as scaffolds, supporting cell viability, proliferation, and differentiation, allowing repair, regeneration, maintaining and improving tissue structure and function. For those reasons, scaffolds play a fundamental role in tissue engineering (Figure 8.7).

8.5 Mesenchymal stem cells for cartilage regeneration

Recently, attention has turned to stem cells as an alternative to chondrocytes for the treatment of chondral and osteo-chondral lesions. Stem cell populations are present in most adult tissues. Involved in tissue homeostasis, they are critical for tissue viability and maintenance, and response to external stimuli. They are the source of all newly formed tissues, participate in reparative and remodelling processes and are guided in their activity by "signal" molecules that control their activation, proliferation, migration, differentiation and survival. Progenitor cells, originating from stem cells, are able both to proliferate and to progress to a different or more differentiated phenotype. Friedenstein et al. reported for the first time the ability of these cells to differentiate in culture towards a chondrogenic phenotype, also defined as chondrogenic potential. In particular, the cells were isolated from bone marrow in culture by removing the non-adherent ones. The cells remained quiescent for a few days and then began to proliferate and produce small areas of cartilage- and bone-like tissues (Figure 8.8). However, subsequent studies have shown that 2 dimensional (2D) culture models are scarcely efficacious in inducing and maintaining the chondrocyte phenotype, while 3D

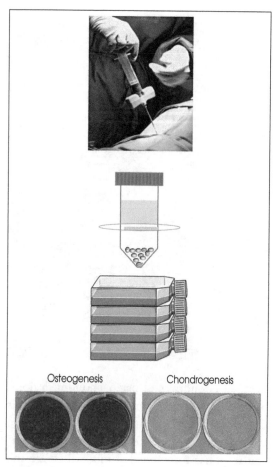

Figure 8.8. Isolation and differentiation *in vitro* of mesenchymal stem cells from bone marrow.

environments better mimic cartilage physiological conditions (i.e. low oxygen pressure). A current methodology to successfully induce MSC chondrogenesis is micro-mass culture used for the first time in 1998 by Johnstone. In this type of culture, chondrocytes can maintain their phenotype without going through a dedifferentiation process, typical of the monolayer culture. In order to form a micro-mass, cells are placed in a tube and centrifuged. TGF-β3, which plays a key role in enhancing chondrogenesis, is then added. This growth factor probably acts by inducing the expression of Sry-related high-mobility-group box-9 which, in turn, regulates the expression of aggrecan, and type II, IX and XI collagen. Other factors have been demonstrated to be effective in inducing the chondrogenic process: IGF-1,

in synergy with TGF-β1; bone morphogenetic proteins and Fibroblast Growth factor-2 (FGF-2) in combination with dexamethasone, glycosaminoglycans and aggrecan. FGF-2 and TGF-β2 have also been shown to enter the composition of Platelet Rich Plasma (PRP) ,a fraction of blood having a platelet concentration above baseline; the growth factors released from platelets are known to potentiate tissue regeneration.

Despite the above reported potential of MSCs, there are some concerns associated with their use for the regeneration of articular cartilage. In particular, some studies have shown the expression of hypertrophic markers in the neoformed tissue, such as type X collagen, metalloproteinase-12, alkaline phosphatase, receptor for the parathyroid hormone and Vascular Endothelial Growth Factor (VEGF). Since hypertrophy leads to ossification, scientists have raised doubts about the clinical application of MSCs for the regeneration of cartilage defects. To overcome these problems, co-cultures of MSCs and mature chondrocytes have been set up, resulting in a diminished expression of hypertrophic markers. This effect appears to be due to the parathyroid hormone-related peptide secreted by chondrocytes. The regenerative potential of MSCs has been investigated also *in vivo*, generally using rabbits as an animal model. The cells have been implanted alone or, loaded onto a biomaterial. Some authors implanted MSCs isolated from rabbit bone marrow in artificially created defects. The histological evaluation carried out 14 weeks after the intervention showed the formation of cartilaginous tissue showing better characteristics than the controls treated without cells. MSCs have been loaded onto different types of biomaterials, such as collagen or hyaluronic acid. A rabbit animal model was still utilized, but the pathology to treat was osteoarthritis, surgically induced by resection of the anterior cruciate ligament. The results highlighted the efficacy of these cells for early lesions. Even large animals, such as sheep, have been used both for osteochondral and meniscal defects and for arthritic lesions, with satisfactory results. The injected cells demonstrated being able to regenerate the damaged tissues and delay the progression of the pathology.

Concerning clinical trials, at present there are only a few aimed at the evaluation of the efficacy of MSC treatments for the regeneration of articular cartilage, and even fewer are randomized. The clinical studies that are currently underway can be found by consulting the site https://clinicaltrials.gov/. Some authors have performed treatments with MSC in a limited number of patients. In some cases, the cells were injected together with collagen gels. The observed histological results were very good, highlighting the regeneration of cartilage tissue. From a clinical point of view, the participants reported pain relief and return to normal activity in a period of time.

Recently, adipose tissue-derived stem cells (ASC) are considered ideal for application in regenerative therapies, since they show multi-lineage differentiation ability, and hence they can form bone and cartilage. ASCs reside in the stromal vascular fraction (SVF) of adipose tissue, which can be considered the non-cultured form of ASCs. Since cultured-expanded ASCs need high manipulation in a laboratory setting, while SVF can be more easily harvested after collagenase treatment, SVF has been as well tested for orthopaedic clinical settings. ASCs appear similar to MSCs, in terms of characteristics and functions, but are present in a higher percentage (5% compared to 0.01%) in the source tissue. Indeed, it has been shown that they perform an immunosuppressive function both *in vitro* and *in vivo* and are able to decrease local inflammation processes. Moreover, ASCs possess a protective effect towards MSCs. Based on these considerations, the use of ASCs was hypothesized to slow down the progression of osteoarthritis. As previously reported, the chondrocytes of osteoarthritis patients secrete a number of inflammatory cytokines, in particular IL-1β, TNF-α, IL-8, IL-6 and other inflammatory molecules, such as cyclooxygenase-2 (COX-2) and inducible nitric oxide synthase (iNOS) with the consequent production of prostaglandin E-2 (PGE-2) and nitric oxide (NO). Several pre-clinical studies have been performed, showing how ASCs protect chondrocytes from degenerative processes *in vitro* and how the injection of ASCs into rats and rabbits contrasts the evolution of osteoarthritis with a mechanism that is still under investigation.

In recent times, attention has turned towards the use bone marrow concentrate (BMC) or SVF for the regeneration of both traumatic and degenerative cartilage lesions. This allows to keep the mutual interactions in the stem cell niche unaltered as much as possible. It is important to underline the fact that the activity of stem cells, rather than being the expression of one or more of their intrinsic properties, is the result of the interaction between other cells and the surrounding microenvironment (or "niche"). Concentrated bone marrow or SVF allows to obtain a cell suspension that can be quickly processed, even intra-operatively for immediate re-implantation (Figure 8.9). Both SVF and BMC can be used alone or, frequently, with adjuvants like Platelet-Rich Plasma (PRP).

A main advantage of the use of medullary aspirate is given by the high cell concentration, equal to about 40 millions nucleated cells and about 2,000 connective progenitors per milliliter. This allows avoiding cell expansion in culture and related risks. The use of concentrated marrow for the regeneration of cartilage lesions has been reported by various authors, both in animal models and in humans, with satisfactory results. In conclusion, the literature shows that at present there is no standardization of the procedures adopted for the production of both expanded and concentrated cells. On the other hand, from the clinical point of view, the reported studies differ as to follow-up times, types of lesions (aetiology, size, location) and patients (age, sex and associated diseases). All these variables influence the robustness and reliability of the experimental results. Therefore, further randomized clinical trials and

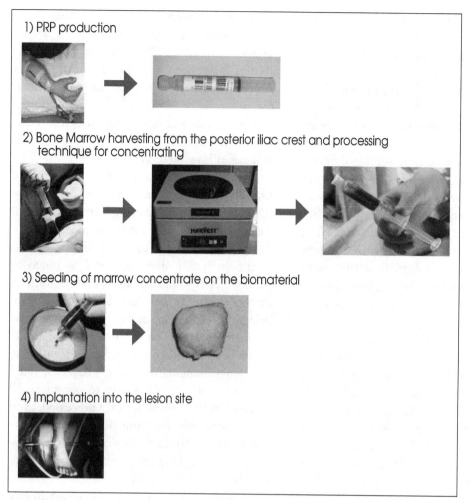

1) PRP production

2) Bone Marrow harvesting from the posterior iliac crest and processing technique for concentrating

3) Seeding of marrow concentrate on the biomaterial

4) Implantation into the lesion site

Figure 8.9. "One step" bone marrow procedure.

longer follow-up will be needed in order to confirm the effectiveness of these therapies for cartilage regeneration over time.

Recommended reading and references

1. Pelletier JP, Martel-Pelletier J. "Articular cartilage". In: Schumacher HR, Klippel JH, Koopan WK, eds. *Primer on the Rheumatic Diseases*. Atlanta: Arthritis Foundation Publ; 1993: 8-11.

2. Schenk RK, Eggli PS, Hunziker EB. "Articular cartilage morphology". In: Kuettner KE, Scheleyerbach R, Hascall Vc, eds. *Articular Cartilage biochemistry*. New York Raven Press 1986: 3-22.

3. Hunziker EB. "Articular cartilage structure in humans and animals". In: Kuettner KE, Schleyerbach R, Peyron J, Hascall VC, eds. *Articular cartilage and osteoarthritis*. New York: Raven Press; 1992:97-130.

4. Eyre DR, Wu JJ, Niyibizi C, Chun L. *The cartilage collagens: Analysis of their cross-linking interactions and matrix organization*. In: Maroudas A, Kuettner KE, eds. *Methods in research*. London: Academic Press; 1990:28-33.

5. Kuettner KE, Kimura JH. *Proteoglycans: an overview*. Cell Biol Chem. 1985; 27:327-36.

6. Cawston TE. *Metalloproteinase inhibitors and the prevention of connective tissue breakdown*. Pharmacol Ther. 1996;70(3):163-82.

7. Goldring MB, Goldring SR. *Skeletal tissue response to cytokines*. Clin Orthop Relat Res. 1990 Sep;(258):245-78.

8. Mankin HJ. *Current concepts review: the response*

of articular cartilage to mechanical injury. J Bone Joint Surg (Am) 1982, 64: 460-466.

9. Mankin HJ. *The reaction of articular cartilage to injury and osteoarthritis.* N Engl J Med. 1974 Dec 19;291(25):1335-40

10. Gay S, Kuchen S, Gay RE, Neidhart M. *Cartilage destruction in rheumatoid arthritis.* Ann Rheum Dis. 2002 Nov;61 Suppl 2:ii87.

11. Shapiro F, Koide S, Glimcher MJ. *Cell origin and differentiation in the repair of full-tickness defects of articular cartilage.* J Bone Joint Sur. 1993; 75/A: 532-553.

12. Griffith LG, Naughton G. *Tissue Engineering-current challenges and expanding opportunities.* Science 2002; 295 (5557): 1009-14.

13. Vacanti CA, Vacanti JP. The science of tissue engineering. Orthop Clin North Am 2000; 31: 351-6.

14. Sittinger M, Bujia J, Rotter N, Reitzel D, Minuth WW, Burmester GR. *Tissue engineering and autologous transplant formation: pratical approaches with resorbable biomaterials and new cell culture techniques.* Biomaterials 1996; 17:237-42.

15. Mistry H, Connock M, Pink J, Shyangdan D, Clar C, Royle P, Court R, Biant LC, Metcalfe A, Waugh N. *Autologous chondrocyte implantation in the knee: systematic review and economic evaluation.* Health Technol Assess. 2017 Feb;21(6):1-294.

16. Goldberg A, Mitchell K, Soans J, Kim L, Zaidi R. *The use of mesenchymal stem cells for cartilage repair and regeneration: a systematic review.* J Orthop Surg Res. 2017 Mar 9;12(1):39.

17. Peterson L, Brittberg M, Kiviranta I, Akerlund EL, Lindhal A. *Autologous chondrocyte transplantation. Biomechanics and long-term durability.* Am J Sports Med. 2002; 30: 2-12.

18. Sittinger M, Perka C, Schultz O, Haupl T, Burmester GR. *Joint cartilage regeneration by tissue engineering.* Z Rheumatol 1999 Jun;58:130-5.

19. Muschler GF, Midura RJ. *Connective tissue progenitors: practical conceps for clinical applications.* Clin Orthop. 2002;345: 66-80.

20. Friedenstein AJ, Chailakhjan RK, Lalykina KS. *The development of fibroblast colonies in monolayer cultures of guinea-pig bone marrow and spleen cells.* Cell Tissue Kinet. 1970 Oct;3(4):393-403.

21. Johnstone B, Hering TM, Caplan AI, Goldberg VM, Yoo JU. *In vitro chondrogenesis of bone marrow-derived mesenchymal progenitor cells.* Exp Cell Res. 1998

22. Pelttari K, Winter A, Steck E, Goetzke K, Hennig T, Ochs BG, Aigner T, Richter W. *Premature induction of hypertrophy during in vitro chondrogenesis of human mesenchymal stem cells correlates with calcification and vascular invasion after ectopic transplantation in SCID mice.* Arthritis Rheum. 2006;54:3254–3266 .

23. Wakitani S, Goto T, Pineda SJ, Young RG, Mansour JM, Caplan AI, Goldberg VM. *Mesenchymal cell-based repair of large, full-thickness defects of articular cartilage.* J Bone Joint Surg Am. 1994;76:579–592.

24. Zuk PA, Zhu M, Ashjian P, De Ugarte DA, Huang JI, Mizuno H, Alfonso ZC, Fraser JK, Benhaim P, Hedrick MH. *Human Adipose Tissue Is a Source of Multipotent Stem Cells* Mol Biol Cell 2002;12: 4279-4295.

25. Sampson S, Botto-van Bemden A, Aufiero D. *Autologous bone marrow concentrate: review and application of a novel intra-articular orthobiologic for cartilage disease.* Phys Sportsmed. 2013 Sep;41(3):7-18.

26. Spradling A, Drummond-Barbosa D, Kai T. *Stem cells find their niche.* Nature 2001; 414: 98-104.

Bone stem cells

9

Nicola Baldini   Gemma Di Pompo
Gabriela Ciapetti

9.1 Bone tissue

Bone is a specialized type of dense connective tissue consisting of cells, fibres and highly mineralized extracellular matrix that confers strength, rigidity, and resistance to compression, traction and torsion. Based on these properties, bone represents a scaffold providing support and protection to the whole body. Since the bone matrix stores high amounts of calcium salts, bone also finely regulates calcium homeostasis.

Despite its apparent static stiffness, bone tissue is extremely dynamic: the macroscopic balance resulting from its mechanical integrity is the consequence of *bone remodelling,* a continuous and coordinated sequence of tissue degradation (*resorption*), followed by the deposition of new bone matrix (*formation*); these processes occur due to a close functional correlation between *osteoblasts* and *osteoclasts*, whose activities of formation and resorption, respectively, are balanced in physiological conditions. Constant remodelling provides repair and regeneration of damaged bone throughout life.

From a macroscopic point of view, two types of bone can be distinguished: *compact* and *spongy* bone (Figure 9.1). Compact bone is found in the diaphysis of long bones and covers the spongy tissue of short and flat bones; its main unit, the *osteon*, is composed by the *Haversian canal* - containing the blood vessels and oriented in parallel to the central axis of the bone - and by parallel layers of bony lamel-

lae arranged concentrically around it. Spongy bone is mainly found in short and flat bones, and in the epiphyses of long bones; the lamellae of spongy bone are arranged in layers that aggregate to form more or less thick and variously intertwining trabeculae to delimit intercommunicating spaces (*medullary cavities*) containing *haematopoietic bone marrow* or *red marrow*. Otherwise, adipose *yellow marrow* occupies the entire *diaphyseal cavity* inside the long bones.

The external surface of bones is covered by the *periosteum*, a fibrous layer of connective tissue made up of intertwined bundles that is absent at the articular surfaces (covered by cartilage) and at the insertional areas of tendons and ligaments. In the diaphysis of long bones, the medullary canal is covered by a thinner fibrous connective tissue: the *endosteum*.

Bone marrow consists of a supporting connective tissue called *stroma (yellow bone marrow)* and a haematopoietic parenchyma made of blood cell precursors (*red bone marrow*, or *myeloid tissue*). The bone marrow stroma contains an extremely heterogeneous cell population, including fibroblasts, macrophages, adipocytes, osteoblasts and endothelial cells, in association with an extracellular matrix; together, these elements provide the structural scaffold, spatial context and physiological and trophic stimuli regulating the maintenance and function of *haematopoietic stem cells* (HSC). However, these are not the only type of stem cells within the bone marrow; indeed,

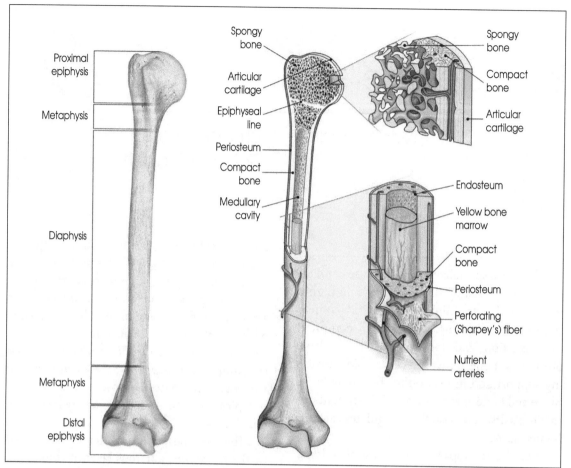

Figure 9.1. Macroscopic structure of bone tissue.

also *endothelial stem cells* able to regenerate the endothelial tissue and other stem cells localized in the stroma reside in the bone marrow. In particular, the stem cells of the bone marrow stroma are equipped with properties of multipotency and self-renewal which make them able to differentiate and contribute to the regeneration of tissues of mesenchymal origin, such as bone, cartilage, muscle, ligaments, tendons, and adipose tissue.

9.2 The discovery of a new population of bone marrow stem cells: stromal stem cells

The presence of a new population of stromal stem cells in the bone marrow was first suggested in 1867 by Julius Friedrich Cohnheim. He considered the bone marrow as a potential source of adherent non-haemato-poietic mesenchymal progenitors, with fibroblast-like morphology, able to migrate to the sites of tissue injury and to deposit collagen fibres as a normal damage repair mechanism.

Subsequent evidence of the presence of non-haematopoietic mesenchymal precursors in the bone marrow stroma was provided in 1968 by Alexander Friedenstein, Maureen Owen and co-authors, who set up an *in vitro* culture of bone marrow, removing the non-adherent haematopoietic cells after 4 hours. The Friedenstein group was the first to test the clonogenicity of a fraction of the stromal population, demonstrating its ability to generate colonies of fibroblast-like cells (*Colony Forming Unit-Fibroblasts* or *CFU-F*). Moreover, once inoculated *in vivo*, these non-haematopoietic adherent cells proved to be able to differentiate into bone tissue and medullary stroma, confirming the hypothesis that the bone marrow microenvironment is the biological "niche" of two distinct populations of progenitors: haematopoietic cells and stromal cells. Before then, the scientific world's attention to the bone marrow stroma was limited to its essential role in supporting myeloid tissue and regulating haematopoiesis. Thanks to the discovery of Friedenstein and collaborators, the interest of scientists focused on its stemness potential.

The cells thus identified were initially named *stromal stem cells*. Then, *in vivo* studies led many authors to propose different nomenclatures: *mesenchymal stem cells (MSC)*, *mesenchymal progenitor cells (MPC)*, or *skeletal stem cells (SSC)*, among others.

Although there is no single nomenclature to date, all the definitions listed above refer to a particular type of adherent, mononuclear cells, with fibroblast-like morphology, a small amount of cytoplasm, a few mitochondria and a poorly developed Golgi apparatus; such cells can be expanded *ex vivo* and have the peculiar ability to spontaneously differentiate, both *in vitro* and *in vivo*. From now on, we will refer to the complex and heterogeneous population of cells just described as MSCs, or adult stromal cells of mesenchymal origin.

Despite the ubiquitous nature of MSCs and the consequent chance of isolating them from various tissues such as fat, dental pulp, the liver, fetal blood, umbilical cord blood and amniotic fluid, bone marrow is the most studied and accessible source of isolation of MSCs.

MSCs are present both in the postnatal bone marrow and in the adult bone marrow, with a proportion decreasing with age increase. Within the bone marrow, MSCs represent 0.001-0.1% of total *mononuclear cells (MNC)*, and are usually isolated from bone marrow samples obtained from the posterior iliac crest and from the medullary compartments of the tibia and the femur. The selection of these cells out of the whole bone marrow MNCs is usually based on their ability to adhere to a plastic substrate. However, the resulting cell population appears to be extremely heterogeneous both from a morphological and a functional point of view.

9.2.1 Heterogeneity of MSCs: limitations in selection and characterization of the mesenchymal stem fraction

The heterogeneity of the bone marrow stromal cell population had already been recognized by the pioneering study of Friedenstein who observed that not all the CFU-F were highly proliferative and multipotent.

Indeed, cells isolated from the bone marrow generate colonies of different size and morphology: some appear fusiform and fibroblast-like, others flattened and large. Their differentiation potential is also variable: within the heterogeneous population of MSCs isolated from the bone marrow, some CFU-F are able to differentiate in osteogenic, adipogenic and chondrogenic lineages, while others are less multipotential. In particular, in healthy donors, about 50% of the MSCs that form colonies generate clones with multipotency and high proliferative ability, while 10-20% generate exclusively osteogenic clones.

The heterogeneity of the bone marrow stromal cell population was also confirmed by *in vivo* studies: when single cell colonies derived from CFU-F are transplanted into an animal model, only a fraction proves able to completely regenerate an organ in which bone cells, supportive stroma and adipocytes originate from the donor; on the contrary, the haematopoietic and vascular elements are derived from the host. This result further confirms that not all clonogenic cells are in fact multipotent stem cells.

This morphological and functional variability also includes phenotypic differences: unlike HSCs and their progeny, under *in vitro* culture conditions, bone marrow stromal cells express a series of non-specific surface markers that are not useful for their selection and enrichment, either individually or in combination.

The morphological and phenotypic heterogeneity of bone marrow stromal cells represents a considerable limitation to the effort to identify and isolate the real mesenchymal stem fraction. The mismatch between cell behaviour in the *in vitro* culture system and what happens in the physiological microenvironment must also be added to this limitation. For this reason, the International Society for Cellular Therapy (ISCT) has established minimal identification requirements. According to the criteria established by the ISCT, the MSCs should:

a. adhere to a substrate *in vitro*, proliferate and originate osteoblasts, chondrocytes, adipocytes and reticular stroma to support haematopoiesis under appropriate differentiation stimuli;

b. express CD73 (SH3/4), CD90 (Thy1) and CD105 (SH2), and not haematopoietic (CD34, CD45, CD14) or endothelial (CD34, CD31, VWF) markers.

9.2.2 *In vitro* phenotypic markers

Although not expressed by expanded MSCs *in vitro*, CD34 may be expressed by cells immediately isolated from the bone marrow, and lost during *in vitro* cell culture passages. The CD34 marker is common to haematopoietic, stromal, epithelial and endothelial cells: these different types of CD34-positive cells share the features of progenitor and stemness, as well as a high differentiation ability. It is likely that the presence of CD34, together with tissue-specific markers, indicates a particular progenitor for a specific type of tissue. In general, *in vitro* culture conditions, such as adhesion to plastic substrates, bovine fetal serum, and exogenous growth factors that are used to culture cells, can modulate the loss or acquisition of surface receptors, thus altering the cell phenotype.

MSCs express a wide range of adhesion molecules (CD44, CD29, CD90), typical markers of stromal cells (SH-2, SH-3, SH-4) and receptors for cytokines such as interleukins and *Tumor Necrosis Factor* (*TNF*-α).

The anti-SH2 monoclonal antibody identifies an epitope of SH2 antigen known as *endoglin* (CD105) or *type III Transforming Growth Factor receptor* (TGFBR3); it is a glycoprotein on the surface of endothelial cells, erythroblasts, monocytes and stromal cells of the connective tissue that binds TGF-β3 with high affinity. It plays an essential role in the interactions between endothelial cells and during vessel development, mediates interplay between MSCs and haematopoietic cells in the marrow, and appears to play a key role in chondrogenic differentiation.

The anti-SH3 and anti-SH4 monoclonal antibodies recognize two different epitopes of CD73, an antigen expressed by many cell types and in particular by the lymphoid tissue, and that is not expressed by haematopoietic precursors or osteocytes. This marker is present on *in vitro* expanded stromal cells. In the bone marrow microenvironment, CD73 may mediate cell-cell interactions and represents a common element in stromal and lymphocyte development.

The anti-SB10 monoclonal antibody specifically recognizes the SB10 antigen, identified as CD166 or ALCAM (Activated Leukocyte-Cell Adhesion Molecule), a glycoprotein involved in osteogenic differentiation, although the mechanism underlying its function has not yet been elucidated.

It has been shown that SB-10, SH-2, SH-3 and SH-4 monoclonal antibodies are not able to stain haematopoietic cells; however, other known epitopes on the MSC surface used for their isolation, such as CD44, CD29 and CD90, are not exclusively expressed by the MSCs, but also by other cell types.

Another antibody used for MSC isolation is Stro-1, which recognizes a surface antigen typical of non-haematopoietic bone marrow MNC progenitors. The selection of Stro-1 positive cells allowed 10-20-fold enrichment of the number of isolated CFU-F compared to the bone marrow samples not subjected to this separation technique. In summary, all Stro-1 positive cells generate colonies, but not all CFU-F express Stro-1.

9.2.3 *In vivo* phenotypic markers

Most of the data concerning the phenotypic properties of stromal stem cells are based on *in vitro* studies, while little information is available on the features of the primary clonogenic precursors responsible for priming the *in vivo* growth of bone marrow stromal cells. Furthermore, as already mentioned, there is often a mismatch between the behaviour of these cells in the *in vitro* culture system and what happens in their physiological microenvironment. Unfortunately, the *in vitro* use of single or combined antibodies, as already mentioned, does not favour the enrichment of the mesenchymal stem fraction contained in the most heterogeneous population from which they originate, since the antigens are not specific to the MSCs, but are also expressed by other cell types. This lack of specificity makes the *in vivo* study of the MSC phenotype extremely difficult. Furthermore, *in vitro* markers allow only a prospective "recognition" of MSCs, not their actual *in vivo* identification. However, even today, the efforts of the scientific community are aimed at satisfying the cogent need of a phenotypic characterization that is as unique as possible and consistent with the *in vivo* cellular behaviour. Analyzing the properties of MSCs in their physiological bone microenvironment is in fact an essential requirement for developing more sophisticated approaches of cell isolation and culture and developing cell therapies.

To fill this need, several researchers have made an effort to characterize the *in vivo* phenotype of MSCs and to establish their localization and distribution within the bone marrow stem cell niche. In 2013, Rasini and collaborators analyzed the positivity for the expression of typical MSC markers in different cell types distributed within three main micro-anatomical bone compartments: the intratrabecular space of the marrow, the endosteal surface localized along the trabecular bone (interface between the trabecular bone and the medullary cavity), and the area around the vessels, namely the endothelial compartment. This study showed the presence of cells positive for CD10, CD31, CD73, CD140b, CD271 and GD2 in the intratrabecular space of the bone marrow, in addition to haematopoietic elements expressing CD45. The anti-CD31 antibody stains large multinucleated cells very similar to megakaryocytes. On the other hand, the cellular elements positive for CD73 and negative for CD45 are osteogenic mesenchymal precursors. The cells positive for CD10 are small in size and with oval morphology. CD10 is a zinc-dependent metalloprotease expressed both by MSCs *in vitro*, and by normal and neoplastic progenitors belonging to different tissues and organs. It is involved in various signalling pathways capable of influencing cell migration, angiogenesis, tumorigenesis, and immunomodulation. Although a minimal part of CD10-positive cells is represented by mesenchymal progenitors, the other small CD10-positive cells appear to be of haematopoietic origin, since this antigen is typically expressed by normal lymphoid progenitors and, sometimes, by myeloid precursors. CD271-positive mesenchymal cells were also identified within the medullary cavity. CD271, also known as *Nerve Growth Factor* (NGF) *receptor*, is considered to be one of the selective markers for isolating and characterizing bone marrow MSCs. The lack of CD45 in these CD271-positive cells confirmed the *in vivo* existence of such non-haematopoietic mesenchymal progenitors. In the vicinity of CD271-positive cells, CD140b-positive cells were identified. CD140b, known as *platelet-derived growth factor receptor-b* (PDGFR-β), is considered a new marker of MSCs; nevertheless, this antigen could not be identified in *in vitro* culture conditions.

So-called *bone lining cells* (BLC), are fusiform cells, positive for CD73, CD140b, CD271, GD2 and negative for CD10, CD31, CD146, CD34, CD45, and have been identified at the endosteal surface covering the cavities of trabecular bone. The compartment of these cells is connected to the reticular system found within the intratrabecular space of the bone marrow.

The positive expression of the MSC markers described so far is found *in vivo*, in both reticular and non-reticular cells. CD10 and CD146 are typical of stromal reticular cells, whereas non-reticular cells co-express CD73, CD140b, and CD271.

Finally, in the endothelial compartment, the expression of the phenotypic markers varies according to the structure and distribution of the vascular system. The sinusoids within the medullary cavity consist of a discontinuous layer of endothelial cells expressing CD31, CD34 and CD146 and negative for CD10, CD45, CD73, CD140b, CD271. The *tunica intima* of larger vessels contains cells positive for CD31, GD2 and CD34 and negative for CD10, CD45, CD73, CD146 and CD271. In the outer layers there is an additional cell population positive for CD146 and GD2 and negative for CD31, CD34, CD45, CD73 and CD271.

This investigation, together with further *in vivo* studies aimed at identifying both the phenotype and the localization and distribution of MSCs within the physiological bone microenvironment, has led to a better definition and understanding of the bone marrow stem cell niche.

9.3 The bone marrow stem cell niche: a more in-depth definition

"Stem niche" means a specific microenvironment, located in adult tissues, in which cellular elements and molecular signals regulate the function and maintenance of the stem cells inside it.

The stem cell niche is responsible for controlling the balance between quiescence, self-renewal and cell differentiation, as well as the use of specific cellular programs in response to stress conditions.

On the basis of the experimental data related to the behaviour and localization of MSC within the physiological bone microenvironment, the concept of bone marrow niche has now been expanded, and includes cells that had not been precisely defined in the past. From a conceptual point of view, it can be divided into two main functional sections: the *endosteal niche* and the *perivascular niche* (Figure 9.2).

The endosteal niche consists of mesenchymal cells and their osteoblastic progeny residing at the interface between the endosteal surface and the bone marrow cavity; it provides a protective microenvironment that guarantees the maintenance and self-renewal of HSCs, isolat-

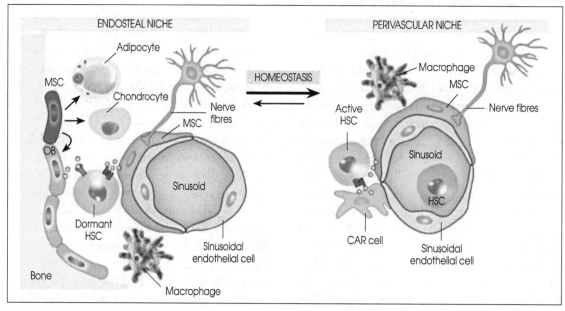

Figure 9.2. Representation of the bone marrow stem cell niche.

ing them from differentiating and pro-apoptotic stimuli that would reduce the stem cell reserve. In particular, the role of MSCs is to keep HSCs in a quiescent state.

The vascular niche includes sinusoidal endothelial cells and CD146⁺ subendothelial stromal cells and controls the differentiation of HSCs and the release of mature haematopoietic cells in the vascular system. In 2006, Takashi Nagasawa's research group identified a small population of reticular cells with long dendritic processes and uniformly distributed within the murine bone marrow. Since these cells secreted high levels of CXCL12, they were defined as *CXCL12-abundant reticular* (CAR) *cells*. CAR cells surround the sinusoidal endothelial cells and express antigenic markers, such as the *vascular cell adhesion molecule 1* (VCAM1), CD44 and PDGFRα/β, while they are negative for typical haematopoietic markers, such as Sca-1 and CD45, or for CD31.

Currently, CD146⁺ subendothelial cells are considered as the human equivalent of the murine CAR cells identified by Takashi Nagasawa's research group. The expression of CD146 by stromal cells of the bone marrow has indeed been associated with differentiation into smooth muscle cells of the vessels.

9.4 Bone marrow stromal cells as cells of the vascular wall: the theory of pericytes

CD146, also known as *melanoma cell adhesion molecule* (MCAM), is an adhesion molecule typically used as an endothelial marker. It is believed to function as a receptor for the alpha-4 subunit of *laminin*, a molecule of the cellular matrix widely expressed within the vascular wall.

Therefore, CD146 is highly expressed in the cells that assemble the wall of blood vessels, including endothelial cells, smooth muscle cells, and pericytes.

The identification of cells that are positive for this marker and negative for the typically haematopoietic markers, such as CD45, located in the perivascular area of the bone marrow,

and endowed with clonogenicity, self-renewal properties and ability to *in vivo* regenerate the bone, the stroma and the haematopoietic microenvironment, has suggested the existence of an intimate relationship between the MSCs and the cells identified as *pericytes*, due to similarities in the behaviour and in the *in vitro* and *in vivo* potential of these two populations.

The pericyte is a type of contractile connective cell that partially surrounds the endothelial cells of capillaries and venules, performing a blood flow control function. Pericytes reside in the external surface of the sinusoids and express *proteoglycan NG2, alpha smooth muscle actin* (αSMA), and PDGFR-β, other than CD146. Under *in vitro* culture conditions, the pericytes are characterized by a good proliferative rate and share morphology, mitotic activity and surface antigens, i.e. CD44, CD73, CD90 and CD105, with MSCs. The *in vitro* affinity between pericytes and MSCs also affects their differentiation potential: under appropriate exogenous stimuli, pericytes are able to differentiate into bone, cartilage and adipose tissue in the same way as MSCs. Furthermore, human pericytes from different sources are able to regenerate muscle, bone, and even skin, both *in vivo* and *in vitro*.

Overall, these data suggest that at least a fraction of the multipotent stem cells found in primary cultures isolated from different fetal and adult organs originates from vascular pericytes. As a further support to this hypothesis, pericytes residing in their original tissue natively express the typical MSC markers, such as CD44, CD90, CD73 and CD105, as already mentioned.

The morphological and phenotypic affinity with pericytes and the evidence of the perivascular localization of MSCs in the bone marrow suggest that all the tissues of our organism host their own MSC population, and that adult MSCs are ubiquitous. According to this hypothesis, pericytes are believed to represent perivascular precursors which will differentiate into tissue-specific MSCs under the influence of their niche. This makes them similar to each other, but with some distinct features and differentiation abilities.

The perivascular localization of pericytes in different tissues results in the expression of adhesion molecules (MCAM/CD146) and surface receptors or antigens involved in the regulation of perivascular cells (PDGFR-β/CD140b; CD105/endoglin). This may represent an important prerequisite for the identification of protocols aimed at isolating specific categories of progenitors to be used in the regeneration of specific tissues and organs.

Despite the morphological and phenotypic affinity with pericytes and the evidence of the perivascular localization of MSCs in the bone marrow, recent research has demonstrated that pericytes do not behave like MSCs *in vivo*, and that not all MSCs can act as pericytes, suggesting that MSCs and pericytes are likely to be different cell types residing at the same anatomical sites.

9.5 Stem cells and bone regeneration

Bone is a highly vascularized and dynamic tissue, subject to a constant remodelling process that makes it able to regenerate without the formation of scar tissue. This property does not apply only to the sequence of events triggered by a fracture, but also when the insertion of an artificial implant or the resection of a bone segment are needed.

The molecular mechanisms of bone repair reflect skeletal formation during embryonic development. Multiple factors, including the cytokines and growth factors stored in the extracellular matrix, interact with different cell types recruited at the site of tissue damage, i.e. MSCs, bone and cartilage cells, and endothelial cells. These factors regulate the intra- and extra-cellular signalling mechanisms that are responsible for *osteoconduction* and *osteoinduction* by priming cell migration, proliferation, chemotaxis, differentiation and synthesis of extracellular proteins.

Bone healing is characterized by three phases: an early stage of inflammation, which leads to the formation of granulation tissue; a repair phase, characterized by the formation of cartilaginous callus and immature bone, and subsequent replacement with lamellar bone; a final remodelling phase to restore the original bone morphology.

Inflammation. In case of fracture, bone undergoes a loss of its skeletal integrity and of the precious vascular supply of nutrients at the site of the lesion. This results in reduced oxygen tension and destruction of the bone marrow architecture. The haematoma that occurs between the fracture ends is a source of signal molecules, such as growth factors and cytokines, for monocyte-macrophage and osteo-chondroblastic precursors. Macrophages and other inflammatory cells recruited at the site of the lesion secrete *fibroblast growth factor* (FGF), TNF-α, PDGF, TGF-β, *insulin-like growth factor I* (IGF1), and a variety of cytokines, including *interleukin 1* (IL1) and *interleukin 6* (IL6). In turn, these factors exert a chemoattractant effect on inflammatory cells and osteoblastic precursors. During the early phase, the mesenchymal precursors proliferate and differentiate into osteogenic and chondrogenic lineages; furthermore, the formation of new blood vessels occurs by budding from pre-existing vascular structures through a complex network of events: enzymatic degradation of the basement membrane, migration of endothelial cells towards angiogenic stimulus, proliferation, maturation and organization of endothelial cells in capillary tubes. This phenomenon is regulated by FGF, *vascular endothelial growth factor* (VEGF) and *angiopoietin 1* (Ang-1) and *2* (Ang-2).

Repair. *Intramembranous ossification* begins a few days after tissue damage, while *endochondral ossification* develops within about one month and involves tissues adjacent to the fracture site. The subperiosteal area and the soft tissues immediately surrounding the fracture site form the so-called "hard callus" and directly generate new bone tissue. In this process, the mesenchymal precursors recruited at the site of the injury directly differentiate into the osteoblastic lineage and produce both compact and trabecular bone without inducing cartilage formation. Instead, endochondral ossification involves the recruitment and proliferation of multipotent progenitors and their differentiation into cartilage. The proliferation of MSCs is already evident a few days after fracture. Chondrogenesis leads to the formation of a cartilaginous callus that fills and stabilizes the site of the fracture. Type II collagen and aggrecan are deposited by chondrocytes of the cartilaginous callus adjacent to the bony callus. After 2 weeks, these cells undergo hypertrophy and produce type X collagen. Subsequently, the partially mineralized membrane is resorbed and replaced with matrix mainly composed of type I collagen. Chondrocytes release phosphatases and proteases to prepare the matrix for the subsequent mineralization. The activity for phosphatases consists in making phosphate groups available; phosphate groups react with calcium released by the mitochondria, causing the precipitation of calcium phosphate and therefore the calcification of cartilage. Proteases degrade proteoglycans that prevent mineralization, allowing chondrocytes to control the speed and chemical-physical behaviour of the cartilage mineralization process. After 4-5 weeks, chondroclasts, i.e. multinucleated cells responsible for the degradation of calcified cartilage, are activated. During the resorption of the cartilage matrix, chondroclasts send signals that allow blood vessels to enter the tissue, attracting perivascular MSCs that will differentiate into osteoprogenitor cells. Endothelial cells, together with other cell types that express metalloproteases, support vascular invasion and the removal of septa and residual cartilaginous structures. The tissues resulting from intramembranous and endochondral ossification proliferate until they join each other, and a combination of calcified cartilage and new reticular bone is observed after 6-7 weeks. The conversion of cartilage to bone involves a series of programmed cell removal and matrix modification events, during which chondrocytes undergo apoptosis.

Remodelling. Complete healing of the fracture is achieved during the remodelling phase, in which osteoblasts and osteoclasts cooperate to transform the fracture callus into a bone structure capable of supporting physiological mechanical loads. Unlike what happens during the development of long bones, in which the periosteal appositional growth is balanced by the resorption of the endosteal surface, in the remodelling of the fracture callus there is an external removal of the bone and an apposition on the internal surfaces. The resorption of trabecular bone is mediated by osteoclasts that form a resorption cavity called *Howship's lacuna*. Each cell acidifies the local extracellular space and secretes lysosomal enzymes, serine proteases, collagenases and *tartrate-resistant acid phosphatase 5b* (TRAP5b), which degrade the bone matrix. The enzymatic degradation of the bone matrix causes the release of different proteins, including the growth factors previously stored during bone formation. Together with the cytokines produced by osteoclasts and other cells, these factors recruit to the site of injury osteoprogenitors that differentiate into osteoblasts. The osteoblasts penetrate into the resorption cavities, produce new intertwined or lamellar bone matrix and, once trapped inside it, they differentiate into osteocytes. Finally, some osteoblasts, called *bone lining cells* (BLC), acquire a flat morphology and place themselves on quiescent bone surfaces.

9.5.1 MSCs and bone regeneration

MSCs are critical elements of the bone regeneration process as they are the precursors of osteoblasts and chondrocytes, and modulate the tissue healing mechanism, as described in the previous section. The strong interest in the therapeutic potential of MSCs in the field of bone regenerative medicine arises from the easy accessibility of their sources, as well as their ability to migrate into damaged tissues, differentiate into mesenchymal tissues and induce tissue repair and regeneration.

The latter property has been extensively investigated in different animal models of disease and bone injury, in which the ability of MSCs to generate bone and to promote the healing of bone defects has been demonstrated. Another important feature of MSCs is their immunomodulatory function, i.e. the ability to modulate the immune response. This property has been successfully used in *graft versus host disease* (GVHD) following haematopoietic stem cell transplantation. The immunomodulatory properties of MSCs have also been used to reduce inflammation in Crohn's disease and in the immune response to organ transplantation.

9.5.2 Sources of MSCs for bone regeneration

The MSCs that are involved in bone regeneration may be endogenous or derive from sources other than bone. In the bone tissue, they are primarily involved in regeneration and are located in the bone marrow, periosteum, endosteum, and mineralized bone.

MSCs isolated from the bone marrow. The number of MSCs in the bone marrow is significantly lower than that of other resident cells. Under *in vitro* culture conditions, mouse bone marrow-derived MSCs (BM-MSCs) form a smaller number of colonies than MSCs isolated from adipose tissue or periosteum (AD-MSCs and P-MSCs, respectively); however, in the initial phase of culture they are characterized by an increased expression of *alkaline phosphatase* (ALP), a marker of early osteoblastic differentiation, and, at a later stage, by a higher expression of *osteocalcin*, a marker of late osteoblast differentiation, and a higher mineralization ability. In addition to being an accessible source of MSCs, bone marrow contains skeletal progenitors with a high expansion potential.

MSCs isolated from mineralized bone. MSCs can be isolated directly from the mineralized bone, taken by milling the medullary cavity during joint replacement. The fragments thus obtained are purified from residual bone marrow and enzymatically digested with collagenase. The culture medium is then filtered to remove bone fragments, and the residual cells are kept in culture and expanded. Alternatively, the bone fragments derived from the medullary cavity can be placed directly in culture, avoiding the enzymatic digestion. Cells derived from mineralized bone are able to differentiate into osteoblasts, chondrocytes and adipocytes, and show a gene expression profile similar to that of BM-MSCs, both in the pre- and post-differentiation phases. Samples from trabecular bone are able to form significantly more colonies than those generated from the marrow aspirate. This suggests the presence of a greater quantity of MSCs inside trabecular bone.

Recently, even compact bone has become a source for MSC isolation (B-MSCs). The isolation is similar to that described above for trabecular bone: compact bone undergoes dissection into fragments and enzymatic digestion with collagenase. Cells are able to form colonies as early as three days after isolation. An additional advantage of isolating MSCs directly from mineralized bone is the possibility of reducing contamination from the haematopoietic elements. B-MSCs are similar to BM-MSCs in differentiation potential and expression of surface markers.

MSCs isolated from the periosteum. The periosteum is crucial for bone repair since it represents the niche of progenitors of osteoblasts and chondrocytes involved in the endochondral and intramembranous ossification that occur during prenatal development and postnatal fracture healing. The isolated MSCs are characterized by an antigen profile according to the minimum criteria established by the ISCT, are multipotent cells and have a high proliferation rate.

The periosteum is an abundant source of MSCs. Given its massive contribution to the local formation of new osteoblasts and chondrocytes, it is a valid alternative to the most classic source of MSCs, the bone marrow.

MSCs isolated from adipose tissue. Although adipose tissue is not an endogenous source of MSCs for *in vivo* bone repair, it may represent a valuable source for therapeutic purposes. Like MSCs isolated from bone, AD-MSCs have the ability to differentiate into osteogenic, chondrogenic, and adipogenic lineages. However, several studies have shown that the osteogenic potential of AD-MSCs is lower than that of BM-MSCs. For instance, AD-MSC exhibit an ALP activity lower than that of BM-MSCs and P-MSCs in mouse models. Once implanted in the muscle, AD-MSCs are able to generate ectopic bone; however, this is smaller if compared to the bone generated by BM-MSCs and P-MSCs. Indeed, AD-MSCs have little or no ability to osteo-differentiate *in vivo*; on the contrary, they are able to recruit the host cells capable of stimulating bone formation.

Similarly, in the light of their paracrine activity, genetically modified AD-MSCs could be used for the administration of growth factors capable of stimulating bone formation, such as *bone morphogenetic protein* (BMP). Although their endogenous potential for osteogenic differentiation appears limited, the major advantages of AD-MSCs include a higher number of stem cell progenitors from an equivalent amount of tissue harvested, a less invasive procedure of cell harvesting, and the abundance of their source. The adipose tissue is in fact easily collected by lipoaspiration, and the resulting material can be used directly for the isolation of AD-MSCs.

9.5.3 Factors regulating MSCs during bone regeneration

Wnt signalling pathway. Wnt proteins belong to a family of glycoproteins that bind the *Frizzled* (FZD) transmembrane receptors by activating two distinct signal transduction pathways: the canonical and the non-canonical pathway of Wnt. The first involves the formation of a complex between the Wnt proteins, FZD, and the co-receptor named *low density lipoprotein receptor-related protein* (LRP) 5 or 6. In the non-canonical pathway, Wnt5a binds the FZD receptor and activates the heterotrimeric G proteins, resulting in an increase in intracellular calcium through C-dependent protein mechanisms, or by inducing Rho- or c-Jun N-terminal kinase (JNK)-dependent changes in cytoskeletal actin. Wnt proteins regulate growth, differentiation, function and cell death, and play an essential role in the biology of bone tissue. The binding of Wnt proteins with the FZD/LRP5/6 complex in the canonical pathway triggers a signal transduction cascade involving the Dishevelled, Axin and Frat-1 proteins and results in the inhibition of *glycogen synthase kinase 3 β* (GSK3). In this pathway, the β-catenin phosphorylation and the consequent ubiquitin-mediated degradation are inhibited, and the β-catenin translocates into the nucleus where it cooperates with the transcription factor *T-cell factor/lymphoid enhancer factor* (TCF/LEF) to regulate the expression of target genes. It is possible that the activity of ß-catenin is required for the activation of specific osteogenic transcription factors, such as the *Runt-related transcription factor 2* (Runx2), whose lack in the osteochondroprogenitors determines chondrogenic differentiation.

TGF-β Signalling. Several members of the TGF-β superfamily, such as BMPs, exert powerful osteogenic effects. BMP activity was first identified in the 1960s; however, the proteins responsible for osteogenesis remained unknown until the time of purification and sequencing of bovine BMP3 (*osteogenin*) and of human BMP2 and BMP4 cloning in the 1980s. BMPs bind to two different types of serine/threonine kinase receptors, leading to the phosphorylation of Smad proteins and therefore to their activation as transcription factors. Among the genes targeted by the activity of these proteins, Runx2 is one of the main regulators of osteogenesis. Although Smad proteins are critical regulators in the TGF-β signalling pathway, BMP2 can also activate Smad-independent responses, which involve the MAP kinase pathway (ERK, JNK and p38) and regulate alkaline phosphatase and osteocalcin expression in osteoblasts.

FGF signalling. The polypeptides of the FGF family regulate the endochondral and membranous ossification through four related tyrosine kinase receptors (FGFR1-FGFR4).

FGFR1 is expressed in the hypertrophic chondrocytes and has stage-specific effects on osteoblast maturation: it stimulates the differentiation of osteoblast precursors, and blocks the maturation of the differentiated osteoblasts. FGF2, 9 and 18 probably interact with FGFR1 expressed by osteoblasts. Although FGF9 and 18 are the main mediators during embryonic development, FGF2 appears to be the most relevant in the postnatal period. In the differentiated osteoblasts, FGF2 activates Runx2 via the MAPK pathway and plays an important role in the regulation of bone mineralization and formation. The expression of FGFR2 is induced in quiescent chondrocytes and inhibited in proliferative chondrocytes. The receptor undergoes tissue-specific alternative splicing, thereby generating an epithelial (form b) and a mesenchymal (form c) variant with different binding specificities. FGF18 is the physiological ligand of FGFR3, which regulates the growth and differentiation of proliferating chondrocytes and the cortical density and thickness of the bone.

Notch signalling. Since the Notch receptors and their ligands (Delta 1, 3, 4 and Jagged 1, 2) are transmembrane proteins, the signal transduction cascade is activated as a result of cell-cell interaction. Notch 1 and Notch 2 are expressed by osteoblasts, while Notch 3 and Notch 4 have been identified in subgroups of the osteogenic lineage. Experimental data support the dimorphic function of Notch signalling, which seems able to positively regulate the expression of osteoblast differentiation genes, but also to repress the maturation of osteoblasts induced by BMP, inhibiting the transactivation activity of Runx2.

9.5.4 Bone repair mechanisms mediated by MSCs

MSCs respond to bone damage through two different repair mechanisms:

a. *direct repair mechanism*: MSCs differentiate into osteoblasts and chondrocytes under the effect of the regulatory factors described in the previous section.

b. *indirect repair mechanism*: MSCs can regenerate bone tissue by secreting paracrine factors able to stimulate the proliferation and/or differentiation of other stem cells in the bone, to inhibit apoptosis favouring the survival of damaged cells, and to regulate the function of the immune system by inducing or inhibiting the migration of different immune cells to damaged tissues, or by altering the secretion of pro-inflammatory cytokines.

Among the paracrine factors secreted by MSCs to promote bone regeneration, an important role has recently been attributed to *exosomes*, a class of nanovesicles ranging in size from 50-100 nm and deriving from specific intracellular compartments known as *early endosomes* or *multivesicular bodies*. The ability to transport and transfer proteins and genetic material (i.e. *microRNA*) to cells gives the exosomes the important role of mediators of cellular communication. Once secreted, they can be internalized by target cells located near the cell of origin, or disseminated through blood or other body fluids to more distant sites. In light of these features, exosomes can be isolated from MSCs and administered systemically or locally in order to mimic the trophic effect of parental cells in the context of tissue regeneration.

Considering the regenerative, immunosuppressive, and migratory properties of the MSCs of origin, exosomes derived from this type of cells could also be subjected to genetic manipulation in order to express high levels of microRNA of specific interest. Finally, if the tropism of the exosomes does not reflect that of the MSCs of origin, or if the exosomes have to be transferred to a target tissue different from the bone, they could be engineered to express tissue-specific receptors on their surface.

9.5.5 MSC-based therapy

MSCs can be administered systemically or directly at the injury site. However, most of them do not survive after *in vivo* implantation.

This occurs because the MSCs injected systemically or implanted locally die of "anoikis", due to loss of adhesion to substrates. In addition, the majority of systemically inoculated MSCs are trapped within the lung, and after 24 hours from inoculation they are found in other organs, such as the liver and the spleen, or migrate under the effect of chemotactic signals derived from inflamed or damaged tissues. As a result, only a small proportion of MSCs can reach the target site. For this reason, local administration of MSCs is preferred to systemic inoculation.

An additional limitation of MSC-based therapy is the influence of the *in vitro* conditions by which cells are expanded before inoculation. It is now well established that *in vitro* culture modifies the MSC phenotype. For instance, *in vitro* expanded MSCs show an altered expression of CD105, CD146 and CD271: overexpression of these markers is required to ensure cell adhesion to plastic substrates and cell motility. In line with these phenotypic alterations, the morphology of MSCs also changes in the early stages of culture: cells become elongated and fibroblast-like, reaching even 20 μm in diameter. This diameter is larger than that of the pulmonary micro-capillaries, so it is not surprising that most MSCs remain trapped at these sites. The *in vitro* culture conditions have also been shown to modify other cell features, making MSCs an easy target to be lysed by natural killer cells after both allogeneic and autologous transplantation. *In vitro*, MSCs are also not recognizable by macrophages, thereby triggering an immunosuppressive effect. In conclusion, at least some of the side effects observed after MSC administration depend on the properties acquired by MSCs *in vitro*.

Regarding the actual mechanisms by which MSCs, once administered, induce repair/regeneration of damaged tissues, the current hypotheses are:

- a small fraction of MSCs escapes death and migrates to sites of damage and inflammation;

- MSCs are able to 'transfer' their effect rapidly to other cells that subsequently mediate tissue repair or immunomodulation;
- MSCs may secrete paracrine factors (i.e. VEGF, bFGF) enhancing the growth of endothelial and smooth muscle cells; furthermore, it is possible that, when attracted to an injured tissue, the soluble factors secreted by MSCs help the survival of the surrounding hosting cells.

9.5.6 Therapeutic applications of MSCs in clinical practice

MSCs have long been used for cell therapy purposes, individually or in combination with different natural or synthetic substrates, to repair bone defects. The advantages of MSC-based therapy in comparison to the most conventional regenerative technique of autologous bone grafts are the greater availability of the source of isolation, the possibility of having a greater cell concentration, the reduction of surgical times, and a lower morbidity.

The major disadvantages of MSC-based therapy are the high costs, the risk of infection, and the unpredictable efficacy.

Despite their osteogenic potential, MSCs require an osteoconductive environment to proliferate and differentiate. For this reason, in clinical settings they are often used in combination with osteoconductive substrates designed to improve cell adhesion, survival and proliferation.

Since the predefined program of MSC differentiation is osteogenic, the formation of new bone tissue would seem a relatively simple objective to achieve. However, there are still many factors restricting the clinical use of MSCs, including the high number of required cells, the limited percentage of non-haematopoietic stromal cells within the bone marrow, the difficulty in expanding the cells without decreasing their regenerative properties, and the risk of bacterial contamination during prolonged *in vitro* manipulation. Furthermore, at the time of inoculation, MSCs must overcome the stress generated by transplantation and survive the environmental factors that characterize the site of the damage, including inflammation and ischaemia: in fact, inadequate vascularization greatly compromises both the function and survival of inoculated MSCs.

◼ Recommended reading and references

1. Bianco P. *Bone and the hematopoietic niche: a tale of two stem cells. Blood* 2011; 117:5281-8.

2. Dominici M, et al. *Minimal criteria for defining multipotent mesenchymal stromal cells. The International Society for Cellular Therapy position statement.* Cytotherapy 2006; 8:315-7.

3. Bianco P, et al. *The meaning, the sense and the significance: translating the science of mesenchymal stem cells into medicine.* Nat Med 2013;19:35-42.

4. De Souza LE, et al. *Mesenchymal Stem Cells and Pericytes: To What Extent Are They Related?* Stem Cells Dev. 2016;25:1843-1852.

5. Guimaraes-Camboa, et al. *Pericytes of multiple organs do not behave as mesenchymal stem cells in vivo.* Cell Stem Cell 2017;20:345–359.e5.

6. Ciapetti G, et al. *Human bone marrow stromal cells: in vitro expansion and differentiation for bone engineering.* Biomaterials 2006;27:6150-60.

7. Baglio SR, et al. *Mesenchymal stem cell secreted vesicles provide novel opportunities in (stem) cell-free therapy.* Front Physiol 2012;3:359.

8. Granchi D, et al. *Gene expression patterns related to osteogenic differentiation of bone marrow-derived mesenchymal stem cells during ex vivo expansion.* Tissue Eng Part C Methods 2010;16:511-24.

9. Ruetze M, et al. *Adipose-derived stromal cells for osteoarticular repair: trophic function versus stem cell activity.* Expert Rev Mol Med 2014;16:e9.

10. Abdel Meguid E, et al. *Stem cells applications in bone and tooth repair and regeneration: New insights, tools, and hopes.* J Cell Physiol. 2018;233:1825-1835.

11. Confalonieri D, et al. *Advanced Therapy Medicinal Products: A Guide for Bone Marrow-derived MSC Application in Bone and Cartilage Tissue Engineering.* Tissue Eng Part B Rev. 2018;24:155-169.

12. Eggenhofer E, et al. *The life and fate of mesenchymal stem cells.* Front Immunol 2014;5:148.

Dental stem cells 10

Giovanna Orsini   Thimios Mitsiadis

10.1 Tooth Development and Dental Regeneration

Tooth development proceeds through a series of morphological stages that necessitate sequential and reciprocal interactions between the oral epithelium and the underlying cranial neural crest-derived mesenchyme. The oral epithelium thickens and invaginates the mesenchyme and progressively acquires the bud, cap and bell configurations (Figure 10.1). At the bell stage, two mesenchymal cell populations can be distinguished: the dental follicle and the dental pulp. Pulp cells adjacent to the dental epithelium differentiate into odontoblasts, while epithelial cells juxtaposing the dental pulp differentiate into ameloblasts. Odontoblasts are polarized columnar cells with processes that are formed at their distal part. Odontoblast processes penetrate the dentin and participate in the secretion of dentin organic matrix and minerals. This specific matrix is composed mainly of collagen (90%), while non-collagenous proteins represent 10% of the dentin matrix. Apatite minerals are deposited on the matrix forming the mature calcified dentin, 70% of which is mineralized. Following initial dentin deposition, the epithelium-derived ameloblasts polarize and start to secrete the enamel matrix along the dentin-enamel junction (Figure 10.1). The enamel matrix is principally composed of amelogenins and non-amelogenins hydrophobic proteins. In its mature state, enamel becomes the hardest tissue of the body, containing 96-97% minerals. Moreover, once human teeth have erupted in the oral cavity, enamel cannot be regenerated since the ameloblasts are degraded.

While the cells of the dental pulp differentiate into odontoblasts, cells from the dental follicle are involved in root development by the formation of cementum, periodontal ligament (PDL) and alveolar bone. The PDL connects the tooth root cementum to the alveolar bone and contributes to tooth stability and homeostasis.

Traumatic injuries and various external harmful agents, such as bacteria and acids, jeopardize tooth integrity. Periodontal disease and carious lesions are mainly responsible for pathologies affecting the dental hard tissues. Dental pathologies combined with age constitute important factors that can trigger tooth loss. The reparative capability of the dental pulp and periodontium is often insufficient to entirely restore the damaged tissues. Moreover, enamel loss is usually substituted with sophisticated biomaterials, ceramics and precious metals, since the enamel cannot be repaired naturally. Therefore, there is an increased need of specific dental biomaterials that can be used in clinics for dental tissue repair and regeneration. Novel dental materials are successfully used for partial dental tissue repair, while a new generation of dental implants is used for tooth replacement. These materials are often used in conjunction with signalling molecules

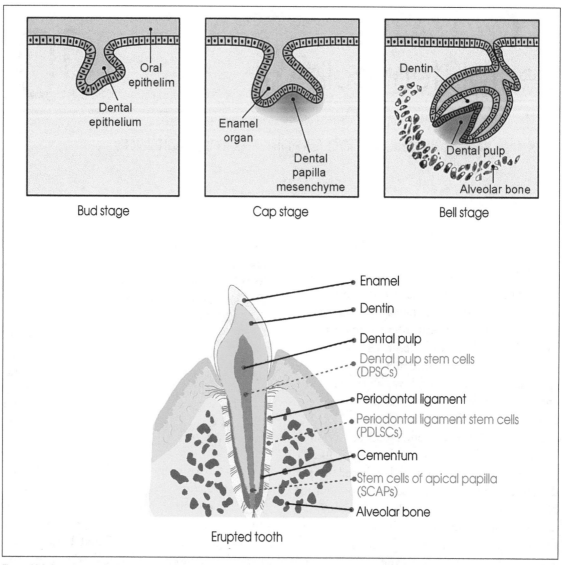

Figure 10.1. Development of human tooth; stem cell niches in the adult tooth.

to enhance the repair of the dental tissues and alveolar bone.

To complement traditional dental restorative or surgical techniques, novel stem cell–based therapeutic approaches have been developed and many efforts in this direction have been shown to be promising and challenging. Most studies focus on partial dental tissue repair/regeneration for diseases that commonly affect the dental tissues. However, several attempts have also been made to regenerate entire teeth.

10.2 The tooth as a source of stem cells

Stem cells are characterized by their potential to self-replicate and differentiate into a vast variety of cell populations. Pluripotent epithelial and mesenchymal cell populations are present in the vast majority of adult human tissues and organs, including teeth. Dental mesenchymal stem cells (DMSC) were found in dental pulp of deciduous and permanent teeth in humans. These cells were also identified in the apical part of the dental papilla, dental follicle, and periodontal ligament. DMSCs are responsible for homeostasis and regeneration of the dental pulp and periodontium, and are able to form dentin, cementum, and alveolar bone. In contrast, dental epithelial stem cells (DESC) are very rare in adult human teeth, thus limiting the capability to naturally repair or regenerate enamel. The current knowledge on DESCs has been obtained from studies in rodents, in which DESCs are responsible for the renewal of the continuously growing incisors. Various dental cell populations have been characterized and are currently used for experimental regenerative purposes. DMSCs have been isolated from dental pulp, deciduous teeth, dental papillae and follicle, as well as from the PDL and the periosteum (Figure 10.1).

Dental pulp stem cells (DPSC) are the most common source of DMSCs (Figure 10.1). Due to the lack of specific DMSCs markers, generic mesenchymal stem cell markers such as STRO-1, CD146, and CD44 are commonly used for the identification of DPSCs populations. Additional identification procedures that rely on the morphology, selective adherence properties, proliferation and differentiation potential, and tissue repair abilities of these cell populations are in use. DPSCs are capable of differentiating into odontogenic, osteogenic, chondrogenic, adipogenic, myogenic, and neurogenic cells *in vitro* and *in vivo*. Dentin has been generated after ectopic transplantation of DPSCs mixed with hydroxyapatite/tricalcium phosphate. Furthermore, clinical trials using autologous human DPSCs combined with collagen scaffolds for alveolar bone reconstruction were successfully performed some years ago.

Stem cells from human exfoliated deciduous teeth (SHEDs) were isolated using the same procedure leave as it is DPSCs. Like DPSCs, SHEDs express surface molecules STRO-1 and CD146, and several neural and glial markers, such as nestin and β-III tubulin. These cells are capable of differentiating into odontogenic, osteogenic, chondrogenic, adipogenic, myogenic, and neurogenic cells *in vitro*. SHEDs proliferate very fast but have a limited capacity to form the dentin/pulp complex *in vivo*. However, transplantation of SHEDs seeded in biodegradable scaffolds into human tooth slices resulted in the formation of dental pulp-like tissue. It has been shown that SHEDs are able to induce bone and dentin formation *in vivo*.

Stem cells from the apical part of the dental papilla (SCAP) are mesenchymal cells located at the apex of the developing root of the tooth. SCAPs are highly proliferative and exhibit increased migratory and regenerative potentials. These cells express the same surface markers as DPSCs, as well as the SCAP- specific marker CD24, for which DPSCs are negative. SCAPs have the potential to generate odontogenic and adipogenic lineages *in vitro*, and are able to form dentin *in vivo*, when transplanted on hydroxyapatite/tricalcium phosphate carriers.

Stem cells from the dental follicle (DFSC) are progenitor cells for the PDL, alveolar bone and cementum, and express the STRO-1 and CD44 markers, as well as type IA, IB and II BMP receptors. DFSCs transplanted into immune-deficient animals were able to form cementum and PDL-like tissues.

Periodontal ligament stem cells (PDLSC) also express the cell-surface markers STRO-1, CD146 and CD44. These cells are able to differentiate into adipogenic and osteogenic cells under defined culture conditions *in vitro*. PDLSCs can contribute to the regeneration of the periodontium by giving rise to cementum/PDL tissues, after their injection into immune-compromised animals *in vivo*. Another PDLSCs population that is located close to the alveolar bone has shown higher osteogenic and adipogenic capabilities when compared to PDLSCs.

Periosteum-derived stem cells can be isolated from the maxillary and mandibular periosteum, which is a dense layer of vascularized connective tissue enveloping all the bones. These stem cells possess a great potential to differentiate into osteoblasts.

Dental epithelial stem cells (DESC) can be isolated from the third molar that develops late after birth. Another source of DESCs is the epithelial root sheath that disintegrates into strands of epithelial cells, which express epithelial stem cell markers, such as Bmi-1, E-CAM, and p75, as well as embryonic stem cell markers, such as Oct-4 and Nanog.

Lastly, *induced pluripotent stem cells* (iPSC) have the capacity to differentiate into various cell lineages and can be technically produced from patients' cells. The iPSCs technology can be progressively applied for the regeneration of dental tissues. iPSCs are able to differentiate into ameloblast-like cells and mesenchymal odontogenic cells.

10.3 Dental Repair and Regeneration

Dental pathologies (e.g. periodontal and carious diseases), fractures, injuries, and genetic aberrations represent a frequent socio-economical problem. In clinical practice, damaged pulp is usually amputated and substituted with artificial materials. We can imagine that in the near future dentists will focus on pulp regeneration for the treatment of these clinical cases. Periodontitis is a disease that is triggered by microorganisms of the oral cavity and often causes severe damage on the periodontal tissues, resulting in tooth loss. Dental implants have been the only solution for the replacement of missing teeth. Although the development of novel biocompatible materials has improved the quality of treatment, there are several limitations in the functionality and longevity of dental implants due to their strong dependence on the quantity and quality of the surrounding bone. To overcome this problem, new ideas and approaches have emerged recently from the fields of stem cell biology, tissue engineering, and nanotechnology. Different therapeutic approaches that depend on the degree of tooth damage are required. Current therapies are mainly oriented towards partial dental tissue repair, where injured dental tissues are substituted with appropriate materials. Dental tissue regeneration is based on the replacement and functional restoration of the damaged (or pathological) tissue by the same healthy biological tissue.

Pulp-dentin regeneration. Proper regeneration of the dentin-pulp complex allows new dentin formation under the pathological site and requires the re-vascularization and re-innervation of the pulp. Signalling molecules and numerous growth factors have been used to stimulate and increase the natural regenerative response of dental pulp. DPSCs are able to differentiate into odontoblasts, endothelial cells, and neurons when placed in contact with dentin *in vitro*. *In vivo* studies in mice have shown that transplanted DPSCs can regenerate the pulp-dentin complex after pulpotomy. Similarly, transplantation of human DPSCs and SCAPs seeded on biodegradable scaffolds into the empty root canal space of mouse teeth gave rise to a brand-new vascularized pulp-dentin complex. Although these and other findings clearly show that DPSCs can be used for dental pulp regeneration, further studies and regulations are needed for their definitive application in dental clinics.

Periodontal tissue regeneration. Using different scaffolds, it has been possible to induce differentiation of PDLSCs or DPSCs into the various cell types of the periodontium *in vitro*. Human PDLSCs transplanted into immune-compromised animals participate in the regeneration of the periodontium, thus indicating their potential for future cell-based therapies in dentistry. Equally important for the development of these therapies is the use of signalling molecules, various morphogenetic proteins and commercialized amelogenin extracts. The combination of stem cells, signalling molecules, and desirable scaffold materials is under investigation for the regeneration of periodontal tissues. While these procedures appear to improve tissue regeneration, their true effectiveness for achieving durable repair is still unclear. Therefore, to ultimately provide definitive conclusions, further investigations *in vivo* are needed.

Enamel regeneration. It is the most difficult tissue to be regenerated. Porcine epithelial rests have been shown to differentiate into ameloblast-like cells after co-culture with dental pulp cells *in vitro*, thus forming enamel after transplantation *in vivo*. Other attempts using the iPSC technology are promising.

Whole tooth regeneration. The formation of a brand new tooth would be the ideal therapeutic approach after tooth loss and can be realized using two approaches. The first consists in the association of DESCs and DMSCs *in vitro*, allowing the formation of a tooth germ that could then be transplanted into the alveolar bone, where the tooth germ would develop, erupt and become a functional tooth. The second approach to obtain a functional tooth is the implantation into the jaw of tooth-shaped polymeric biodegradable scaffolds that are filled with both DESCs and DMSCs. The three-dimensional structure of the scaffolds should drive the differentiation of the transplanted cells into odontoblasts and ameloblasts. These bioengineered teeth have been produced in ectopic sites and are still missing some essential elements, such as a complete root or the correct crown morphology. However, recent experiments in mice have shown that it is possible to obtain functional teeth with roots using bioengineered approaches. The formation of all dental tissues allows the eruption and full integration of the bioengineered teeth into the recipient alveolar bone.

10.4 Nanotechnological applications in regenerative dentistry

The combination of the above-mentioned stem cell populations with advanced nanotechnology platforms holds great promise for applications in regenerative dentistry. The control of tooth initiation, pattern and mineralization necessitates a thorough understanding at the cellular and molecular level. Understanding when and how signalling molecules con-

trol these events will open new horizons and create great challenges. The identification and characterization of dental epithelial and mesenchymal stem cells together with tissue engineering techniques/approaches can offer new perspectives in dental treatment.

The development of novel nanostructured materials (i.e. on the scale of 1-100 nm) could be useful in manipulating stem cells for tooth regeneration. Nanomaterials can be also used for stem cell tracking, gene and protein delivery, and the formation of artificial stem cell niches. This knowledge could be used for designing appropriate scaffolds that will host dental stem cells before transplantation, and will allow the evaluation of the various therapeutic effects, when exposed to specific microenvironments, before any clinical application. The creation of artificial microenvironments would direct dental stem cells towards a precise role and function. The size, surface chemistry and shape of the natural and artificial nanostructures are important parameters for the development of cell adhesion sites that modulate stem cell behaviour. Nanoscale assemblies, such as nanotubes, could be used for the creation of particular dental microenvironments, such as the apex of the root and the pulp chamber. The nanostructure of biocompatible and bioresorbable scaffolds is essential in the regulation of dental stem cells' survival, differentiation potential, and three-dimensional organization. Such scaffolds, once transplanted, may act as temporary niches that guide the formation of new specific extracellular matrices.

These innovative technologies offer exciting perspectives in regenerative dentistry, providing new non-invasive procedures for dental tissue repair and regeneration. In particular, the use of nanostructured materials could be pivotal in the fine modulation of stem cell behaviour to drive proper pulp and periodontal regeneration, avoiding tissue fibrosis and misdifferentiation, while simultaneously providing proper tissue reinnervation and vascularization.

Recommended reading and references

1. Mitsiadis TA, Orsini G, Jimenez-Rojo L. *Stem cell-based approaches in dentistry*. Eur Cell Mater. 2015;30:248-57.

2. Orsini G, Pagella P, Mitsiadis TA. *Modern Trends in Dental Medicine: An Update for Internists*. Am J Med. 2018; 131:1425-1430.

3. Orsini G, Pagella P, Putignano A, Mitsiadis TA. *Novel Biological and Technological Platforms for Dental Clinical Use*. Front Physiol. 2018;9:1102.

4. Pilipchuk SP, Plonka AB, Monje A, Taut AD, Lanis A, Kang B, et al. *Tissue engineering for bone regeneration and osseointegration in the oral cavity*. Dental materials: official publication of the Academy of Dental Materials. 2015;31:317-38.

5. Larsson L, Decker AM, Nibali L, Pilipchuk SP, Berglundh T, Giannobile WV. *Regenerative Medicine for Periodontal and Peri-implant Diseases*. J Dent Res. 2016;95:255-66.

Skin regeneration

11

Davide Melandri   Valeria Purpura
Catuscia Orlandi   Paola Minghetti   Elena Bondioli

The continuous innovations in the field of Regenerative Medicine has led in the last years to the development of therapeutic strategies able to regenerate damaged and/or missing tissues, as well as to provide cell enrichment, activation and/or their genetic modification. To date, research in this field has been growing and new biological products based on cells, tissues or genes are now commercially available and used for the treatment of different pathological conditions, offering patients new and more effective therapeutic options. In fact, the loss of a functional organ and/or tissue is one of the most disabling, frequent and costly aspects in the field of health and the use of conventional surgical and/or pharmacological treatments are frequently not sufficient to solve the problems. An example of a frequent clinical condition in which tissues are damaged or lost are non-healing wounds, such as burns or ulcers, in which cutaneous tissue is damaged or absent and continuously fails to heal.

11.1 The skin: organ histology and function

The skin is the more extensive organ of the human body, with an area of 1.5 - 2 m² and it alone represents 16% of body weight. It is composed of three distinct tissues - the epidermis, the dermis and the hypodermis - and shows a different thickness depending on the body district, from a minimum of 0.5 mm to a maximum of 5 mm. It also contains blood and lymphatic vessels branching along the dermal tissue, sensory receptors for the transmission of different information to the central nervous system and skin appendages - such as hair follicles, nails and glands - that have a synergistic interplay with the skin to carry out different functions essential for the organism. The skin's ability to cover the entire surface of the organism and the presence of different properties, such as elasticity, mechanical resistance and impermeability, make it a protective natural barrier against various external - physical, chemical and thermal - insults and pathogenic microorganisms. Moreover, it also plays a key role in thermoregulation by modulating blood supply and removing both liquids and metabolism products via the secretory glands. The production of vitamin D_3 by the skin is essential for the regulation of calcium and phosphorus levels in the body, so that a metabolic role is also evident. The presence of sensory receptors and nerve endings also ensures recognition of and response to pain and tactile, thermal, pressure stimuli. The correct functioning of all these processes in the skin is the result of the specific characteristics of each component and their mutual interaction.

11.1.1 Dermis

The dermis derives from the mesodermal layer and is thicker than the epidermis, ranging from 0.6 mm to 3 mm depending on the body district. It is distinguished in papillary and reticular dermis depending on the type and the level of aggregation of the dermis fibrous components (Figure 11.1). The papillary dermis is so named for the presence of the "dermal papillae", extroflexions of the dermal layer into the epidermis, able to provide nutrition to the overlying epidermal cells. The connective tissue is composed of fibrocytes, the inactive form of fibroblast cells, and collagen/elastic fibres immersed in the ground substance, an amorphous, semi-fluid matrix, composed of an aqueous dispersing phase - containing metabolic substances, organic salts, gases in addition to enzymes, vitamins and hormones - and a dispersed phase – consisting of macromolecular complexes, such as glycosaminoglycans (GAG), proteoglycans and glycoproteins. The ground substance is ideal for cell life, since it allows nutritive exchanges by the diffusion of water and molecules from blood vessels to cells as well as the maintenance of a water reserve. The papillary dermis also shows a level of vascularization and innervation higher than that of the reticular dermis, lymphatic vessels and sensory receptors. On the other hand, the reticular layer is the deepest layer of the dermis, composed of a poor amorphous substance and compact and large bundles of collagen/elastic fibres that create a dense network arranged parallel to the skin's surface. This structure confers to skin elasticity and a remarkable resistance to movements and changes in body volume. It also shows mechanical properties due

to its ability to resist to compression and plays a defensive role due to its viscosity that is able to interfere with the diffusion of foreign substances. Furthermore, the amorphous matrix is directly involved in the processes of cellular differentiation, proliferation and migration. The cells physiologically resident in the dermis are fibrocytes, macrophages, vascular and mast cells, in addition to elements of blood origin. The fibrocytes are the characteristic dermal cells that, in their activated form of fibroblasts, are responsible for the maintenance of the correct amount of intercellular substances through periodic cycles of synthesis and degradation. The frequency of this turnover can be altered during pathologies or injuries compared to physiological conditions. The macrophages derive from monocytes, cells present in the blood, and are involved in the defensive mechanisms of the organism and in the renewal of the extracellular matrix by removing its degraded components. When infections or injuries occur, these cells increase their phagocytic activity and the secretion of bioactive molecules that act as chemotactic factors for different cell types, in order to stimulate proliferation, angiogenesis and vascular permeability during the process of wound healing. Among the less represented cellular components, the mast cells are located along the vessels of the dermis and are responsible for the secretion of molecules involved in the inflammatory

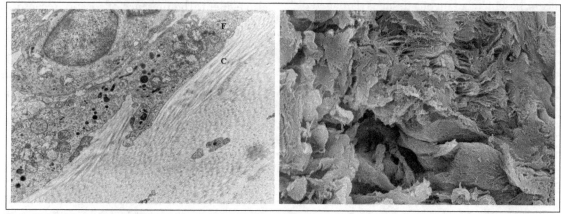

Figure 11.1. Left panel: production of collagen from fibroblast (C). Transmission Electron Microscope (TEM) image. Right panel: organization of the dermis. Scanning Electron Microscope (SEM) image.

and immune response. Other cells usually low in number in physiological conditions are myofibroblasts that show a contractile activity for the regulation of the interstitial fluid volume and pressure. During wound healing, these cells significantly increase their involvement in the formation of scar tissue. In fact, they adhere and exert a traction to the collagen fibres, resulting, in turn, in the retraction of tissue and the closure of wound margins. These cells increase in number by the differentiation of precursors recruited from different sources: the most common appear to be fibroblasts able to migrate in response to alterations of the extracellular matrix and cytokines and to terminally differentiate in myofibroblasts that undergo apoptosis after the repair of the damaged area. Another cellular source is represented by mesenchymal cells that also contribute to the healing process, satisfying the transient cellular requirement. To date, the exact origin of myofibroblasts and the relative contribution of the different sources is still widely debated; it is proving difficult to establish a hierarchy in the differentiation processes and cell identity in the heterogeneous populations constituting organs and tissues. Different cells such as lymphocytes and granulocytes, are also transiently recruited in the dermal layer during pathological events.

11.1.2. Dermal-epidermal junction

The dermal-epidermal junction is a highly specialized basal membrane able to ensure communication, anchorage and mechanical support between the dermis and the overlying epidermal layer. It is also a selective barrier able to control the cellular and molecular exchanges with the external environment, so that it results essential for the maintenance of cutaneous homeostasis. Moreover, it also regulates the proliferation and differentiation of the germinal keratinocytes of the basal layer by the maintenance or loss of cell-junction contact in response to specific signals. It also regulates cell migration during embryonic development and the wound re-epithelializa-

tion phase during the healing process. The dermal-epidermal junction is composed of three overlapping layers known as lamina reticularis, lamina densa and lamina lucida. The reticular lamina is produced by fibroblasts and promotes the adhesion between dermis and epidermis. It is composed of anchoring fibrils of type VII collagen that interact with the type I and III collagen of the dermis, with the type IV collagen of the lamina densa and with the laminin 5 of the lamina lucida. The lamina densa controls the permeability of the junction and appears as an amorphous matrix for the structural organization of type IV collagen. On the other hand, the lamina lucida is involved in the keratinocytes' anchorage at the junction. The synthesis and the structural organization of these two layers depend on the epithelial cells.

11.1.3. Epidermis

The epidermis derives from ectoderm and is the most superficial layer of the skin, with a thickness ranging from 0.08 mm to 0.5mm. It is composed of 5 different layers, mainly made up of densely-packed keratinocytes with a different status of differentiation, known as the stratum (layer) basale, stratum spinosum, stratum granulosum, stratum lucidum and stratum corneum (Figure 11.2). The basal layer is composed of a single layer of cells linked together by desmosomes and connected with the dermal-epidermal junction below by hemidesmosomes. It contains several stem, proliferating keratinocytes able to both maintain the correct amount of germinative cellular component and to produce cells that undergo the differentiation process moving progressively towards the keratinized epidermal surface. During this migration, keratinocytes undergo different morpho-functional modifications in the different layers until the final, complete cornification with detachment from the body. The spinosum layer is composed of 8-10 layers containing cells with irregular shape characterized by several, small extroflexions able to synthesize keratin and to partially maintain the mitotic activity active. The granulosum layer is

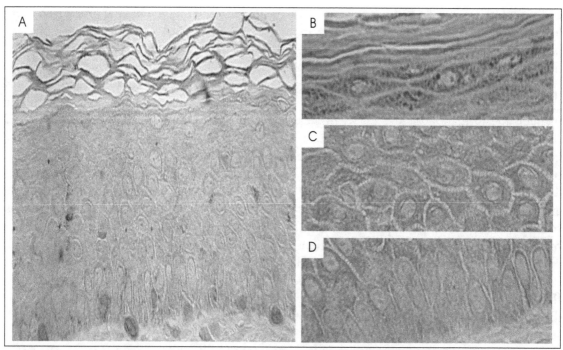

Figure 11.2. . Epidermal sections: immunohistochemical staining S100 to identify Langerhans cells (brown) and all layers except the lucidum (a); haematoxylin and eosin staining of the granulosum and corneum layers (b), spinosum (c) and basal (d) layers.

composed of 3-5 layers of keratinocytes that totally block their proliferation and start the process of cornification producing large quantities of keratin and keratohyalin. During the production of keratin, cells become thin, flat and less permeable. On the other hand, keratohyalin forms dense granules in the cytoplasms inducing both cell dehydration and aggregation/crosslink among fibres. The nuclei appear in regression with the final cell death. The lucidum layer is identified in thick areas of the skin, such as the palms of the hands, and contains flattened cells that contain a material insoluble in water, eleidin, in the centre, while in the peripheral part they continue the corneal transformation. The last phase of the differentiation process is the formation of the stratum corneum. It is composed of 15-30 layers of keratinized, dead cells, called corneocytes, that show a strongly thickened and rigid membrane due to the aggregation of keratin filaments in a proteic matrix. The corneocytes remain in this layer for about two weeks before their definitive removal, providing a protective

barrier over time. On the external side, cells show a lipid wrap that - together with the secretion of sebum and sweat - contributes to form a thin hydrolipidic film on the skin's surface. This barrier has an acid pH and it plays an extremely important role in preventing the penetration of pathogenic microorganisms. It also regulates the loss of water from the body, known as trans-epidermal water loss (TEWL). Thus, a balance between cell proliferation in

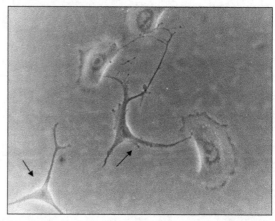

Figure 11.3. Co-culture of melanocytes (arrows) and keratinocytes. Optical microscope, magnification 20X

the basal layer and superficial desquamation of corneocytes is required to maintain a correct amount of epidermal cells. The time of renewal required to complete the process of cell differentiation from the basal to the superficial layers ranges from 3-4 weeks. A further three cell types identified in epidermis are melanocytes, Langerhans and Merkel cells. The melanocytes (Figure 11.3) are located in the basal layer of the epidermis, where they interact with adjacent keratinocytes by their extensions. In particular, these cells play an important, protective role against the ionizing effects of electromagnetic radiation by producing melanin and transferring it to the keratinocytes by a mechanism of phagocytosis. Langerhans cells are dendritic cells derived from bone marrow able to activate the immune response in the skin presenting antigens to the lymphocytes. Merkel cells, located at the epithelial-dermal junction, are tactile sensors of neuroectodermal origin.

11.2 Cutaneous stem cells

The self-renewal of skin tissue constantly protects the organism against external insults: this ability is ensured by the high amount of stem cells present in the dermis, epidermis and in the adipose tissue.

11.2.1 Stem cells in the dermis

The dermis is composed of two layers, reticular and papillary, that differ by the structural organization and amount of cells. Among the cellular components identified in both these layers, a subgroup of cells known as skin derived precursors (SKPs) shows stem properties. These cells, initially obtained as non-adherent dermal cells capable of growing as spheroids, show characteristics similar to the mesenchymal stem cells of adipose tissue, such as the expression of markers and their ability to differentiate towards the adipogenic, chondrogenic and osteogenic line. On the other hand, SKPs show less efficiency in the formation of colonies and take longer to differentiate. The current hypothesis considers the SKPs a heterogeneous population with a high similarity to adipose mesenchymal cells, although less abundant and with a lower degree of staminality. The SKPs have been localized in niches at the perivascular level, so that their concentration is higher in the reticular layer around the cutaneous appendages, in particular the hair bulbs. On the other hand, the capillaries at the dermal-epidermal junction provide support for the epidermis. It has been observed *in vivo* that the basal keratinocytes, located near the SKPs, have high levels of p63, a fundamental transcription factor, for both epidermal development and the maintenance of the proliferative and differentiating potential of keratinocytes.

11.2.2. Epidermal stem cells

The epidermis can be divided into two regions: the epidermal hair follicle (HF), obtained by introflection of the epidermis into the dermal layer containing the piliferous formations, and the interfollicular epidermis (IFE) (Figure 11.4). In the HF, the keratinocytes involved in the development and maintenance of the hair are localized in the matrix forming the medulla, cortex and cuticle layers and are gradually pushed towards the surface, increasing the length of the hair. The process of keratinization in the HF is widely different from that in the IFE due to the cellular organization and synthesis of keratin, so that cells are called trichokeratinocytes and each piliferous formation is considered a single functional unit. The keratinocytes of the HF also form an outer covering sheath which is in continuity with the interfollicular epidermis. On the other hand, the IFE is organized in proliferation units containing an average of 10 basal cells able to produce 7-14 suprabasal layer cells and 5-7 corneocytes. Studies on stem cells in these two layers of epidermis have mainly been carried out since the development of the Rheinwald-Green method in 1975. In fact, this method made possible the maintenance and enhancement of keratinocytes in culture for a long time, in order to study their proliferative ability *in vitro*. In addition to this method, the use of animal models and the improvement of analytical studies, such as cell tracking, have allowed knowledge in this field to exponentially grow over the last 20 years. When cultured, only 0.15-3.8% of the isolated keratinocytes show clonogenic activity. In particular, they can be classified in three different subpopulations depending on their proliferative potential: 28% of cells are holoclones with a high proliferative potential due to their ability to do 140 divisions before senescence; 49% of cells are meroclones with an intermediate proliferation ability; lastly, 24% of cells are paraclones, which differentiate after about 15 divisions. In particular, the population identified as epidermal stem cells are the holoclones, characterized by a high *in vitro* clonogenic ability and a low *in vivo* duplication rate. On the other hand, the meroclones and paraclones are transit progenitor cells at different stages of differentiation that show a more limited number of divisions *in vitro* and an active proliferation in the epidermis. The niche of stem cells identified in the HF is the bulge region, which consists of multiple digitiform formations located in the middle part of the hair, between the sebaceous gland and the bulb, connected to a bundle of the erector muscle. After the periodic loss of hair, the stem cells are induced to produce transit progenitors that migrate towards the bulb, where the interaction with cells of the dermal papilla causes their differentiation into cells that will give rise to a new piliferous structure. Moreover, the cells of the bulge also play an important role during wound healing, in which they represent a reserve of cells. On the other hand, an independent group of stem cells are evident in the basal layer of the IFE, where they take care of maintenance and repair. The mechanism of epidermal homeostasis regulated by these stem cells is not yet well understood, since they are not physically separated from the other differentiating cells. In fact, the basal membrane is distributed along the whole tissue, so that the proliferation unit of the IFE is only a theoretical concept, unlike the bulge and the piliferous unit, which are also anatomically distinct. Complete understanding of the biology of epidermal stem cells is strongly limited by the difficulty to identify them unequivocally. The two populations, in fact, are not exactly complementary, with regard to both the expression of markers and the differentiating potential. The stem cells of the IFE are not able to reconstitute the follicle structures, while the stem cells of the bulges can also reform an interfollicular epidermis. Moreover, the two cell types are not rigidly distinct, since

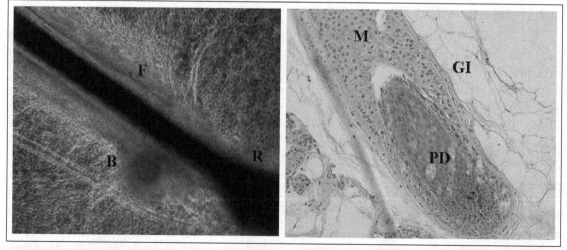

Figura 11.4. Left panel: Hair follicle composed by root (R), hair shaft (F) and bulge (B). Optical microscope, magnification 10X. Right panel: haematoxylin and eosin staining of the root in which the dermal papilla (PD), the medulla (M) and the inner sheath (GI) are evident. Optical microscope, magnification 25X.

the basal layer of the IFE is connected with the outer sheath of the follicle and, consequently, with the bulge. The identification of the pro-liferative/differentiative fate of these cells is also difficult, since the divisions in vertebrates can be both symmetric and asymmetric. In the asymmetric division (deterministic model), the stem cell duplicates itself generating simulta-neously two daughter cells: one identical to itself and the other one able to begin the pro-cess of differentiation, generating first a high number of progenitors, then of precursors and, finally, of mature cells. On the other hand, in symmetric division, stem cells are able to gen-erate two daughter cells with the same phe-notype producing alternatively two stem cells (symmetric proliferative division) or two pro-genitors (symmetric differentiative division). In the epidermis, three different models have been proposed for the constant cell renewal induced by the stem component. The first to be hypothesized was the **theory of the hierarchy of the progenitors.**

According to this model, stem cells divide rarely by an asymmetric mechanism giving rise to transit-amplifying progenitors (TA) that undergo a limited number of divisions, grad-ually lose their proliferative and self-renewal ability, to terminally differentiate into post-mi-totic cells. Then, these cells migrate into the spinosum layer and continue their transforma-tion in corneocytes. In this model, the prolifer-ation unit is hierarchically composed of a sin-gle stem cell and 8-10 TA cells with a different state of differentiation. Although this model is supported by a plethora of experimental evidence and explains the *in vivo* presence of cells with a low (stem) and high (TA) dupli-cation activity, some recent cell tracking stud-ies suggest a different mechanism of renewal for the epidermis. The model of the **theory of the single progenitor, also called population asymmetry,** proposes the presence of a single progenitor, called committed progenitor, with a high proliferative ability able to divide asym-metrically or by symmetric proliferative or dif-ferentiative divisions according to a probabilis-

tic ratio of 80:10:10 in a healthy tissue. On the other hand, stem cells are considered quiescent, since their divisions are rare. This theory could explain the different dimensions over time of the proliferation units but is not able to justify both the rapid response of the epidermis to the high demand of cells during the healing pro-cess or the presence of cells at low-frequency of duplication in the IFE. The third model proposed is the **population asymmetry with stem cells** (PAS), in which the progenitors are in active proliferation and the stem cells show a low duplication rate. Both these cell types carry out mitosis with asymmetric, symmet-ric proliferative or differentiative divisions in a ratio of 80:10:10. According to this model, the long-term renewal and repair of the epidermis following injuries is essentially dependent on the stem cells, with a limited contribution from the progenitors.

Recent studies of cell tracking with meth-ods able to simulate the long-term behaviour of single cell types during the renewal of the epi-dermis and the healing of wounds have made possible the evaluation of cellular dynamics for three years, further supporting this model, since it reconciles all the experimental observations and the discordant theories. In fact, the PAS theory seems to reflect the real behaviour of the epidermis, supporting all aspects of homeosta-sis and re-epithelialization, although further confirmation is still required. Some studies also reveal the existence of a putative third stem cell population with intermediate characteris-tics located in the loop of the follicle under the invagination of the epidermis. Considering the functional and structural complexity of the epi-dermis, several studies are still required, espe-cially to discover the relationships between the different types of stem cells and their progen-itors, as well as their effectiveness for clinical applications. In fact, little information is availa-ble on their involvement in the development of diseases such as tumours, or on which cells are the most effective therapeutic targets, or which is the cell type mainly involved in tissue regen-eration.

11.3 Mechanisms of tissue repair

The mechanism of tissue repair is managed by different cell types and can be broken down, regardless of wound type and its extension (Figure 11.5), in the following overlapping phases:

- inflammation (0-3 days)
- proliferation (3-24 days)
- remodelling (from 6-10 days to 12-24 months).

In these phases, the epithelial-mesenchymal interaction plays a predominant role, regulating tissue homeostasis and repair. Inflammation is the first phase of the healing process aimed to stop the bleeding, to recruit immune cells and to form new tissue on the wound area. During the 3 days of inflammation, the main responses of the organism to the injury occur in **vascular, haemostatic and leukocyte phases.** Firstly, the vascular phase induces vasoconstriction by vasoactive amines and polypeptides released by cells that, in turn, reduce the loss of blood, allowing coagulation. The next step is the haemostatic phase, in which a blood clot is produced, stopping the flow of blood. It is a porous, gel-like three-dimensional matrix involved in a complex series of events and composed of aggregated platelets and fibrin;

it also contains blood cells. The fibrin of the blood clot is able to interact with the various growth factors and cytokines required for the induction of the healing process and its deposition also triggers the synthesis of hyaluronic acid by fibroblasts adjacent to the lesion area. Hyaluronic acid plays an important role in the fibrin reticulum, since it integrates with this matrix and increases its volume attracting water, so that it becomes more accessible to cells. Moreover, it also acts as a chemotactic factor, stimulating and regulating the migration of cells derived from blood (neutrophils, macrophages and mast cells) and from connective tissue (fibroblasts, progenitors and mesenchymal stem cells). In the final step of inflammation, the fibrin matrix is degraded and the hyaluronic acid is transformed into a low molecular weight form, for the formation of the extracellular matrix. Moreover, the components of the clot have a chemotactic effect on blood cells, inducing the leukocyte response and, in turn, the recruitment of phagocytes (neutrophils and monocytes) in the damaged area. These cells clean the wound removing contaminants, such as microorganisms and cellular debris, as well as damaged components of the extracellular matrix, by secreting proteolytic enzymes and they synthesize pro-inflam-

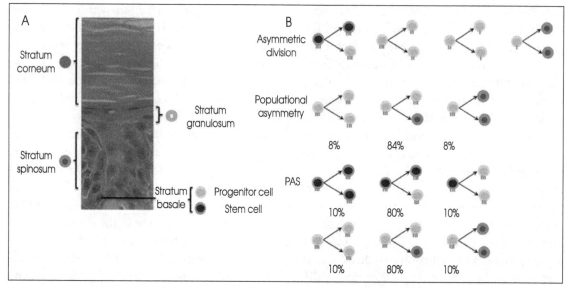

Figure 11.5. Models proposed for the maintenance of homeostasis in the interfollicular epidermis (from Li et al., 2013)

matory cytokines that interact with endothelial cells, fibroblasts and keratinocytes for the formation of new vessels, new connective tissue and the epithelium, respectively. The stimulation of these cells modifies the microenvironment, inducing the formation of granulation tissue and, in turn, the passage to the proliferative phase. It is characterized by neo angiogenesis, required for the transport of nutrients to the newly formed tissue, the colonization of the fibrin and hyaluronic acid matrix by fibroblasts for the formation of granulation tissue, wound contraction, the synthesis of new collagen and the re-epithelialization of the wound. The granulation tissue is transiently used as a support for the reconstruction of the different skin layers. It also appears compact for the presence of myofibroblasts, required due to the contraction of the wound margins in order to reduce the healing time, and is essential for the formation of new vessels, created by the budding of pre-existing venules. At the same time, keratinocytes migrate from the wound margins and hair follicles to induce re-epithelialization. In particular, the epithelium easily re-grows when the basal lamina is intact by the slipping of keratinocytes from the edges of the wound. On the other hand, re-epithelialization depends on the presence of fibrin matrix and, in turn, of granulation tissue when the lesion extends to the connective tissue. The final phase of remodelling and maturation involves the **transformation of the granulation tissue** and the **remodelling of the scar**. In this phase, fibroblasts initially proliferate, produce increasing amounts of extracellular matrix, transforming the granulation tissue in scar. The next step is the **remodelling phase,** in which the fibroblasts reduce their growth, similar to the keratinocytes, that terminate the process of re-epithelialization. In this step, the removal of excess collagen and extracellular matrix is induced by proteolytic enzymes and collagenase that give to the scar a temporary hypertrophic appearance. Thus, a mature scar is obtained, often with an irregular and less elastic appearance, as well as low blood vessels.

The regression of the vessels is then almost total and the granulation tissue is transformed into a white fibrous scar that is disorganized compared to the original tissue, and frequently gives rise to significant aesthetic and functional issues. In some cases, the reparative process can produce hypertrophic scars and keloids or it may also not produce enough tissue, so that an hypotrophic scar is obtained. Some particular conditions may also reduce or completely inhibit the closure of the wound which, in this case, is defined chronic. Wound repair in adults and in fetal tissues widely differs: in adults the process is essentially reparative and is inevitably associated to the formation of a fibrous scar, while in the fetus the process is regenerative, so that it is not accompanied by fibrous scars or contraction of the wound.

11.3.1. Alteration of the wound healing process

The wound healing process is widely affected by the amount of tissue lost that, in turn, is related to the extension and depth of the damaged area. In particular, superficial wounds involve only the loss of epidermal layer, while the damaged area is considered deep when the dermal layer is also compromised. Both these aspects can lead to different modalities of healing defined as first, second or third intention. Wounds with minimal loss of tissue and defined margins, without haematomas, necrosis or infections, such as cutting wounds, undergo first intention healing. In this case, the skin flaps are sutured to reduce the space between the margins, inducing a more rapid filling with scar tissue. On the other hand, the loss of a high amount of tissue heals by second intention modality after a long time, that is required for the massive production of granulation tissue, with poor aesthetic results. In fact, a greater loss of tissue corresponds to a more extensive and contracted scar. Healing by third intention occurs in surgical wounds with a partial or total dehiscence in the post-operative course. Their treatment involves the re-opening, careful cleaning, the removal of necrotic areas and adequate drainage. In addition to loss of tissue, altered reparative mechanisms can also lead to abnormal scars or chronic lesions, with times of recovery greater than 40 days. Some chronic wounds, such as venous ulcers, show a prolonged inflammatory state due to their altered mechanism in the remodelling of the extracellular matrix, with the maintenance of high levels of inflammatory cytokines, as well as proteases that degrade the newly formed granulation tissue. Thus, cell migration, the transition to the proliferative phase and the formation of a mature scar tissue are compromised. In other chronic wounds, such as diabetic ulcers, the high amount and expression of the components of the extracellular matrix subtract growth factors to the wound area, making it unable to overcome the proliferative phase. In this case, the activation of fibroblasts is too low to induce both the paracrine stimulation of keratinocytes and the synthesis of the basal lamina required for the migration of epidermal cells. The synthesis and deposition of collagen is also altered in all cases of abnormal healing, with low levels in hypotrophic and high levels in hypertrophic scars and keloids. In particular, keloids occur when the scar process has the characteristics of irreversibility and extends beyond the margins of the lesion, unlike hypertrophic scars. Moreover, the presence of other factors, such as vascular diseases or infections, can further affect this pathological condition.

11.3.2. Repair and regeneration

The wound healing process in adults is exclusively carried out through tissue repair mechanisms that produce scar tissue with disabling effects, since the native tissue is definitely lost. For this reason, new medical approaches, such as tissue engineering, aim to regenerate tissues and organs. Although we are still far from attaining this goal, the mechanism of tissue repair in adults has been compared with the complex molecular mechanism of fetal regeneration. Regarding skin lesions, it has been observed that the fetal and adult tissues have intrinsic regenerative and reparative characteristics, respectively. In fact, the transplantation of fetal tissue in the subcutaneous adult skin does not alter its regenerative ability and adult skin, transplanted in the fetus, maintains a phenotype similar to scar tissue. In addition to these cell-specific characteristics, differences have also been identified both in the different stages of the healing process and in the elements involved, such as cells, extracellular matrix, growth factors and intercellular junctions. For example, fetal healing implies a shorter and less intense inflammatory phase compared to adults and, at the same time, the beginning of wound contraction. Thus, the required granulation tissue is reduced and the fibres within the forming tissue show a better organization. Moreover, the migration of keratinocytes occurs concomitantly to the activation of the connective cells, unlike what happens in adults in whom a phase of pause is evident and cell migration is carried out with different mechanisms. In fact, fetal keratinocytes proliferate along the opposite margins of lesions, determining their closure by growth in concentric lines. As a consequence, the cellular junctions are maintained and the structural modifications are low, so that re-epithelialization times are reduced. Moreover, the consistent presence of high molecular weight hyaluronic acid in fetal wounds - compared to the lower molecular weights in adults - counteracts platelet aggregation and their granule secretion, decreasing, in turn, the recruitment and infiltration of inflammatory cells to the lesion area. In fact, the establishment of a low inflammatory state, both in terms of time and intensity, seems to be a key aspect of the regenerative mechanism. Regarding cells, fetal fibroblasts are able to proliferate and produce matrix at the same time, while these phases are mutually exclusive and occur sequentially in adults. Moreover, the fetal extracellular matrix shows a higher content of type III collagen and high molecular weight hyaluronic acid, in contrast to the typical low weight form identified in adults, hindering the infiltration of immune cells into the temporary matrix. Fetal hyaluronic acid is also more potent in promoting fibroblast migration and modulates angiogenesis more effectively than the adult form. The regenerative and reparative mechanisms also show a different secretion of bioactive molecules, partially due to different inflammatory cells. Based on these observations, the current hypothesis is that the main difference between regenerative and reparative mechanisms resides in cellular hyper activation, a condition required from adult cells to restore lesions. In fact, the proliferative abilities of cells decrease during development and, they need to be intensely stimulated to induce healing: this could explain the different levels of inflammation found in fetal and adult lesions. A reduction of differentiating abilities, as well as synthesis, are also evident in adults that prevent the reconstruction of tissue identical to the tissue lost.

11.4 Clinical application of tissue engineering for skin care

Skin wounds, regardless of their origin, are clinical conditions characterized by loss of tissue integrity, proportional to injury extension, that affects the functional and aesthetic properties of the damaged area, increasing the risk of infection. Moreover, the occurrence of pathological scarring or chronic conditions in the wound area complicates the healing process. The management of skin wounds has always been a serious medical problem due to its extent, considering the high number of patients affected and the long time and resources required for a total healing of the lesion area. In fact, healing time for hard-to-heal wounds is usually over a year and their treatment requires an annual cost, in the United States alone, of more than 25 billion dollars. Patients affected by ulcers in the lower limbs alone represent 1% of the total population, reaching 3.6% when patients over 65 years are taken into account. Many patients ranging from 8% to 25% can also suffer from pressure or decubitus ulcers during

their hospitalization. In general, all the clinical conditions in which non-healing skin wounds occur are considered a challenge in the medical field and several research strategies have been developed for their treatment. The main aims of these new approaches are the stimulation/acceleration of wound closure by a mechanism of regeneration of the lesion area, in order to reduce scar tissue formation. Taking into account the scientific advances on the cellular and biochemical mechanisms underlying the healing process, the actual elective treatment is based on the use of advanced dressings, able to cover and interact with the damaged area, promoting its healing in different ways. Among them, Integra™ is a three dimensional porous matrix of cross-linked bovine tendon collagen and glycosaminoglycan frequently used for its ability to provide a template that is easily vascularized and repopulated by cells. Moreover, acellular dermal matrices are also highly used in the field of wound treatment for their regenerative ability. In fact, the biological properties of these scaffolds make them able to provide a suitable environment for cell growth, stimulating, in turn, the healing process. Among the acellular matrices derived from human dermis, the Human Decellularized Matrix (HDM) produced at Emilia Romagna Regional Skin Bank is distributed in Italy for the treatment of wounds alone or in combination with allograft or autograft skin in cases of osteo-tendineous exposure; it is also used for tissue reconstruction post oncologic mastectomy and in the surgical repair of the rotator cuff. Another commercially available acellular dermal matrix that is frequently used for the treatment of skin wounds is Alloderm. In general, the absence of cells makes these biological, cell-free scaffolds widely used a regenerative templates in several fields of Medicine or Surgery. A supporting role is also performed by materials, such as foams, hydrogels, hydrocolloids and alginates, that allow the maintenance of a wet environment required to absorb exudate, as well as to control infections and, in the case of collagen and hyaluronic acid, to release degradation compounds of low molecular weight with a stimulating effect on cells. Although the use of these different dressings is frequently able to reduce the healing times producing good scars, it is also insufficient, especially in the case of non-healing wounds. In these cases, the best choice of treatment is the use of cells for their active participation to the healing process by the release of active molecules that interact with the microenvironment of the lesion area. In these types of treatments, matrices or **scaffolds** are frequently combined with cells, in order to create skin substitutes that, as products of **tissue engineering**, are considered drugs according to current legislation, able to both enhance cell effects and to facilitate their application on the damaged area. The additional use of advanced dressings, such as colloidal silver or growth factors, in combination with engineered products also enhances the effectiveness of these regenerative treatments. Skin substitutes are used to replace the epidermal or dermal skin layers. In particular, the epidermal substitutes are composed of a thin lamina corresponding to the basal membrane in which keratinocytes are cultured. Despite the high amount of active molecules released by cells and, in turn, the bioactivity of epidermal substitutes, this type of engineered product is mainly useful for the treatment of superficial lesions due to its thinness. On the other hand, the dermal substitutes show a three-dimensional structure similar to connective tissue containing fibroblasts, so that their use is recommended on deep or full-thickness wounds. Based on cell source, skin substitutes can also be classified as allogeneic or autologous. In the first case, the cells are obtained from a donor and, in turn, immediately available for the patient since the growth of autologous cells is not required. For this reason, allogeneic skin substitutes are a temporary graft quickly replaced by the patient's cells and their effectiveness mainly depends on the release of different molecules, such as growth factors or cytokines, active on the wound microenvironment. Due to their characteristics, allo-geneic skin substitutes are usually applied in superficial lesions as bioactive dressings or in deep lesions until autologous substitutes are available. On the other hand, autologous skin substitutes are used for deep skin wounds as a permanent dressing, since they contain cells derived from the same patient affected by the lesion and, in turn, avoid problems of rejection, ensuring a total engraftment on the wound area. In this case, the presence of the patient's cellular component, in addition to active molecules released from cellular component, reduces healing times producing good scar tissue. Skin substitutes can be also classified, according to the origin of the scaffold used, in biological, when materials such as hyaluronic acid, collagen or fibrin are used, or synthetic. In order to have the best clinical effect, the application of a dermal substitute in a first phase followed by an epidermal graft is frequently preferred to the simultaneous application of both substitutes. In fact, the first application of the dermal substitute is able to induce its vascularization that is required for the growth of cells placed in the epidermal substitute. To date, although these engineered products appear highly effective for the treatment of wounds, they have the real limitation of requiring high amount of cells from a small skin biopsy in short times.

11.4.1. Regulatory framework

From a legal point of view, the products of tissue engineering are part of Advanced Therapy (AT) together with gene therapy, in which the sequence of DNA replaced is the pharmaceutical substance, and cell therapy that uses living cells with a therapeutic, diagnostic or preventive action. In particular, they are defined as products "**containing or composed of engineered cells or tissues administered to humans with the purpose to regenerate, repair or replace a human tissue**". All advanced therapies involve significant cell manipulation, such as their *in vitro* enhancement, or a different cellular function in the receiving patient; consequently, they are considered drugs. For these reasons, ATs are very different from other cell-based products frequently used in medicine, such as bone marrow transplants, blood transfusions or the clinical use of cells derived from tissues and organs, since these different products only share some steps in their processing, such as their collection and isolation, conservation in authorized centres and tissue banks, or the transplantation in the recipient patients, when clinically required. Current legislation classifies and regulates ATs Regulation (EC) n°1394/2007 and Directive 2009/120/EC, so that each step regarding their production, distribution, quality/safety control and clinical trials refers to the European regulatory framework contained in "The discipline concerning medicinal products in the European Union". Chapter 4 is also important since it contains the guidelines of the Good Manufacturing Practices (GMP) that define all criteria required to ensure that these products comply with high standards of quality and safety for public health. Taking into account the peculiarity of ATs, considered as "personal drugs prepared on a non-routine basis", Regulation 1394/2007 was also introduced to permit their preparation and use outside clinical trials, under the unique professional responsibility of a doctor after an individual medical prescription. The individual clinical use of these products is reserved to patients in emergency or life-threatening conditions or when therapeutic alternatives are absent. The production of ATs is allowed only in public structures, such as hospitals, after the authorization and periodic controls of the competent authority, the European Medicines Agency (EMA).

11.4.2. Cells as drugs and the evolution of cell cultures

The growing use of cells in the medical field and the introduction of ATs as drugs for clinical use have necessarily led to changes in the *in vitro* components used for cell amplification. The *in vitro* enhancement of cells for research purposes is usually carried out using serum and molecules, such as hormones and growth factors, derived from animals that

can be unsafe for clinical use. In fact, several risk factors, such as immunogenic response or transmission of xenopathogens, must be taken into account when animal derivatives are used, so that the regulatory framework allows their use only when they are irreplaceable. To date, different culture media, such as DMEM, Ham's and RPMI, are commercially available and, in turn, used for the clinically required amplification of cells. Moreover, other components, such as cytokines, growth factors and hormones, are synthetic or obtained from genetically modified microorganisms, in order to produce human variants. On the other hand, effective alternative sources of fetal serum are still a challenge. The use of human platelet lysate for cell culture is able to enhance several types of cells, although their growth is reduced compared to the use of animal-derived serum. The growth of keratinocytes, the main cellular component of the epidermis, is difficult because of their tendency to differentiate in corneocytes. Moreover, the poor proliferative ability of keratinocytes makes possible the overgrowth of fibroblasts on them, due to their greater proliferative ability when they are present in culture. The use of animal-derived cellular substrates, such as the feeder layer, are required to support the cell growth of keratinocytes *in vitro*. In 1975, Rheinwald and Green developed this nutrient substrate (feeder layer) composed of murine fibroblasts cultured in a specifically formulated medium, also containing calcium, growth factors, hormones, basic nutrients and fetal bovine serum, that resulted able to induce the subculture of keratinocytes. In particular, the feeder layer is composed by 3T3 cells, a spontaneously immortalized cell line derived from embryonic fibroblasts of Swiss mouse established by Todaro and Green, that are used after specific treatments, aimed to obtain post-mitotic cells, preventing, in turn, their overgrowth on epithelial cells. This method is still the most widely used for *in vitro* cell culture, ensuring a high proliferative capacity of cells and, in turn, their amplification in 3/4 weeks starting from a small skin biopsy (2cm²), with the final outcome of a structurally organized culture similar to the normal epidermis, also containing melanocytes. On the other hand, fibroblasts can be amplified in a common medium rich in glucose and glutamine obtaining a high expansion in a ratio of 1:2000 in 3-4 weeks starting from a skin biopsy of 2 cm². During keratinocyte culture, although murine cells decrease in number, they remain present in low quantities until cell confluence, disappearing after 8-10 days. Moreover, the proteins of animal fetal serum are able to create bonds with cells, so that they remain in culture also after serum removal. Thus, epidermal substitutes contain a residue of murine cells and fetal serum proteins when applied on humans, which means that an immune response could be triggered

Table 11.1 Epidermal substitutes.

COMMERCIAL NAME	DESCRIPTION	APPLICATION
BioSeed-S™	• Autologous keratinocytes amplified *in vitro* • Application after resuspension in fibrin glue (3-6x106 cell/ml)	• Acute and chronic wounds • Burns
ReCel™	• Suspension of cells obtained from the dermal-epidermal junction (keratinocytes, melanocytes, fibroblasts, Langerhans cells) • Isolation of keratinocytes with a specific kit ready to be used • Application as spray suspension	• Superficial lesions
CellSpray™	• Autologous keratinocytes amplified *in vitro* • Application as spray suspension	• Burns with a body surface higher than 30%
CellSprayXP™	• Autologous keratinocytes amplified *in vitro* for 48 hours • Application as spray suspension	• Burns with a body surface lower than 30%
Epicel®	• Autologous keratinocytes amplified *in vitro* • Application after transfer on a gauze of petrolatum	• Acute and chronic wounds • Burns
Epidex™	• Autologous keratinocytes derived from the outer sheath of the hair amplified *in vitro* • Plating on silicone membrane (diameter 1cm)	• Ulcers of limited size
Episkin™	• Keratinocytes amplified *in vitro* on collagen membrane using the air/liquid interface method • Obtaining of stratified epidermis	• Tests of irritation, corrosion and photo-toxicity of substances and materials
LyphoDerm™	• Lysate of allogenic keratinocytes amplified *in vitro* • Applied as lyophilized solubilized in a hydrophilic gel	• Venous ulcers
Myskin™	• Autologous keratinocytes amplified *in vitro* • Seeded on a perforated silicone matrix (diameter 60 cm) with polymeric coating and kept in culture untill the semi-confluence • Application of the colonized matrix able to release cells	• Pressure, neuropathic and diabetic ulcers • Superficial burns
Cryoskin™	• Version of MyskinTM obtained with allogenic keratinocytes that are frozen after their plating on the matrix	• Pressure, neuropathic and diabetic ulcers • Superficial burns
Laserskin™ (Vivoderm™)	• Autologous/allogenic keratinocytes amplified *in vitro* • Seeded on a microperforated matrix of a hyaluronic acid ester (dimension 10x10 cm)and maintained in culture until semi-confluence • Application of the colonized matrix respecting cellular polarization. The presence of microperforations allows cell migration on the wound bed.	• Acute and chronic wounds • Burns

in the receiving patient after application, in addition to the risk of pathogenic transmission. It has been previously demonstrated that the application of epidermal grafts on humans induces the production of anti-fetal serum antibodies with different levels depending on the patient treated and the duration of the treatment. Then, they decrease rapidly within 30 days even if they remain detectable for 5-6 months. On the other hand, antibodies directed against components of murine cells were not identified. However, the risk of transmission of potentially immunogenic sialic acid from murine to human cells is possible when the 3T3 cell line is used. Thus, different alternative protocols based on the absence of serum, as well as murine substrate, have been proposed. In particular, several culture media have been developed without the presence of serum (serum-free media), even if the total absence of animal-derived proteins, such as growth factors, hormones and extracts of the bovine pituitary gland (animal-free media), is obtained only in a few formulations. However, these culture media are unfortunately not able to guarantee large-scale cellular growth, as required for clinical applications. The serum of human origin could be an excellent alternative for the growth of keratinocytes but its availability is low compared to clinical needs. As an alternative, the use of platelet lysates requires lower amounts of blood compared to human serum but is not able to similarly support cell growth. An increasing number of studies is also focused on the research of substitutes for the murine substrate, evaluating the possible use of proteins of the extracellular matrix or alternative sources of cells. The use of proteins of the extracellular matrix provides good results. However, the high costs required for the use of human proteins, as well as the lower growth of cultured keratinocytes compared to that obtained with the use of the feeder layer, means that this method is not used for clinical purposes frequently. The use of undifferentiated cells is preferred for their ability to highly sustain cell growth, as evidenced by numerous studies on human embryonic cells amplified in the presence of human fetal fibroblasts (HFF) or human neonatal fibroblasts (HNF). On the other hand, the use of fetal or neonatal stem cells is a limiting factor due to both ethical issues and supply difficulties; the use of mesenchymal cells seems to be a good alternative. In fact, the use of adipose-derived stem cells allows to both amplify keratinocytes for a greater number of passages than 3T3 and to obtain a greater number of cells for each passage.

11.4.3. Engineered dermis

The dermal engineered products currently authorized and commercially available for clinical use differ with regard to the origin of the fibroblasts used and the composition of the three-dimensional support. In **Trancyte ™**, the scaffold is composed of a network of nylon coated with porcine collagen associated with a waterproof silicone film. In this type of support, fibroblasts derived from neonatal prepuce are cultured for 14 days and the final product is then frozen in the absence of cryoprotectants, so that cell viability is lost and only a reserve of proteins of the extracellular matrix and trophic factors are used to stimulate the healing process. It is frequently used for the immediate coverage of the wound bed, especially in second- and third-degree burns, but clinical results are not optimal. In fact, this engineered dermis needs to be removed frequently, since it is not biodegradable and the freezing method used highly affects the effectiveness of the cellular component. Another approach is used in **Dermagraft™**, in which fibroblasts derived from neonatal prepuce are cultured in a partially degradable matrix of polyglycolic acid and polygalactin 910, so that the need to clean the grafting site is reduced. Moreover, the maintenance of cell viability after freezing makes this engineered dermis able to maintain the effectiveness of the cellular component during the healing process. Due to these characteristics, Dermagraft ™ significantly reduces the healing times for venous

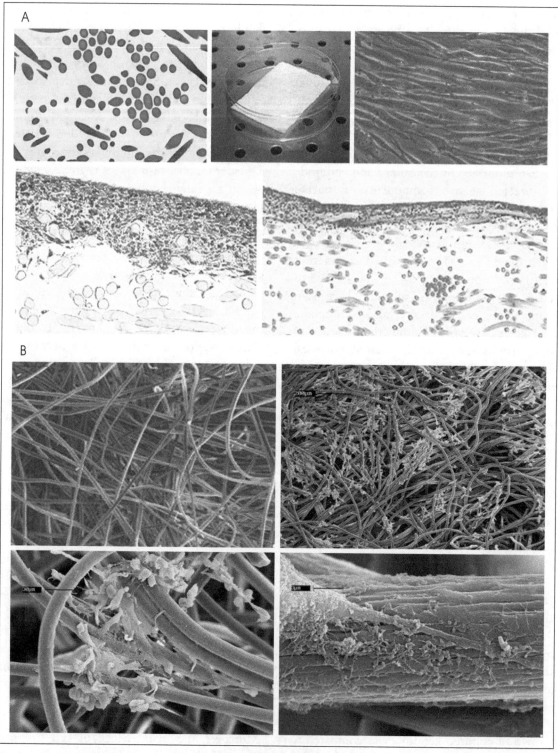

Figure 11.6. A) Upper panels: toluidine blue staining of a HyalograftTM section (magnification 10X) left); scaffold before cell plating (central); confluent fibroblasts (maginification 10X) (right). Lower panels: longitudinal sections stained with Masson's trichrome (left) (magnification 25X) and haematoxylin and eosin (right) (magnification 10X) of engineered dermis after 15 days of culture, in which the cellular colonization of the superficial layers is evident. B) Upper panels: Scanning Electron Microscope (SEM) images of Hyalograft 3DTM before (left) and after (right) 7 days of cell culture. Lower panels: details of cellular adhesion on a fibre with production of collagen (left and right).

ulcers and diabetic foot. On the other hand, its poor biodegradability, small size and high cost mean it is not often applied on burns or extensive wounds. The best compromise is represented by **Hyalograft 3D ™** (Figure 11.6 A and B) in which the scaffold is composed of randomly organized hyaluronic acid fibres, in order to mimic the organization of the collagen fibres in the extracellular matrix, and allogeneic or autologous fibroblasts derived from adult dermis cultured on it. The construct can then be frozen at -80 ° C, preserving an excellent level of viability for at least two years. In addition, it has the advantage of being resistant and manageable compared to other commercial products, so that it is easily applicable in the medical field. When allogeneic products are used, two aspects that may appear contradictory have been taken into account: the cellular component strongly promotes wound healing by the release of bioactive molecules but it also induces a low rejection in the area in which it is applied. The immediate rejection after application is considered positive, since it leads to a rapid degradation of the engineered tissue and, in turn, to the diffusion of active components. On the other hand, the necrosis of cells from the 6th-7th day reduces the healing process. To overcome this limitation, a periodic cleaning of the wound site and the use of several allografts is recommended. Then, the treatment is carried out with autologous grafts when available or when the wound is newly chronicized, in order to induce its complete integration into the damaged tissue.

11.4.4. Engineered epidermis

Several epidermal substitutes are currently available for clinical use (Table 11.3) and can be categorized according to the method used for their production, ranging from how cells are obtained and their level of differentiation to their application on the patients. Some epidermal substitutes are produced using keratinocytes directly isolated from the epidermis, while an *in vitro* step of amplification is required for others. In particular, the methods

of growth used during *in vitro* amplification are able to affect the degree of cell differentiation, which will be low in immersed cultures - especially in sub confluent cells compared to confluent cells - while it will be high, with stratification and formation of the stratum corneum, in the case of air/liquid interface cultures. In both cases, the formation of a thin layer similar to the epidermis is achieved and can be manipulated after its detachment from the growth support. Moreover, epidermal substrates can be variously applied on the lesion area as suspension, layer or combined with different matrices immediately or after some culture steps. In this case, the engineered epidermis can be immediately applied on the lesion or left in culture for a variable time, in order to enhance the cellular component, and then frozen for future applications. To date, the clinical outcomes obtained have shown that only some grafts are able to give significant and reproducible effects on different wounds. When an epidermal substitute is produced, the most important aspect is the high number of keratinocytes with a low level of differentiation obtainable with the method of Rheinwald and Green, preferably using starting sub-confluent cells, in order to apply proliferating, metabolically active cells on wounds. Another important aspect is the maintenance of cellular junctions, in order to allow an immediate interaction and adhesion of the epidermal substitutes with the wound area and, in turn, the effectiveness of the engineered epidermis. For this purpose, Laserskin™ (Figure 11.7 A and B) is frequently used as a bioactive polymer matrix, since the hyaluronic acid lamina is easily manipulated and applied on the wound area, its transparency facilitates observation under the microscope and at the grafting site, and the presence of holes promotes the passage of keratinocytes on the wound site and the transpiration of exudates. The adhesion of the epithelial lamina is affected by the structure of the underlying tissue, with a sufficient number of dermal ridges. Thus, it is essential to establish when the granulation tissue is

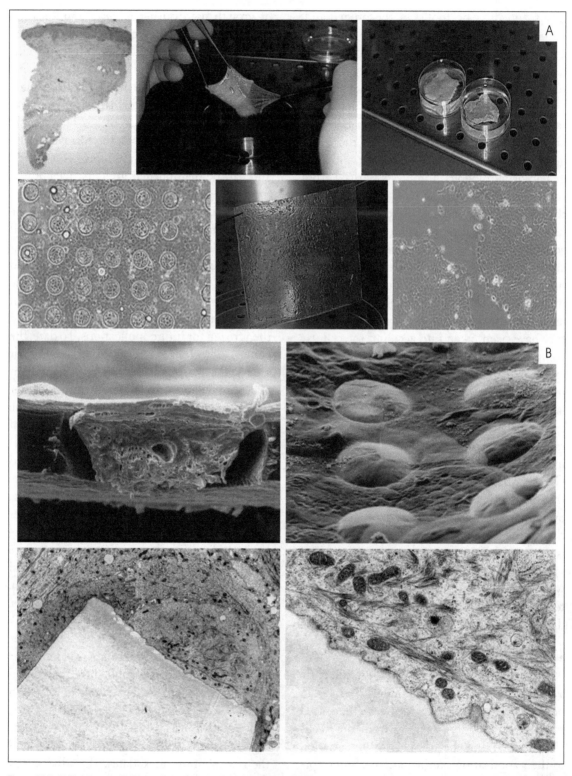

Figure 11.7. A) Upper panels: skin section stained with haematoxylin and eosin (10X) (left), separation of dermal and epidermal layers (central and right). Lower panels: amplification of keratinocytes (right) and their culture on LaserskinTM (central and left) (magnification 10X). B) Upper panels: transversal section of keratinocytes inside a micro-hole of LaserskinTM (left) and the colonized surface of the lamina (right). Lower panels: adhesion of a keratinocyte to the lamina with production of anchoring fibrils and organization of hemidesmosomes *in vitro* (left and right). Scanning Electron Microscope (SEM) images.

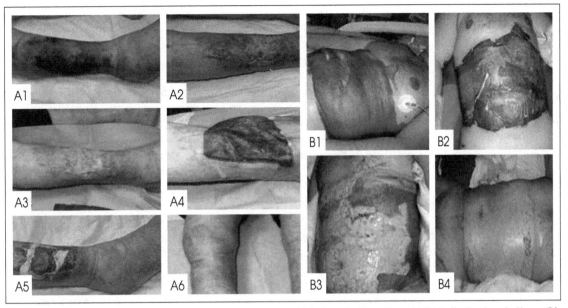

Figure 11.8. Clinical application of Hyalograft 3DTM on ulcers (A1-A6). Clinical application of LaserskinTM for the treatment of burns (B1-B4) in combination with silver nanocrystals.

mature and, therefore, able to cooperate with the keratinocyte lamina for the formation of the basal membrane, required for the adhesion and formation of a complete epidermis. On the other hand, adhesion is negatively affected by the poor attachment of the matrix on the wound area and the formation of haematomas. The healing process is thus improved if the epidermal substitute is applied correctly and is accompanied by infection and pain control. In addition, chronic wounds that are refractory to all other treatments can also be repaired (Figure 11.8). The engineered epidermis is also able to maintain cell viability and structural organization after their freezing so that they can be available when clinically required. The use of allogenic or autologous cells can also influence the clinical outcomes: the engraftment of autologous products is easily obtained, while rejection is induced using allogenic products.

Recommended reading and references

1. Rajkumar VS, Howell K, Csiszar K, Denton CP, Black CM, Abraham DJ (2005) *Shared expression of phenotypic markers in systemic scle-rosis indicates a convergence of pericytes and fibro-blasts to a myofibroblast lineage in fibrosis.* Arthritis Research & Therapy 7:R1113–R1123.

2. Bahar MA, Bauer B, Tredget EE, Ghahary A (2004). *Dermal fibroblasts from different layers of human skin are heterogeneous in expression of collagenase and type I and III procollagen mRNA.* Wound Repair Regen 12:75–182.

3. Alt, E., Yan, Y., Gehmert, S., Song, Y. H., Altman, A., Gehmert, S., ... & Bai, X. (2011). *Fibroblasts share mesenchymal phenotypes with stem cells, but lack their differentiation and colony-forming potential.* Biology of the Cell, 103(4), 197-208.

4. Vaculik, C., Schuster, C., Bauer, W., Iram, N., Pfisterer, K., Kramer, G., ... & Elbe-Bürger, A. (2011). *Human dermis harbors distinct mesenchymal stromal cell subsets.* Journal of Investigative Dermatology, 132, 563-574.

5. Martin, R., Stefan, G., Horst, W., Volker, A., Annette, M., Wolfgang, D., & Anja, K. (2012). *A novel niche for skin derived precursors in non-follicular skin.* Journal of dermatological science.

6. Yang, C. C., & Cotsarelis, G. (2010). Review of hair follicle dermal cells. Journal of dermatological science, 57(1), 2-11.

7. Driskell, R. R., Clavel, C., Rendl, M., & Watt, F. M. (2011). *Hair follicle dermal papilla cells at a glance.* Journal of cell science, 124(8), 1179-1182.

8. Ghadially, R. (2011). *25 Years of Epidermal Stem Cell Research*. Journal of Investigative Dermatology, 132, 797-810.

9. Popova NV, Morris RJ (2004). *Genetic regulation of mouse stem cells: identification of two keratinocyte stem cell regulatory loci.* Curr Top Microbiol Immunol 280:111–137.

10. Doupé, D. P., Klein, A. M., Simons, B. D. & Jones, P. H. (2010). *The ordered architecture of murine ear epidermis is maintained by progenitor cells with random fate.* Dev Cell 18, 317–323.

11. Li, X., Upadhyay, A. K., Bullock, A. J., Dicolandrea, T., Xu, J., Binder, R. L., ... & Smallwood, R. H. (2013). *Skin Stem Cell Hypotheses and Long Term Clone Survival-Explored Using Agent-based Modelling.* Scientific reports, 3.

12. Zhdanov, V. P., & Cho, N. J. (2013). *Kinetics of the maintenance of the epidermis.* Central European Journal of Physics, 11(8), 1016-1023.

13. Kaur, P., & Potten, C. S. (2011). *The interfollicular epidermal stem cell saga: sensationalism versus reality check.* Experimental dermatology, 20(9), 697-702.

14. Barrandon, Y., Grasset, N., Zaffalon, A., Gorostidi, F., Claudinot, S., Droz-Georget, S. L., ... & Rochat, A. (2012). *Capturing epidermal stemness for regenerative medicine.* In Seminars in Cell & Developmental Biology. Academic Press.

15. Doupé, D. P., & Jones, P. H. (2012). *Interfollicular epidermal homeostasis: dicing with differentiation.* Experimental dermatology, 21(4), 249-253.

16. Namazi, M. R., Fallahzadeh, M. K., & Schwartz, R. A. (2011). *Strategies for prevention of scars: what can we learn from fetal skin?* International journal of dermatology, 50(1), 85-93.

17. Sonnemann, K. J., & Bement, W. M. (2011). *Wound repair: toward understanding and integration of single-cell and multicellular wound responses.* Annual review of cell and developmental biology, 27, 237-263.

18. Marazzi M, De Angelis A, Ravizza A, Ordanini MN, Falcone L, Chiaratti A, Crovato F, Calo D, Veronese S, Rapisarda V (2007) *Successful management of deep facial burns in a patient with extensive third-degree burns: the role of a nanocrystalline silver dressing in facilitating resurfacing.* Internation Wound Journal 4(1):8-14.

19. Marazzi, M. (2010). *Le ulcere cutanee: l'importanza dell'approccio preparatorio della ferita per raggiungere la guarigione. Il debridement.* Rivista della Società Italiana di Medicina Generale N.

20. Coolen NA, Ulrich MMW, Middelkoop E (2010) *Future perspectives of tissue-engineered skin: xenobiotic-free culture systems.* Adv Wound Care 1: 432-7.

21. Green, H., Kehinde, O., & Thomas, J. (1979). *Growth of cultured human epidermal cells into multiple epithelia suitable for grafting.* Proceedings of the National Academy of Sciences, 76(11), 5665-5668.

22. Varki NM, Varki A (2007) *Diversity in cell surface sialic acid presentations: implications for biology and disease.* Lab Invest 87: 851-7.

23. Lu W, Yu J, Zhang Y, et al (2012) *Mixture of fibroblasts and adipose tissue-derived stem cells can improve epidermal morphogenesis of tissue-engineered skin.* Cells Tissues Organs 195: 197-206.

24. Tosca, M. C., Chlapanidas, T., Galuzzi, M., Antonioli, B., Perteghella, S., Vigani, B., ... & Faustini, M. (2015). *Human adipose-derived stromal cells as a feeder layer to improve keratinocyte expansion for clinical applications.* Tissue Engineering and Regenerative Medicine, 12(4), 249-258.

25. Weninger, W., & Wiedner, M. (2013). *The use of Keratinocytes: Things we should keep in mind!.* European Surgery, 1-7.

Pancreatic progenitor cells and regenerative therapies for diabetes

12

Martina Rossi   Giacomo Lanzoni

12.1 Summary

In this chapter we will discuss the development of the pancreas and the differentiation of pancreatic progenitor cells toward adult pancreatic cell types.

We will outline the molecular events that control these maturative steps, along with the methods for recapitulating such events *ex vivo* to generate mature and functional pancreatic cells. The knowledge gained in the field of embryology has enabled the generation of robust methods for the maturation of insulin-producing islet β cells from progenitor cells. These methods and the resulting cells have a major translational potential for the treatment of diabetes mellitus.

We will highlight the current challenges and opportunities to develop safe and effective therapies for diabetes.

12.2 Introduction

The pancreas is a glandular organ of the digestive system that performs exocrine and endocrine functions. *Exocrine functions* are mediated by pancreatic digestive enzymes. These enzymes are produced in an inactive form by pancreatic acinar cells and transported to the duodenum through the pancreatic ducts. These enzymes are activated in the duodenum, where they participate in the digestion of nutrients. *Endocrine functions*, on the other hand, are mediated by hormones released by the cells of the pancreatic islets. Such hormones regulate glucose metabolism, nutrient uptake, and metabolism. Pancreatic islet β cells produce the hormone insulin. The loss or insufficient function of β cells results in lack of control over the increase in blood glucose, which can result in severe acute and chronic complications.

In type 1 diabetes mellitus (T1D), β cells are lost due to an autoimmune attack, whereas, in type 2 diabetes mellitus (T2D), β cells become dysfunctional due to increased workload and peripheral resistance to the effect of insulin (insulin resistance). There are other, more rare forms of diabetes mellitus, such as monogenic forms of diabetes, where mutations or variants of certain genes cause β cells to fail.

Millions of patients with diabetes mellitus could benefit from cellular and regenerative therapies that restore the physiological function of β cells. The transplantation or the in vivo generation of cells that release insulin in a regulated and glucose-dependent manner could revolutionize the treatment of diabetes mellitus. The transplantation of donor-derived pancreatic islets, a strategy aimed at controlling blood sugar in patients with T1D, can be considered the first successful cell therapy in this field. However, this option is limited to a small number of cases, mainly because of the shortage of organs from cadaveric donors and the need of life-long immunosuppression due to allogeneic donor derivation. These problems have stimulated research on alternative strategies to obtain insulin-producing cells. Several cellular sources have been explored. Recently, studies have centred on two main lines of research for the replacement of islet β cells. The first is focused on stem and progenitor cell differentiation, the second aims to achieve reprogramming or transdifferentiation of adult cells.

Progress in human embryonic stem cell (hESC) differentiation has stimulated clinical translation, with the initiation of phase I/II clinical trials in the United States. In addition, the plasticity of pancreatic cells has been the subject of intense studies, and innovative approaches have been developed to induce cell conversion from the non-endocrine compartment of the pancreas in the absence of genetic manipulation.

12.3 Glossary

Islets of Langerhans (or Pancreatic islets). The islets of Langerhans are groups of endocrine pancreatic cells interspersed within the pancreas. They constitute about 1-2% of the organ. Their main function is to maintain glucose homeostasis through the secretion of hormones, such as insulin and glucagon, in the bloodstream. The cells present in the islets can be classified as: α cells (glucagon-secreting cells), β cells (insulin-secreting cells), δ cells (somatostatin-secreting cells), PP cells (pancreatic polypeptide-secreting cells), ε cells (ghrelin-secreting cells). The islets are highly vascularized, hence they also contain endothelial cells, pericytes, and other connective cells.

β-cells. β cells are the main cellular components of pancreatic islets. Their main function is to sense glucose concentration and secrete insulin in the bloodstream in a glucose-dependent manner. They are lost due to an autoimmune attack in type 1 diabetes (T1D). The lack of β cells leads to pathological hyperglycaemia and to the need for exogenous insulin in T1D patients. β cells progressively lose function in type 2 diabetes (T2D, the most common form of diabetes mellitus) due to increased workload and peripheral insulin resistance. The administration of exogenous insulin is required also in the most severe cases of T2D. Certain genetic mutations can cause β cells to develop improperly or mature into dysfunctional cells (monogenic forms of diabetes). Strategies of β cell replacement and regeneration could be applied in T1D, in the most severe cases of T2D, as well as in certain monogenic forms of diabetes.

Diabetes Mellitus. Diabetes mellitus refers to a group of diseases characterized by high levels of glucose in the blood (hyperglycaemia). Symptoms of diabetes include frequent urination, increased thirst, and increased hunger. Diabetes can lead to a plethora of complications, including acute complications (diabetic ketoacidosis, hyperosmolar hyperglycaemic state, death) and chronic complications (retinopathy, neuropathy, nephropathy, cardiovascular disease, stroke, non-healing ulcers). Diabetes mellitus can result from insufficient insulin production, as in the case of type 1 Diabetes (T1D) - a disease characterized by severe loss of pancreatic insulin-producing β cells due to an autoimmune attack. In rare cases, insufficient insulin production can be due to genetic mutations or variants in genes encoding proteins involved in β cell maturation, insulin production, and insulin release (monogenic diabetes).

Diabetes mellitus can also result from the diminished ability of the cells of the body to respond to the action of insulin (insulin resistance). This is the case of type 2 diabetes (T2D), the most common form of diabetes mellitus, connected to diet and lifestyle choices. β cells can become impaired due to a protracted increased workload, and a lack of insulin may develop in advanced-stage T2D.

Islet transplantation. Islet transplantation is a procedure by which the islets of a pancreas from a donor are separated from the non-endocrine pancreas fraction, and subsequently transplanted into mechanica processing and a recipient. Isolation is currently performed by mechanical processing and enzymatic digestion of the organ, followed by separation of the different pancreatic fractions with a density gradient. Isolated islets are usually transplanted into the recipient's liver via infusion into the portal vein, although ongoing clinical trials are exploring alternative sites for the transplantation, such as the omentum (a highly vascularized fold of the peritoneum). Allogeneic islet transplantation is an effective cell therapy for T1D, performed clinically in many countries. However, this therapy has important limitations, including the scarcity of cadaveric donor pancreata and the need for immunosuppressive therapy. Autologous islet transplantation can be utilized in the treatment of severe forms of pancreatitis: when the surgical removal of the pancreas is required, islets can be isolated and reinfused into the patient to avoid the development of diabetes mellitus.

Exocrine pancreas (or non-endocrine compartment). The secretion of digestive enzymes is the main function of the exocrine pancreas, which constitutes more than 95% of the organ. This tissue is mainly composed of acinar and ductal cells. Pancreatic acinar cells produce zymogen granules and release them into a space surrounded by centroacinar cells, which are a component of the pancreatic ductal system. The ductal tree, formed by structures that start from centroacinar cells and converge into ducts of increasing calibre, carries secretions and digestive enzymes into the duodenum. The exocrine pancreas also includes populations of non-endocrine pancreatic cells residing in the pancreatic duct glands and in the large-calibre ducts.

Pancreatic progenitors. Pancreatic progenitors are non-terminally differentiated cells with the potential to mature into multiple pancreatic cell types. Pancreatic progenitors can be multipotent (if they have differentiation potential towards multiple lineages, including endocrine and exocrine types) or oligopotent i.e. with the potential to mature into a limited range of cell types, such as pancreatic endocrine progenitors, (cells that can give rise to islet endocrine cell types).

Pluripotent stem cells (PSC). Pluripotent stem cells are stem cells with the ability to proliferate indefinitely *in vitro* under the appropriate conditions maintaining their pluripotency, i.e. the ability to differentiate along all the lineages of the three embryonic sheets (endoderm, ectoderm, and mesoderm).

Human embryonic stem cells (hESC) represent an example of PSCs: they are obtained from the inner cell mass of a pre-implantation human embryo (day 5 – day 6 blastocyst) and can give rise to all cell types of the adult. These cells are considered the standard of pluripotency. Embryonic germ (EG) cells are an example of native pluripotent stem cells. More recently, conditions have been identified that allow the generation of pluripotent stem cells that do not exist in nature. These cells are called **induced Pluripotent Stem Cells (iPSC)** and are derived from genetically reprogrammed adult cells; iPSCs can be obtained theoretically from any individual, which could allow a wide range of personalized cell therapies. iPSCs and hESCs are functionally equivalent.

Reprogramming. The term 'reprogramming' refers to methods that determine the conversion of one cell type into another, typically involving genetic or epigenetic manipulation.

12.4 Pancreas development

Pancreatic progenitors develop during embryonic life from the endoderm of the cephalic portion of the primary digestive tube (foregut). The maturation of these progenitors will give rise to pancreatic endocrine cells (α, β, δ, PP, and ε cells of the pancreatic islets) and pancreatic exocrine cells (pancreatic acinar cells, pancreatic ductal cells, and pancreatic duct gland cells).

Most of our knowledge of the pancreatic developmental program is based on studies of gain and loss of function and lineage tracing in animal models, mainly in mice. Most genetic and molecular components involved in pancreatic development appear to be highly conserved between rodents and humans, but there are differences.

Moreover, a major proportion of the studies has focused on pancreatic endocrine and β cell maturation. Pancreatic development, with emphasis on β cell maturation, can be subdivided in the following sequence of steps: (a) generation of the endoderm and of the foregut (Figure 12.1, 12.2), (b) pancreas specification (Figure 12.3), (c) commitment of pancreatic exocrine and endocrine progenitors (Figure 12.4), (d) differentiation towards pancreatic islet β cells (Figure 12.5), and (e) functional β cell maturation (Figure 12.6). A set of transcription factors, acting in a network of interactions, control each maturative step. We will provide a simplified view of these maturational processes.

(a) Generation of the endoderm and the foregut

After the formation of a zygote, a morula develops and gives rise to a blastocyst through a process called cavitation. The blastocyst consists of an Inner Cell Mass (ICM), which subsequently will form the embryo, and an outer layer of cells collectively called trophoblast. At this level, Embryonic Stem Cells (ESC) can be isolated from the ICM. Waves of migration and maturation of the cells of the ICM generate the gastrula. At the gastrula stage, the endoderm begins to differentiate and expresses a combination of transcription factors: Foxa1-2/HNF3β, Mixl1, Eomes, Gata4-6, SOX17 and other transcription factors of the SOX family (Figure 12.1).

Subsequently, the endoderm will give rise to the epithelium of the primary digestive tube. The anterior part of the gut will form the cephalic portion of the primary intestine (the foregut), which will mature into the pancreas, the liver, the biliary tree and the lungs. This initial anterior-posterior organization and patterning of the foregut epithelium is regulated by a Nodal gradient (Figure 12.2).

(b) Pancreas specification

Sonic Hedgehog (Shh) is expressed in almost all of the foregut, but is repressed in a specific region of the endoderm: the one that becomes committed to mature towards pancreatic phenotypes. The cells forming this prepancreatic region express the transcription factors Pdx1 and Ptf1α. Knockout experiments in mice have shown that the entire process of pancreas maturation starts from Pdx1$^+$ progenitors. Together with Pdx1, also Ptf1α is necessary for the initiation of pancreatic differentiation. The ability of these factors to induce the pancreatic phenotype has been demonstrated by the observation that their simultaneous ectopic expression in the posterior endoderm induces pancreatic differentiation. Therefore, the repression of Shh and the activation of Pdx1 and Ptf1α are essential for pancreatic development.

There are two prepancreatic Pdx1$^+$/Ptf1α$^+$ regions: one in the dorsal and one in the ventral area of the foregut. In the dorsal prepancreatic region of the foregut, the suppression of Shh results from the release of pro-pancreatic factors, such as Activin β and FGF2 by the notochord. In the ventral part of the prepancreatic region, signals from the cardiac mesoderm, mainly factors of the FGF family, initially suppress Shh and subsequently induce liver formation, while the same signals at a lower concentration stimulate differentiation of the ventral pancreas. Inhibition of Shh can be obtained *in vitro* with the alkaloid cyclopamine, which induces pancreatic differentiation and PDX1 expression.

The prepancreatic dorsal bud emerges from the foregut on e9.5 in the mouse (week 4 in human development). The ventral bud emerges 0.5 days later in the mouse (6 days later for

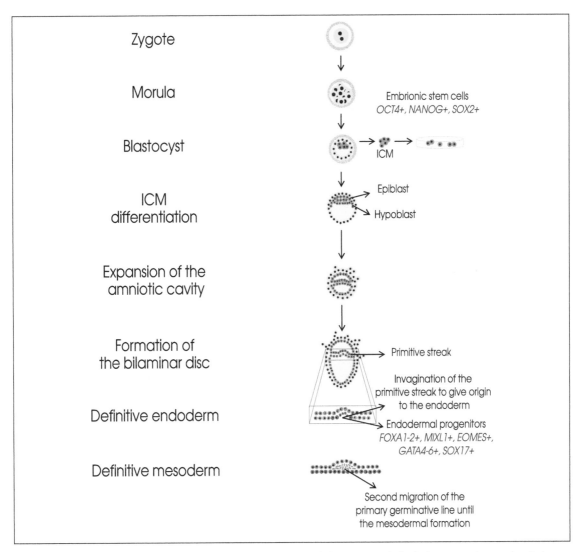

Figure 12.1. Embryonic development from the zygote to the trilaminar gastrula - composed of ectoderm, mesoderm and endoderm.

humans). The first will give rise to the dorsal part of the pancreas, i.e. the body and tail of the pancreas, while the second will mature in the ventral part of the pancreas, i.e. the head of the pancreas, along with the biliary tract, the gallbladder, and the liver.

After the initial patterning signals from the notochord and mesenchyme, blood vessels stimulate the further development of the pancreatic endoderm. At the same time, the prepancreatic region expresses VEGF, which attracts and induces the maturation of the surrounding vessels.

The dorsal bud appears in the proximity of the dorsal aorta, while the ventral bud emerges next to the vitelline veins (which will give rise to the portal vein). Therefore, signals produced by blood vessels are important morphogenetic and differentiation factors for pancreatic progenitor cells (Figure 12.3).

The expansion of the early pancreatic epithelium is characterized by apical branching morphogenesis and by the formation of primitive pancreatic ducts. A rotation of the foregut brings the dorsal and ventral portions of the pancreas into close contact. The main cavity of

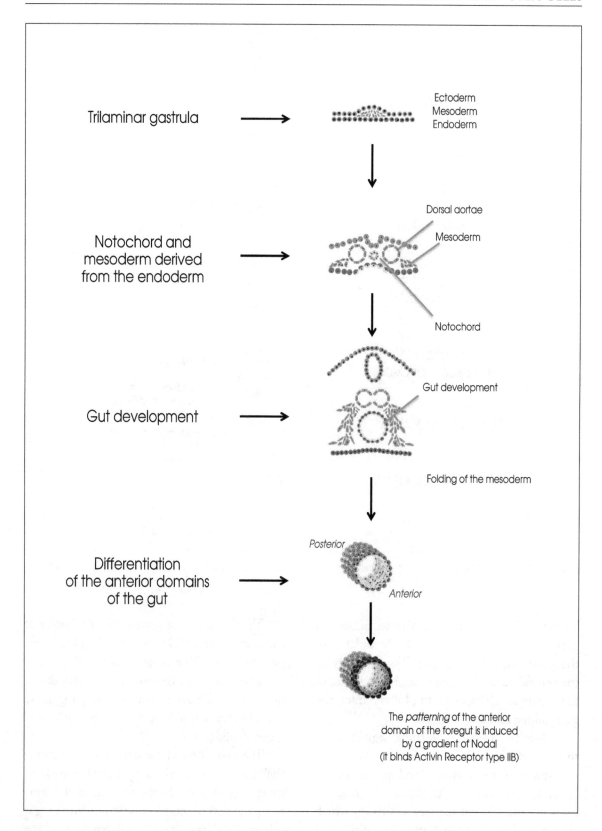

Figure 12.2. Embryonic development from the endoderm to the foregut.

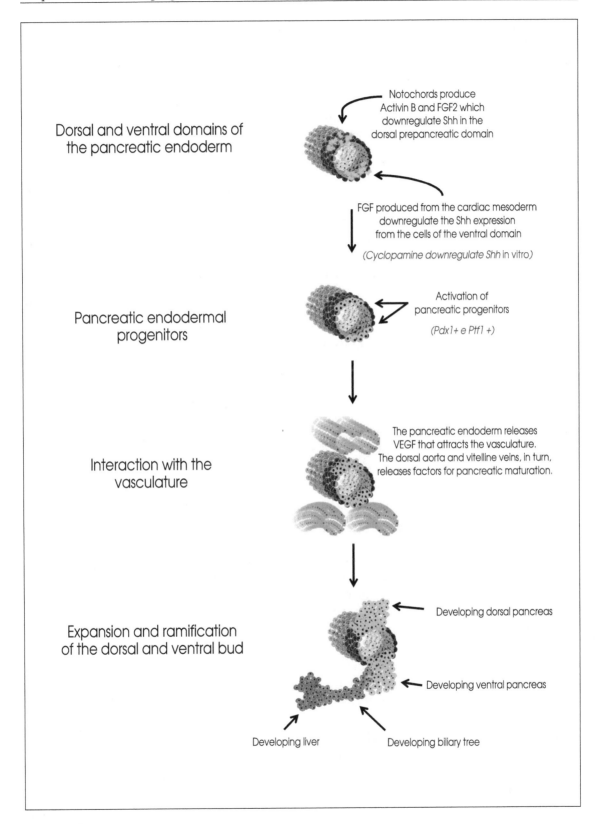

Dorsal and ventral domains of the pancreatic endoderm

Notochords produce Activin B and FGF2 which downregulate Shh in the dorsal prepancreatic domain

FGF produced from the cardiac mesoderm downregulate the Shh expression from the cells of the ventral domain

(Cyclopamine downregulate Shh in vitro)

Pancreatic endodermal progenitors

Activation of pancreatic progenitors

(Pdx1+ e Ptf1 +)

Interaction with the vasculature

The pancreatic endoderm releases VEGF that attracts the vasculature. The dorsal aorta and vitelline veins, in turn, releases factors for pancreatic maturation.

Expansion and ramification of the dorsal and ventral bud

Developing dorsal pancreas

Developing ventral pancreas

Developing liver

Developing biliary tree

Figure 12.3. Specification of the dorsal and ventral pancreatic buds from the prepancreatic region of the foregut.

the ventral pancreas merges with the distal portion of the largest duct of the dorsal pancreas, giving rise to the Major Pancreatic Duct (also known as Main Pancreatic Duct, or Wirsung's duct). The portion of the dorsal duct closest to the duodenum persists as an accessory pancreatic duct (also known as Santorini's duct).

(c) Commitment of pancreatic exocrine and endocrine progenitors

The pancreatic endoderm will give rise to three main parenchymal cell lineages: pancreatic endocrine, acinar, and ductal cells. Lineage tracing studies have enabled the analysis of the events that determine the development of these cell lineages. The ancestral Pdx1$^+$ progenitors, which form the tip of the primary ducts, give rise to all cells of the pancreatic parenchyma. In the trunk region of the developing ducts, progenitors of the endocrine cells become spacified. These cells are characterized by Neurogenin 3$^+$ (NGN3$^+$) expression. At a later stage, exocrine progenitors (Hes1$^+$, Gata4$^+$, Sox9$^+$, Ptf1a$^+$, Nkx6.1$^-$) form the tip of the developing ducts. These cells will give rise to ductal cells (Pdx1$^+$, Sox9$^+$) towards the internal side, and acinar cells (Sox9$^-$, Carboxypeptidase A1$^+$) towards the external side (Figure 12.4).

The progenitors of endocrine cells are characterized by transient activation of the transcription factor Ngn3, which results from a suppression of the Notch signal. Acinar cells derive from Pdx1$^+$/Ngn3$^-$ cells where both the Notch signalling and the expression of Ptf1α are active. Finally, ductal cells derive from committed progenitors that acquire the expression of Pdx1 between E9.5 and E11.5 (in the mouse) and that do not express Ngn3 (Figure 12.4).

It is thought that the key signal leading epithelial progenitors to enter the endocrine lineage may be the loss of the Notch signalling through a lateral specification process. The binding of ligands, such as Delta, to the Notch receptor stimulates the expression of high levels of HES1, a powerful suppressor of

the proendocrine transcription factor Ngn3. At this level, the activation of the Notch signalling is associated with the proliferation of progenitor cells. Pancreatic acinar and ductal cells represent the progeny of HES1$^+$ progenitor cells.

The action of multiple transcription factors, such as Pdx1, Sox9, HNF6, HNF1B, and Foxa2, coordinates the activation and maturation of Ngn3 endocrine progenitors. The crosstalk between endocrine cells and blood vessels represents an inductive interaction, occurring both in the early stages of pancreatic differentiation and in the more advanced phase of endocrine cell specification.

(d) Differentiation towards pancreatic β cells

The pathway of β-cell differentiation from endocrine progenitors (Ngn3$^+$/Hes1$^-$/Ptf1a$^-$)has been analyzed extensively. Studies have shown that several transcription factors play a key role in the steps leading to β cell differentiation (Figure 12.5).

Animal studies have shown that two members of the family of the NK homeodomain proteins, namely Nkx2.2 and Nkx6.1, are involved in the generation of β cells. Nkx2.2 is expressed in the prepancreatic endoderm and then decreases in the Ngn3$^+$ progenitors. It is expressed in all the endocrine cells excluding δ cells. Similarly, Nkx6.1, expressed in the prepancreatic endoderm, is active in multipotent pancreatic progenitors and endocrine progenitors. Its expression becomes progressively restricted to β cells. Another transcription factor that plays a central role in the function of β cells is β2/NeuroD. Pax6 is a transcription factor with an important role in endocrine progenitors and α cells. RFX6 acts downstream of Ngn3 and promotes the maturation of progenitors towards all endocrine cells, except those that produce pancreatic polypeptide (PP). Pax4 acts downstream of Ngn3, Nkx2.2, and Nkx6.1 and is the main switch in the definition of β/δ cell progenitors, inhibiting Arx and inhibiting maturation in α/PP cells. Pax4 has a peculiar role in the development of the β lineage, since it becomes repressed in the δ cells. Endocrine progenitors and immature β cells express

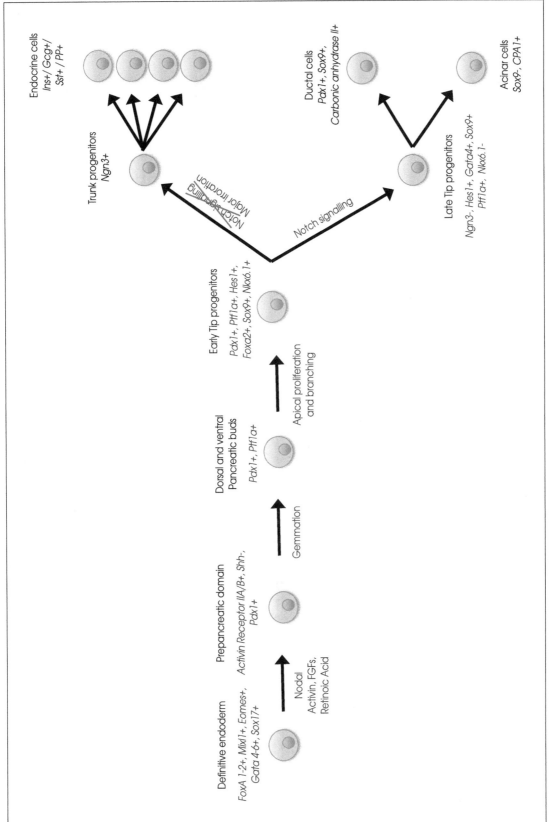

Figure 12.4. Commitment of pancreatic exocrine and endocrine progenitors.

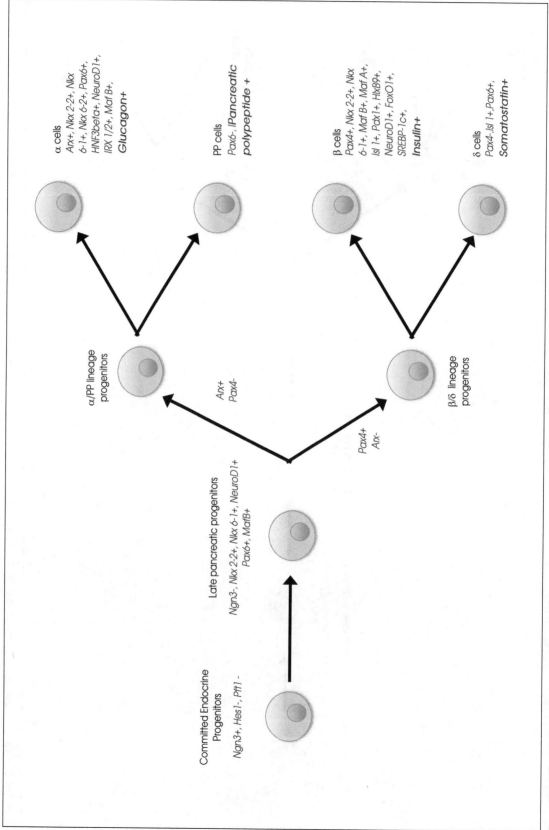

Figure 12.5. Differentiation from endocrine pancreatic progenitors (also know as trunk progenitors) to islet endocrine cells.

MafB. Proceeding towards the late stages of β maturation, MafB is switched off and MafA production begins. In these maturing cells, Pdx1 becomes expressed at high levels, and finally insulin is expressed.

MafA has been identified as specific for the differentiation of β cells in the pancreas: it acts in the β-specific reactivation of Pdx1 and is a regulator of the insulin gene in mature β cells. MafA is crucial for the differentiation of insulin-producing cells, and its role is fundamental in the functional regulation of glucose-mediated insulin secretion in mature β cells.

(e) Functional β cell maturation

Pancreatic islet β cells are cells specialized in synthesizing, processing and storing insulin. They are also able to detect glucose concentration in the extracellular environment and to secrete insulin in response to increases in glucose concentration (Figure 12.6).

The β cell depends on glucose as a substrate for energy metabolism, and neither fatty acids nor amino acids can act as substrates to support the production of ATP.

The internalization of glucose from the extracellular environment is mediated by glucose transporters of different types (GLUT2 in mice, GLUT1, 2 and 3 in humans). Unlike many other tissues, glucose metabolism in β cells is mainly mediated by glucokinase (GK), an enzyme that acts as a glucose sensor. GK activity increases dramatically in response to small increases in blood glucose concentration, and this ultimately results in an increase in insulin release.

After GK-mediated glucose phosphorylation, glycolysis leads to an increase in the ATP/ADP ratio.

An increase in intracellular ATP leads to the closure of the potassium (K^+) channels, preventing K^+ from leaving the cell. The accumulation of positive charge (K^+ ions) in the cytosol initiates a depolarization that results in the opening of voltage-dependent calcium channels. An influx of calcium ions (Ca^{++}) stimulates the exocytosis of the insulin granules and the secretion of the hormone into the bloodstream.

Multiple waves of action potentials occur in islets exposed to increased glucose concentrations. β cells release insulin in two phases. The first phase is rapid and is characterized by the release of the insulin stored in the granules. The second phase is prolonged, involving the synthesis and release of insulin as long as blood glucose levels remain high. After the blood glucose has decreased to normal levels, the insulin granules are regenerated, and stored ready for the next rapid phase.

The administration of oral glucose induces a faster and longer secretion of insulin compared to intravenous glucose administration. This is due to the action of intestinal factors (incretins) that are released into the bloodstream and signal to β cells the impending inflow of glucose. The most characteristic incretin hormone is glucagon-like peptide 1 (GLP-1), which is released from the intestinal L cells. GLP-1 is a powerful incretin that enhances the release of insulin stimulated by glucose through the binding and activation of its receptor (GLP-1R) on β cells. This potentiation of insulin release probably results from the modulation of three types of ion channels: ATP-dependent potassium channels (K^+ATP), voltage-dependent calcium channels, and voltage-dependent potassium channels (Kv). The function of these channels is indirectly modulated by glucose and has an effect on insulin secretion.

The schematic representation (Figure 12.6) shows in a simplified way the main molecular events that determine and control the glucose-dependent release of insulin. Insulin can also be expressed in immature cells, but glucose-dependent release functionality is a characteristic of late β cell maturation. Mature β cells are thus characterized by combined expression of insulin, along with proteins that impart sensitivity to glucose concentration (GSK, GLUT1,2,3), proteins involved in insulin production and processing (PCSK1, PCSK2), and receptors that modulate β cell function (e.g. GLP-1R).

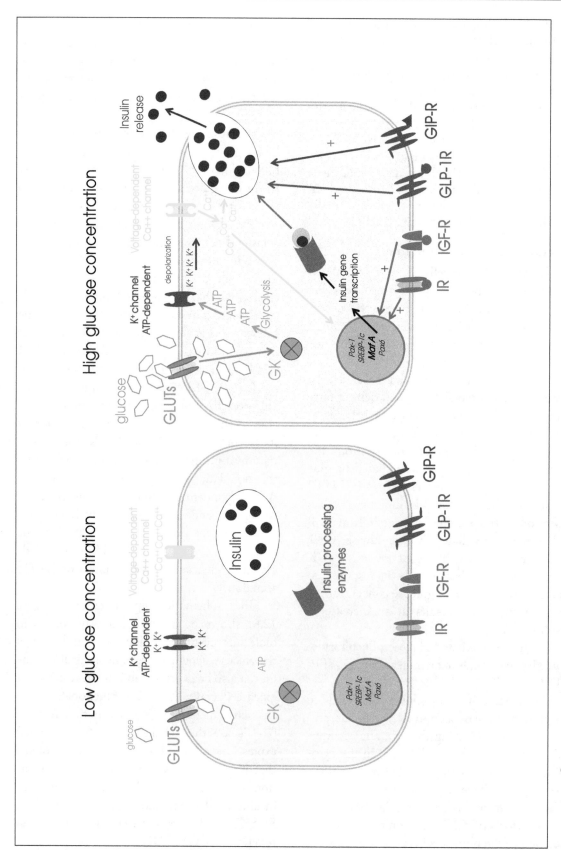

Figure 12.6 Main β cell characteristics: insulin production, glucose-dependent release, modulation by soluble factors.

12.5 Stem cells, progenitors and other sources of β cells for diabetes therapy

The insulin-producing β cells of the pancreas, together with other types of islet endocrine cells, are responsible for maintaining glucose homeostasis. In type 1 diabetes (T1D), β cells are targeted and destroyed by autoimmune T cells. In T1D, the administration of exogenous insulin is a life-saving, chronic and life-long therapy for patients. Insulin therapy, unfortunately, fails to prevent long-term complications, which include blindness, vascular disease, kidney failure, impaired wound healing. The transplantation of pancreatic islets from cadaveric donors is a successful cell therapy for T1D. The development of steroid-free immunosuppression protocols and, more recently, T-cell reduction interventions, has ensured the long-term function of transplanted islets. However, the application of islet transplantation on a large scale is limited by the shortage of donors and by the need for permanent immunosuppression. The first, pressing problem could be addressed by using cell sources, such as stem or progenitor cells, with the potential to mature into β cells. The development of such a strategy could also have applications in type 2 diabetes (T2D), the prevalent form of diabetes mellitus. Despite its different aetiology, T2D in the most severe or advanced cases is characterized by insufficient insulin production, and could, therefore, benefit from β cell transplantation or regeneration. The possibility of inducing the maturation of stem cells towards functional insulin-secreting β cells is therefore very promising. In recent years, several differentiation protocols for stem cells and progenitors have been developed. The most successful protocols have been designed to replicate *in vitro* the different steps of pancreatic organogenesis. During development, progression from ancestral stem cells to pancreatic progenitors and then to mature pancreatic islets cells is regulated by the intricate interaction of the inductive signals and regulatory elements discussed in the previous section.

However, closely replicating this sequence of events still represents a major challenge.

Several cell sources have been explored to generate new β cells and islet cells. Recently, studies have centred on two main lines of research for the replacement of islets. The first focuses on the differentiation of stem and progenitor cells, while the second aims to achieve reprogramming or transdifferentiation of adult cells.

Progress in the differentiation of pluripotent human embryonic stem cells (hESC) has stimulated clinical translation, with the first phase I/II clinical trials launched in the U.S (ViaCyte, Inc.). The differentiation of pluripotent stem cells, primarily hESCs, towards the β cell lineage has considerably galvanized the field of investigation. However, none of the methods for differentiating hESC/iPSCs has yet provided a product fully equivalent to adult β cells, and the current techniques are not completely devoid of drawbacks and pitfalls.

In parallel, the differentiation potential and plasticity of cells in the adult pancreas have been intensively studied, and techniques have been developed to induce the conversion of non-endocrine pancreatic cells into β cells with and without genetic manipulation. Therapeutic strategies based on these techniques could employ the non-endocrine pancreatic tissue (~95-98% of the pancreas), or subpopulations of progenitor cells currently discarded after isolation of the islets. Cells of pancreatic origin could be transdifferentiated into endocrine cell types and subsequently transplanted. Alternatively, if robust differentiation or transdifferentiation could be induced *in situ*, transplantation may not be necessary. Some of these studies may soon reach the clinical phase.

A successful approach for the cure of T1D should preserve the residual β cells, restore β-cell function, and protect the transplanted insulin-producing cells from allo- and/or autoimmune destruction. The use of stem cells holds great promise for new and effective therapies for T1D .

12.5.1 Differentiation of ESCs and iPSCs through β cells

The first method to stimulate the maturation of human embryonic stem cells (ESC) towards endoderm and insulin-producing cells was reported in 2006 by Novocell (now Via-Cyte, Inc.). This method was received with high expectations: cells matured *in vitro* had an insulin content almost comparable to that of β cells. However, the β-like cells obtained were limited in number and had not gained a key function: the ability to release insulin in response to glucose concentration. It was thought that further changes to this protocol (Table 12.1) could lead to substantial improvements in efficiency, and that functional β cells could, therefore, be efficiently generated both *in vitro* and *in vivo* after transplantation. More than ten years later, this objective cannot be considered fully achieved. Several variations of the above method have been reported, which have improved yields in the derivation of pancreatic progenitors (Table 12.1). The conditions leading to the functional maturation of insulin-responsive glucose-producing cells have yet to be agreed upon. Most protocols result in the generation of immature cells *in vitro*, more similar to fetal β cells, which sometimes co-express insulin and glucagon and/or are not glucose-responsive, possibly due to defects in KATP channels or lack of the GLUT1 glucose transporter.

Table 12.1						
	Definitive endoderm	Foregut	Foregut pancreatic progenitors	Pancreatic progenitors	Endocrine progenitors	Insular endocrine cells
D'Amour K. 2006	RPMI 1640 Activin A Wnt3 +0.2% FBS	RPMI 1640 2% FBS FGF10 Cyclopamine	DMEM 1% B27 FGF10 Cyclopamine Retinoic Acid	DMEM 1% B27 +/- DAPT Exendin-4	DMEM 1% B27 +/- DAPT Exendin-4	CMRL 1% B27 +/- Exendin-4 IGF-1 HGF
Kroon E. 2008	RPMI 1640 Activin A Wnt3 + 0.2% FBS	RPMI 1640 2% FBS KGF	DMEM 1% B27 Cyclopamine Retinoic Acid Noggin	DMEM 1% B27	DMEM 1% B27	Progenitor transplanted *in vivo*: maturation in 3 months
Jiang J. 2007	RPMI 1640 B27 Activin A Sodium Butyrate	RPMI 1640 B27 Activin A Sodium Butyrate	RPMI 1640 B27 EGF bFGF Noggin	RPMI 1640 B27 EGF bFGF Noggin	RPMI 1640 B27 EGF Noggin	RPMI 1640 0.5% BSA Nicotinamide IGF-II + Followed IGF-II-
Rezania A. 2012	RPMI 1640 0.2% FBS thereafter 0.5% Activin A Wnt3a+ thereafter Wnt3a-	DMEM/F12 2% FBS FGF7	DMEM (H) 1% B27 Noggin Retinoic acid SANT-1	DMEM (H) 1% B27 Noggin Alk5 inhibitors TBP	DMEM (H) 1% B27 Noggin Alk5 inhibitors TBP	Progenitor transplanted *in vivo*: maturation in 3 months

Table 12.1. Differentiation of pluripotent stem cells towards the β cell lineage
Methods for differentiating pluripotent stem cells have been developed mainly using human embryonic stem cells (hESC). There are many variations for the main protocols. Most studies are characterized by a procedure to induce stem cells into sequential stages of development: definitive endoderm, foregut prepancreatic endoderm, pancreatic progenitors, endocrine precursors, and islet endocrine cells (a more recent acquisition). The cells in the progenitor phase are currently being tested in phase I/II clinical trials in patients with type 1 diabetes. Further *in vitro* steps can lead to the generation of insulin-producing cells with β-like functionalities.

Starting from the standard protocol, it has been discovered that the regulation of oxygenation at levels similar to those of the pancreatic islets allows the differentiation of pancreatic progenitors with separation of α and β phenotypes *in vitro*. This supports the idea that oxygenation is an important inducer of maturation also in the pancreas. Significant improvements in the methods used resulted in more efficient protocols, leading to measurable β-like functionality after differentiation. These cells mature functionally after transplantation *in vivo*: cells transplanted at the progenitor stage require approximately 40 days to become competent. It has been observed that the use of BMP inhibitors in maturation protocols determines the differentiation towards β-like cells too early, resulting in a drastic reduction of the yield in functional β cells *in vitro*. The removal of these inhibitors increased the yield of β cells, although the resulting cells were not able to correct diabetes in mouse models. There are, therefore, significant limitations in the methods for obtaining *in vitro* a cellular product that is similar to pancreatic β cells (6). The absence of an appropriate tissue structure could contribute to the under-performance of stem cell-derived products. All the organs in the human body are organized in specific structures of multiple cell types. Interactions between different cell types and vascularization, as well as the three-dimensional arrangement of the cells, can play a major role in tissue reconstruction. The progressive improvement of the differentiation methods could, however, enable the generation of a clinically relevant cellular product within a few years.

Methods for differentiating pluripotent stem cells have been developed mainly using human embryonic stem cells (hESC). There are many variations to the main protocols. Most studies are characterized by a procedure to induce stem cells into sequential stages of development: definitive endoderm, foregut prepancreatic endoderm, pancreatic progenitors, endocrine precursors, and islet endocrine cells (a more recent acquisition). The cells in the progenitor phase are currently being tested in phase I/II clinical trials in patients with type 1 diabetes. Further *in vitro* steps can lead to the generation of insulin-producing cells with β-like functionalities.

Since it has been difficult to induce hESCs to mature *in vitro* into fully functional β cells, hESC transplantation protocols have been developed with cells at the pancreatic progenitor stage, before final maturation in insulin-producing β cells. The concept behind these studies is that the microenvironmental conditions provided by a living host may support the maturation of β cells. In a study reported by ViaCyte, pancreatic endodermal progenitors derived from hESCs were transplanted *in vivo* into mice. The human progenitors matured *in vivo*, and the mature cells prevented the onset of diabetes after animal treatment with streptozotocin (a toxin that at certain dosages selectively destroys murine β cells). The recovery and analysis of the transplanted cells showed that the progenitors had undergone maturation during the post-transplant period and that the acquired functionality allowed to maintain normoglycaemia in the host. In a subsequent realization of this approach, designed for future therapeutic applications, the cells were cultivated into a macroencapsulation device that allows immunoisolation (Encaptra®). This is a thin biocompatible and recoverable bilaminar container. It is designed to maintain cells in an environment protected from the host immune system, while allowing the exchange of oxygen, nutrients, and hormones. Subsequent studies have revealed that the production of hormones increases by an order of magnitude in the 20-30 weeks post-transplant. After this period, the transplanted tissues are largely composed of pancreatic endocrine cells expressing a single hormone, which exhibit basal insulin production, although the insulin content per cell is still less than half that of human islets and glucose-induced insulin synthesis remains suboptimal. Despite these limitations, ViaCyte™ has developed scalable methods for hESC expansion, banking, and suspension differentiation into pancreatic progenitor cells for clinical applications. In 2014, the U.S. Food and Drug Administration (FDA) gave the green light to the first clinical trials to evaluate the safety of the product VC-01™, composed of endodermal pancreatic cells derived from hESCs (PEC-01™) transplanted into the Encaptra® immunoisolation device. A phase I/II multicentre trial is now underway to evaluate VC-01™ in patients with T1D (clinicaltrials.gov identifier: NCT02239354). Beyond the justified enthusiasm for reaching the clinical phase, it will be necessary to obtain important answers on the long-term risks of this type of transplantation. In the most recent versions of the protocol, the risk of iatrogenic tumorigenesis seems irrelevant, and the device and immune competence of the host should constitute the second and third level of risk containment. However, uncertainty remains about the efficacy of transplantation, the long-term duration in an autoimmune context, and the eventual function of cells with an unwanted phenotype.

12.5.2 Generation of β cells from adult cells

Among the various approaches with therapeutic potential for T1D, the use of pluripotent stem cells, such as ESCs and iPSCs, has generated great interest. As discussed above, however, the differentiation process is not free of obstacles. Different categories of cells present in the adult organism could represent sources for the generation of new β cells. These are β cells with replication capacity, cells derived from pancreatic islets, progenitor cells that can mature into β cells via differentiation, and non-endocrine pancreatic cells that can be reprogrammed to β cells. At the cellular level, reprogramming (also called transdifferentiation) is defined as a phenotypic change that is not caused by differentiation. Reprogramming is frequently achieved by the ectopic expression of specific transcription factors, but in some cases it has been achieved with inductive molecules or growth factors. The fact that some cells once considered terminally differentiated may

act as facultative progenitors, and that some growth factors may stimulate 'reprogramming', therefore, shows that the boundaries between differentiation and reprogramming are rather blurred. In most of the β-cell reprogramming studies reported, it is not clear if the conversion takes place in mature cells from the exocrine tissue or in specific subpopulations of responding cells, which could, therefore, be progenitors.

12.5.3 Generation of β cells from islet cells

β cells, once considered postmitotic, may actually function as facultative progenitors for new β cells. During the early years of life, human β cells proliferate actively, but this proliferative activity becomes much lower in adults. In adults, following damage, the main pathway to β cell regeneration appears to be replication from β cells. β cells proliferate *in vitro* after manipulation of the cell cycle with cyclin D3 and CDK6. They also proliferate in response to harmine analogues. Another strategy developed to expand islet β cells is based on *in vitro* culture of dissociated islet cells, which causes an epithelial-mesenchymal transition (EMT), a process of dedifferentiation of β cells. After *in vitro* expansion, the cells can be induced to redefferentiate by activin A, exendin-4, nicotinamide, and high concentrations of glucose.

There is some degree of plasticity among pancreatic islet cells, and the interconversion of α cells into β cells has been observed in animal models. In the human and murine adult pancreas, multipotent cells expressing insulin have also been described: they are rare but characterized by a broad differentiating potential. Since these multipotent cells express the insulin gene, the conclusions of lineage tracing studies using insulin as a marker for terminal β cells differentiation should be reconsidered.

12.5.4 Generation of β cells from acinar and ductal pancreatic cells

Pancreatic exocrine cells, commonly called pancreatic acinar cells, can be divided into several subpopulations. Acinar cells are responsible for the production of pancreatic digestive enzymes. Ductal cells of different types (centroacinar cells, cells of the pancreatic ducts of smaller calibre, cells of the pancreatic ducts of larger calibre) enable the transfer of pancreatic digestive enzymes to the duodenum. Pancreatic Duct Gland cells and the epithelial cells of the Major Pancreatic Ducts appear to be more ancestral cells residing in the adult pancreas. Markers that can differentiate these subpopulations have only recently been investigated.

About 30% of the human pancreas is composed of ductal cells. The pancreatic ducts of the adult organ have been hypothesized to harbour progenitors for islet endocrine cells and for other mature pancreatic cells. The observation that endocrine cells appear to 'bud' from ducts is a relatively frequent histological finding, and endocrine cells can sometimes be observed integrated into the ductal epithelium, even co-expressing ductal markers. However, the contribution of ductal cells to endocrine cell regeneration is still under discussion. Interestingly, in response to some pathological conditions, structures with heterogeneous ductal phenotypes expand in the pancreas. Recent observations indicate that with ageing, pancreatic ducts lose their potential for differentiation towards β cells.

In general, the limited ability of these cells to replicate in culture limits the development of methods to generate β cells for clinical translation. A significant advancement on this front is a method based on prospective selection for the isolation of adult pancreatic cells, followed by clonal expansion and genetic reprogramming to endocrine cells through ectopic expression of Ngn3, MafA, and PDX-1.

Even pancreatic acinar cells seem to maintain plasticity, to some degree. They have been reported to give rise to liver cells, pancreatic ductal cells, and β-like cells. A reprogramming of the acinar tissue was obtained by transferring genetic material with the combination of three transcription factors necessary for differentiation into β cells: Pdx1, Ngn3,

and MafA. This combination was used with some success also in previous attempts at reprogramming cells from liver to pancreatic fates. The over-expression of these transcription factors, induced *in vivo* in the pancreas by adenoviral vectors, led to the generation of β-like cells. These cells, already detected 3 days after the injection, increased in number in the following 3 months - that is, long after the elimination of the viral vectors. Treated diabetic mice showed a significant and permanent improvement in blood glucose levels, although diabetes was not completely reverted. This finding may be due to the fact that *de novo* generated β cells did not form islet aggregates, whereas cell-cell communication is essential to obtain glucose-stimulated insulin secretion in islets. The above results have been confirmed *in vitro* using the AR42J acinar cell line and primary cultures of human exocrine pancreatic cells cultivated with TGF-β and ROCK inhibitors, conditions that prevent epithelial-mesenchymal transition (EMT). These results are remarkable because they have shown the reprogramming of human acinar pancreatic tissue into β-like cells, but are difficult to translate in a clinical setting. Such reprogramming requires, in fact, the ectopic expression of transcription factors (Pdx1, Ngn3, MafA, and Pax4) and two agents that remodel chromatin (5-Aza-2'deoxycytidine and sodium butyrate). Reprogramming from pancreatic acinar to endocrine tissue was also achieved by transducing genes for MapK and Stat3.

In two recent studies, on the other hand, reprogramming of pancreatic acinar cells into endocrine cells was obtained in the absence of genetic manipulation, which could be configured as differentiation of progenitors. The first study was conducted in mice with diabetes induced chemically with alloxan and streptozotocin. The simultaneous intraperitoneal administration of epidermal growth factor (EGF) and ciliary neurotrophic factor (CNTF) can stimulate reprogramming from acinar cells to endocrine cells and revert diabetes in ~64% of animals treated with alloxan and ~33% of animals treated with streptozotocin. It is unclear whether transient exposure to these factors results in reprogramming of mature cells or differentiation of progenitor cells, but lineage tracing has led to the conclusion that *de novo* generated β cells are derived from the acinar fraction.

The effect depends on CNTF-mediated phosphorylation of STAT3, and the degree of success of the treatment was directly related to the number of cells of the acinar parenchyma in which the expression of the transcription factor Ngn3 was activated. The second study was conducted using non-human endocrine cells obtained as a subproduct following isolation of the islets. Treatment of the non-endocrine portion of the pancreas with Bone Morphogenetic Protein 7 (BMP7), a clinically approved growth factor with the dual ability to inhibit TGF-β and activate BMP signalling, led to the generation of islet-like endocrine cell aggregates. The cells exposed to BMP7 treatment gained the ability to release insulin in a glucose-dependent manner. Moreover, they produce insulin at levels comparable to those of islets, i.e. 50 times higher than those obtained by previously reported genetic methods. Lineage tracing studies have suggested that BMP7-responsive cells are not acinar or mature ductal cells, but actual pancreatic progenitors. A deeper anatomical and molecular characterization of these cells could allow investigating their regenerative potential after *in situ* stimulation. The link between this field of research and the field of differentiation of pluripotent stem cells lies in a recent observation on BMP inhibitors. These used to be commonly present in differentiation protocols, but they were causing premature generation of endocrine cells, yielding dysfunctional polyhormonal cells. The removal of BMP inhibitors from differentiation protocols solved this problem, suggesting that BMP signalling is important for differentiation into functional β cells.

12.5.5 Generation of cells from adult pancreas progenitor cells

A large number of studies support the hypothesis that pancreatic progenitors similar to embryonic progenitors persist in adult life, but the identity of these cells is subject to intense discussions. The unequivocal identification of an adult cell population that maintains the differentiation potential towards pancreatic islet endocrine cells would have important therapeutic implications for diabetes.

It has been observed that the endocrine and exocrine cells of the pancreas expand in the case of disease or pancreatic damage. During tissue homeostasis and in response to minor lesions, proliferation of pre-existing cells of the same lineage seems to be the main way of replacing adult cells. Lineage tracing studies in rodents have shown that acinar cells give rise to new acinar cells but not to islet endocrine cells, and that islet β cells replicate to generate new β cells. However, these results do not preclude a contribution from multipotent/progenitor stem cell populations, especially following major damage. Impairment or, β cell loss, insulin resistance, and hyperglycaemia may stimulate cell regeneration from endogenous progenitors.

Multipotent cells seem to exist in the adult pancreas, but these cells are rare and have an elusive phenotype. Cells with pancreatic stem characteristics, called biliary tree stem cells (BTSC), have been described in close proximity to the pancreas, in the peribiliary glands (PBG) associated with the biliary tree, mainly in the region of the hepatopancreatic duct. The hepatopancreatic duct is located at the confluence of the common bile duct with the major pancreatic duct and enters the duodenum forming a structure called the ampulla of Vater. These cells have shown robust differentiation towards β-like cells, and transplantation of these cells of human origin into mice rendered diabetic with streptozotocin has led to an improvement in glycaemic control. Within the pancreas, cells with the characteristics of pancreatic progenitors were observed integrated into the ducts of largest calibre and pancreatic duct glands (PDG) (Figure 12.7). PDGs are associated with the main pancreatic duct and its ramifications of largest calibre. They are abundant in the proximity of the hepatopancreatic duct, where they appear similar to PBGs. Surprisingly, PDGs exhibit significant hyperplasia in murine models of chronic pancreatitis. A subset of adult cells located in PDGs have a phenotype consistent with that of pancreatic progenitors, and PDGs contain Ngn3+ cells, putative progenitors of islet cells. These observations suggest that the adult hepatopancreatic duct contains niches of hepato-biliary-pancreatic stem cells, and that the major ducts and PDGs of the adult pancreas contain niches of progenitors commissioned to pancreatic cellular types.

12.5.6 Conclusions and future perspectives

The progress of the last fifteen years of research in the field of stem cells and pancreatic progenitors has led to the first clinical trials for the treatment of type 1 diabetes.

Protocols based on pancreatic progenitors derived from hESCs were the first to reach the clinical trial stage. So far, the functionality of *in vivo* matured β cells seems to be more substantiated by evidence than that of *in vitro* differentiated cells.

New methods have also made it possible to convert abundant pancreatic non-endocrine cells into functional endocrine cells.

While genetic manipulation strategies are facing difficulties in the phase of clinical translation, those using cytokines or growth factors

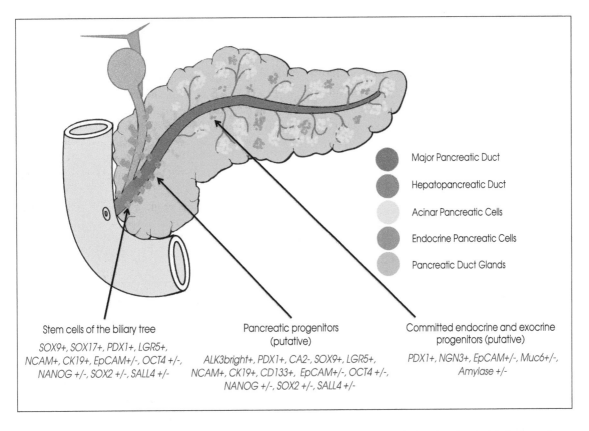

Stem cells of the biliary tree

SOX9+, SOX17+, PDX1+, LGR5+, NCAM+, CK19+, EpCAM+/-, OCT4 +/-, NANOG +/-, SOX2 +/-, SALL4 +/-

Pancreatic progenitors (putative)

ALK3bright+, PDX1+, CA2-, SOX9+, LGR5+, NCAM+, CK19+, CD133+, EpCAM+/-, OCT4 +/-, NANOG +/-, SOX2 +/-, SALL4 +/-

Committed endocrine and exocrine progenitors (putative)

PDX1+, NGN3+, EpCAM+/-, Muc6+/-, Amylase +/-

Major Pancreatic Duct

Hepatopancreatic Duct

Acinar Pancreatic Cells

Endocrine Pancreatic Cells

Pancreatic Duct Glands

Figure 12.7. Biliary tree stem cells and progenitor niches along the pancreatic ducts. Histological and anatomical studies have shown that glands associated with bile ducts and pancreatic ducts of major caliber are rich in stem cells and progenitor cells for pancreatic lineages. Cells with a multipotent phenotype for pancreatic, biliary, and hepatic lineages are located in the biliary tree. Early and late pancreatic progenitors appear distributed along the axis of the Major Pancreatic Duct and its main tributaries.

may reach the clinical trial stage earlier. There are interesting perspectives for the conversion of exocrine pancreatic cells into endocrine, and for the induction of adult progenitor cells into islet cells. Regenerative strategies to stimulate conversion or maturation *in vivo*, in the organ itself, and in patients, are still largely unexplored. In the context of autoimmunity, such as in T1D, specific simultaneous interventions on the immune system may also be necessary.

Thirty years of studies on islet transplantation for T1D have built the foundation to support β cell replacement strategies based on stem and progenitor cells with β cell potential. The goal will be to design transplantation methods and immunomodulatory strategies that promote the long-term survival and function of transplanted cells. Despite considerable advances in immunosuppression protocols, there are still major risks, and methods of inducing immune tolerance are not available. Removable immune isolation devices may solve the problem, at least in part, but their applicability in the context of autoimmunity remains to be assessed. In T2D, there is an opportunity to test β cell replacement approaches in the absence of autoimmunity. The next few years will be crucial for the development of the next generation of therapies for the replacement or regeneration of β cells.

Recommended reading and references

1. Shapiro AM et al. *Islet transplantation in seven patients with type 1 diabetes mellitus using a glucocorticoid-free immunosuppressive regimen.* N Engl J Med. 2000 Jul 27;343(4):230-8.
2. Ricordi C et al. *Clinical islet transplantation: advances and immunological challenges.* Nat Rev Immunol. 2004 Apr;4(4):259-68.
3. Shapiro AM et al. *Clinical pancreatic islet transplantation.* Nat Rev Endocrinol. 2017 May;13(5):268-277.
4. D'Amour KA et al. *Production of pancreatic hormone-expressing endocrine cells from human embryonic stem cells.* Nat Biotechnol. 2006 Nov;24(11):1392-401.
5. Kroon E et al. *Pancreatic endoderm derived from human embryonic stem cells generates glucose-responsive insulin-secreting cells in vivo.* Nat Biotechnol. 2008 Apr;26(4):443-52.
6. Pagliuca FW et al. *Generation of Functional Human Pancreatic beta Cells In Vitro.* Cell. 2014 Oct 9;159(2):428-39.
7. Hrvatin S et al. *Differentiated human stem cells resemble fetal, not adult, beta cells.* Proc Natl Acad Sci U S A. 2014 Feb 25;111(8):3038-43.
8. Greggio C et al. *Artificial three-dimensional niches deconstruct pancreas development in vitro.* Development. 2013 Nov;140(21):4452-62.
9. Nair GG et al. *Recapitulating endocrine cell clustering in culture promotes maturation of human stem-cell-derived β cells.* Nat Cell Biol. 2019 Feb;21(2):263-274.
10. Maehr R et al. *Generation of pluripotent stem cells from patients with type 1 diabetes.* Proc Natl Acad Sci U S A. 2009 Sep 15;106(37):15768-73.
11. Dor Y et al. *Adult pancreatic beta-cells are formed by self-duplication rather than stem-cell differentiation.* Nature. 2004 May 6;429(6987):41-6.
12. Russ HA et al. *Epithelial-mesenchymal transition in cells expanded in vitro from lineage-traced adult human pancreatic beta cells.* PLoS One. 2009 Jul 29;4(7):e6417.
13. Thorel F et al. *Conversion of adult pancreatic alpha-cells to beta-cells after extreme beta-cell loss.* Nature. 2010 Apr 22;464(7292):1149-54.
14. Smukler SR et al. *The adult mouse and human pancreas contain rare multipotent stem cells that express insulin.* Cell Stem Cell. 2011 Mar 4;8(3):281-93.
15. Bonner-Weir S et al. *The pancreatic ductal epithelium serves as a potential pool of progenitor cells.* Pediatr Diabetes. 2004;5 Suppl 2:16-22.
16. Inada A et al. *Carbonic anhydrase II-positive pancreatic cells are progenitors for both endocrine and exocrine pancreas after birth.* Proc Natl Acad Sci U S A. 2008 Dec 16;105(50):19915-9.
17. Xu X et al. *Beta cells can be generated from endogenous progenitors in injured adult mouse pancreas.* Cell. 2008 Jan 25;132(2):197-207.
18. Strobel O et al. *Pancreatic duct glands are distinct ductal compartments that react to chronic injury and mediate Shh-induced metaplasia.* Gastroenterology. 2010 Mar;138(3):1166-77.
19. Razavi R et al. *Diabetes enhances the proliferation of adult pancreatic multipotent progenitor cells and biases their differentiation to more beta-cell production.* Diabetes. 2015 Apr;64(4):1311-23.

20. Wang Y et al. *Biliary tree stem cells, precursors to pancreatic committed progenitors: evidence for possible life-long pancreatic organogenesis.* Stem Cells. 2013 Sep;31(9):1966-79.

21. Lanzoni G et al. *The hepatic, biliary and pancreatic network of stem/progenitor cells niches in humans: A new reference frame for disease and regeneration.* Hepatology. 2015 Nov 2. [Epub ahead of print].

22. Zhou Q et al. *In vivo reprogramming of adult pancreatic exocrine cells to beta-cells.* Nature. 2008 Oct 2;455(7213):627-32.

23. Baeyens L et al. *Transient cytokine treatment induces acinar cell reprogramming and regenerates functional beta cell mass in diabetic mice.* Nat Biotechnol. 2014 Jan;32(1):76-83.

24. Klein D et al. *BMP-7 induces adult human pancreatic exocrine-to-endocrine conversion.* Diabetes. 2015 Dec;64(12):4123-34.

Intestinal stem cells and the gastrointestinal microenvironment

13

Roberta Costa   Giacomo Lanzoni

13.1 Anatomy of the gastrointestinal tract

The intestinal tract is essentially a tube, whose wall is composed of three concentric tissue layers. The outer one, or muscular layer, consists of several sheets of smooth muscle that are fundamental for the peristaltic movements of the intestine. The intermediate layer is composed of connective tissue (or stroma) which contains blood and lymph vessels, nerve fibres and cells of the immune system. Finally, the inner layer, termed the mucosa, is made of a simple epithelium: a single cell layer, strictly connected to the above stroma and responsi-ble for the absorption and processing of nutri-ents. The whole intestinal tract can be divided in two defined segments: the small intestine and the large intestine (or colon). The small intestine's role is to digest and adsorb nutrients and, in order to increase the absorptive surface area, the mucosa is organized in numerous finger-like protrusions that point towards the lumen, named villi, and invaginations into the submucosa, known as crypts of Lieberkuhn. Instead the colon epithelial layer lacks villi and presents only crypts invaginating deep into the submucosa (Figure 13.1).

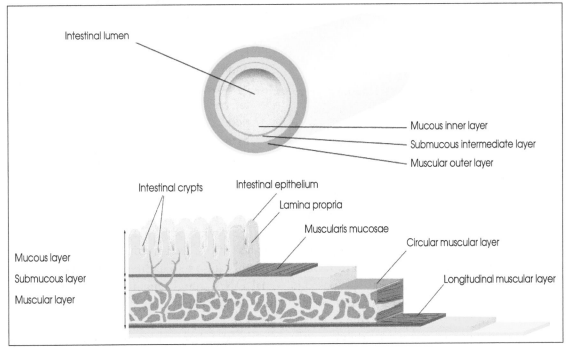

Figure 13.1. Structural organization of the gastrointestinal tract tissues.

The gastrointestinal epithelium is composed of five specialized cell lineages:

1. Enterocytes, the main cell typology in this tissue, which absorb nutrients and release hydrolytic enzymes in the intestinal lumen.
2. Goblet cells which produce mucus to provide a protective barrier.
3. Enteroendocrine cells, that make up less than 1% of the epithelium and secrete gastrointestinal hormones with endocrine or paracrine effect fundamental for gut physiology.
4. Paneth cells which reside at the crypt base and secrete antimicrobial peptides, such as lysozyme, TNF-α and defensins.
5. M cells localized near Peyer's patches, which are involved in antigen recognition and transport.

13.2 Intestinal stem cells

13.2.1 Origin of the intestinal epithelium

The rapid turnover of the intestinal epithelium has inspired various studies on the origin of epithelial cells that derive from endodermal stem cells and from the proliferation and differentiation of progenitor cells. There are two schools of thought with regard to this issue: the "unitarian hypothesis" that affirms the monoclonal origin of crypts, according to which a single multipotent stem cell gives rise to all the cells that compose an adult crypt, while the second hypothesis affirms that there are 4-6 active stem cells in each crypt. Moreover, a third hypothesis has been formulated, that lies in the middle between the previous ones; according to this last hypothesis, intestinal crypts are believed to be generated from one ancestral stem cell that becomes quiescent as soon as it has generated a large subset of cycling stem cells. The rapidly cycling stem cells are responsible for the quick cell turnover in crypts. Potten and colleagues have proposed, in support of the last hypothesis, a hierarchical organization in three layers, with an ancestral stem cell that gives a subset of 4-6 cycling stem cells and that becomes quiescent in the adult

crypt. These cycling cells divide asymmetrically generating one daughter stem cell, which remains in the niche, while the other daughter cell will undergo several cell divisions after which it terminally differentiates.

Among the different hypotheses on the origin of epithelial stem cells, the "unitarian hypothesis", according to which all the terminally differentiated cells in the intestinal epithelium are a clonal population of cells derived from one first stem cell, has gained importance. The best explanation of the validity of this hypothesis comes from the work of Novelli and colleagues on colon cells of a rare XO/XY patient affected by familial adenomatous polyposis (FAP). *In situ* hybridization for chromosome Y revealed that crypts in the normal intestine are entirely made of Y-positive or Y-negative cells. Immunorevelation for endocrine cells confirms that these cells have the same karyotype as the other cells in the crypts, suggesting that cells in intestinal crypts are a monoclonal population derived from only one precursor stem cell.

The hypothesis of monoclonal derivation of crypts arouses interest in the kinetics of crypt stem cells. There are three possible cell division mechanisms for these cells:

- Asymmetric division that gives two daughter cells, one equal to the mother and a second daughter cell that will differentiate;
- Symmetric division that gives two daughter cells, both with stemness characteristics;
- Symmetric division with loss of stemness, that gives two daughter cells that will both differentiate.

The major part of cell divisions is asymmetrical. In this way it is possible to segregate one neo-synthesized DNA strand, that has a higher risk of transmitting mutations induced by replication to daughter cells, while the original DNA strand remains in the stem cells in the deeper part of the crypt, protecting their genome.

Instead less is known on the mechanism by which crypts distribute along the entire intestine. It is possible that the number of crypt units increases by crypt fission, a process in which new crypts form by branching off from existing crypts. This mechanism seems to be responsible for an increasing number of crypts in the postnatal period and in regeneration following exposure to radiation. A "crypt cycle" has also been proposed: a crypt sprouts by fission and grows up until it divides again by fission. In the beginning it was thought that a crypt would start fission once it gained a threshold size, but now attention is focused on the possibility that the number of stem cells in the crypt is the main factor that decides when crypt fission should start.

13.2.2 Cellular and structural organization of the crypt-villus axis

During postnatal life, adult stem cells are responsible for maintaining the functional and structural entirety of intestinal tissues, both in physiological and pathological cell renewal.

The intestinal epithelium is characterized by a rapid turnover of all the cell types in it. Studies on murine small intestine have shown that the epithelium renews every 5 days. This process is based on constant and rapid proliferation, occurs in intestinal crypts and needs a high amount of newly generated cells. This process is fuelled by stem cells, localized near the crypt bottom, that give rise to a population of progenitors that proliferate and differentiate going from the crypt's bottom to the top of the villus. These daughter cells, named transient amplifying population (TA population), divide every 12-16 hours and rapidly amplify the pool of epithelial precursors (300 cells per crypt every day). Along their pathway, TA cells go towards the villus tip, from the proliferation to the maturation area that is localized outside the crypt in the villus for the small intestine, and in the upper third part of the crypt in the colon. Once in the maturation area, progenitor cells differentiate rapidly and irreversibly. Cell proliferation is balanced by apoptosis of terminally differentiated cells once they arrive at the top of the villus, where they shed in the intestinal lumen and are finally substituted. The intestinal epithelial sheet is in a continuous upward movement: epithelial cells produced in the lower part of the crypts migrate up towards an adjacent villus in a coherent and organized column of cells. Six or more independent crypts surround each villus, and this results in an equal number of parallel epithelial cells that migrate from the crypt to the villus tip. Only Paneth cells escape this cell flow and follow an opposite way going towards the bottom-most position of the crypt, where they arrive at the end of the differentiation process and where they stay for 3-6 weeks (Figure 13.2).

The proliferation and differentiation of all these cell types are dependent on the presence of multipotent gastrointestinal stem cells that frequently divide. The presence of intestinal stem cells able to give rise to all the cell types in the gut was first proposed by Stevens and Leblond in 1947, but the evidence of their presence came later. These cells have an immature and undifferentiated phenotype and only recently have some markers been identified (LGR5, BMI-1) that will make a more in-depth study possible. There are also 4 main functional characteristics that permit to identify intestinal stem cells:

1. The undifferentiated phenotype;
2. The continuous production of all intestinal cell lineages;
3. Self-renewal capacity throughout the stem cell's life;
4. The regenerative ability after cell damage.

It is known that stem cells give rise to all the kind of cells in the intestinal epithelium and they do it maintaining a specific cell polarization and hierarchy along the crypt-villus axis. Crypt organization has a well-defined structure, with Paneth cells in the deepest area, while the overhead region is occupied by actively proliferating and differentiating TA cells that go from the crypt towards the villus tip. The localization of stem cells in this hierarchical structure has, for years, been a mystery and has given rise to various hypotheses; only the identification of specific molecular markers expressed by epithelial stem cells has helped to clarify where these stem cells are localized.

Under the epithelium there is a connective tissue, called lamina propria, that controls some epithelial cell functions. This structure contains different cell types, such as fibroblasts, fibrocytes, endothelial cells, smooth muscle cells and a population of myofibroblasts named intestinal subepithelial myofibroblasts (SEMF). These cells, that reside immediately under the basal membrane of the intestinal mucosa and are side by side to the base of epithelial cells, are mesenchymal cells with an ultrastructural phenotype typical of both fibroblasts and smooth muscle cells. They express alpha smooth muscle actin (Alpha-SMA) and vimentin, but they do not express desmin. The localization of SEMFs under the basal membrane suggests that these cells may have a role in regulating some functions of the epithelial cell, such as proliferation and differentiation, or may affect extracellular matrix metabolism or the growth of the basal membrane. SEMFs have been described as a syncytium that extends through the intestinal lamina propria and fuses together with the pericytes that surround blood vessels. SEMFs are also functional and structurally linked to the epithelium: they secrete growth factors (HGF, KGF, TGF-beta 2) essential for regulating epithelial cell proliferation and differentiation. The kinetics of SEMFs, that give the trophic layer for the epithelium, are not completely clarified. It is believed that myofibroblasts have two different origins: the bone marrow and the fibroblasts that are locally activated by TGF-beta, which is a differentiating factor that should induce fibroblast progenitor to differentiate towards myofibroblasts. Lastly, these myofibroblasts surround epithelial stem cells in the intestinal

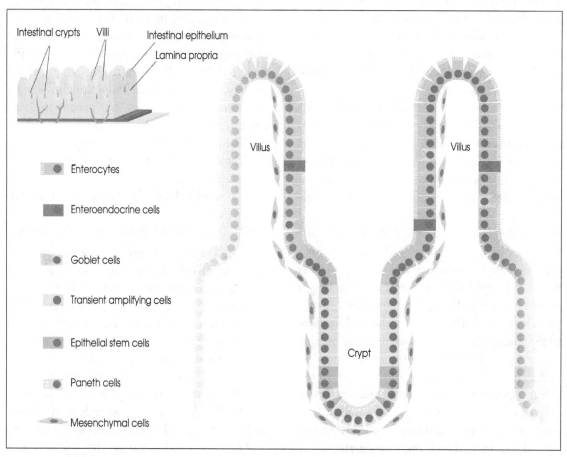

Figure 13.2. Schematic representation of intestinal villi.

crypts and proliferate, migrate and differentiate along the crypt-villus axis thanks to a strict mesenchymal-epithelial interaction.

13.2.3 Identification and localization of intestinal stem cells

Even if the idea that intestinal crypts house a population of stem cells has already been accepted and widely shared, the paucity of specific molecular markers has slowed down the studies focused on identifying intestinal stem cells. There has been a general consensus among scientists on the existence in each crypt of 4-6 independent stem cells, but two schools of thought exist on the exact identity and localization of these cells: the "+4 position" model, proposed in the late 1950s and sustained by Potten and colleagues, and the more recent "stem cell zone" model proposed by Cheng and Leblond in the 1970s. The "+4 position"

model has placed stem cells at position +4 relative to the crypt bottom, while the first three positions in the crypt bottom are occupied by the terminally differentiated Paneth cells. Potten and colleagues supported this hypothesis and they reported the existence in position +4 of cells with a slow cell cycle and that retained the DNA labelling used to mark them; moreover, they observed that the cells in +4 position are extremely sensitive to radiations, a characteristic that would functionally protect stem cells from genetic damage. In addition, the "+4 position" hypothesis sustains that enterocytes, goblet cells and enteroendocrine cells derive from TA cells that are respectively the daughter cells of stem cells in +4 position and that differentiate migrating from the crypt to the villus tip. Conversely, Paneth cells differentiate migrating towards the crypt bottom, but they are also derived from intestinal stem cells in +4

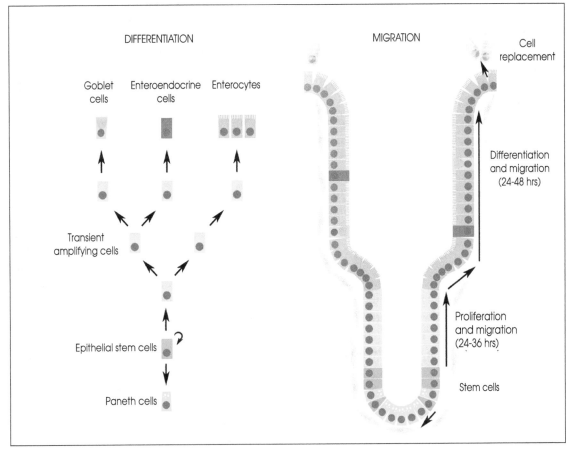

Figure 13.3. Cell renewal of the intestinal epithelium.

position (Figure 13.3). This experimental evidence and the current literature, in absence of a specific stem cell marker, were not able to give a clear insight into the nature of the cellular progeny of +4 cells, so the position of the +4 cells in the epithelial hierarchy remains uncertain, giving rise to further studies. In support of this school of thought, the experimental work of Sangiorgi and Capecchi demonstrated, using transgenic mice, that cells in +4 position were positive for BMI1, a gene involved in the self-renewal of stem cells of other tissues. They also created a system of lineage tracing that permitted to follow over time the cell progeny of BMI1 positive cells (BMI1⁺) in +4 position. These last experiments demonstrated also that BMI1⁺ cells rapidly gave a daughter cell ribbon that moved from the crypt to the villus, sustaining also the multipotency of BMI1⁺ cells in +4 position that seemed the real intestinal stem cells.

The second school of thought on the localization of intestinal stem cells has been proposed by Leblond and coworkers and was based on the identification of small cycling cells between Paneth cells that have been named Crypt Base Columnar Cells (CBC cells). According to the Stem Cell Zone hypothesis, these CBC cells are the real intestinal stem cells from which derive all the precursors of enterocytes, enteroendocrine cells and goblet cells that migrate along a vertical axis towards the villus, while Paneth cell precursors migrate to the crypt bottom. This theory has been sustained by the research group of Clevers which, using systems of lineage tracing and transgenic mice similarly to those used by Sangiorgi and Capecchi, came to completely different conclusions. The approach of these researchers started from the central role of the Wnt pathway on the intestinal epithelium, both physiologically and pathologically. Many factors produced by the intestinal epithelium in the crypt bottom act on the Wnt pathway, creating a gradient of morphogenic signals that acts on the entire crypt-villus axis. Considering that the Wnt pathway represents one of the main actors in

intestinal crypt biology, Clevers and colleagues have hypothesized that some Wnt target genes could be expressed in a specific way by intestinal stem cells. Among 80 target genes of Wnt, many of which are expressed also by Paneth cells and TA cells, researchers have identified the Lgr5 gene as a possible marker since it was expressed in a peculiar way. The Lgr5 gene encodes for a G protein-associated receptor and is a co-receptor for the classical Wnt pathway; it is activated by the binding with a protein, named R-spondin 1 (Rspo1), which in turn results in the activation of Wnt signalling. *In situ* hybridization experiments have showed the expression of Lgr5 in a limited number of cells in the deepest zone of the crypts, in particular a limited number of cells able to rapidly enter the cell cycle and whose morphology corresponded to the description of CBC cells identified by Leblond. Morphological analysis of Lgr5⁺ cells in the deepest region of the crypts has shown that these cells are characterized by a wide base, a flat wedge-shaped nucleus, scarce cytoplasm and few organelles. Moreover, a slender extension of apical cytoplasm reaches between the neighbouring Paneth cells to the crypt lumen and carries some microvilli. The morphology of these Lgr5⁺ cells is completely different from the Paneth cells that are in the same region of the crypts and that are characterized by an abundance of granules and endoplasmic reticulum. The correspondence between the described morphology of Lgr5⁺ cells and those of CBC cells made from Cheng and Leblond, from which is possible to deduce that CBC cells express Lgr5, is very interesting. Moreover, Clevers and coworkers have traced the progeny of Lgr5⁺ CBC cells; researchers observed the appearance of ribbons of cells, coming from Lgr5⁺ CBC cells, that proliferate and migrate outside the crypt towards adjacent villus tips. This behaviour has confirmed the ability of CBC cells to renew the intestinal epithelium and histological analysis has shown their capacity to produce a cell progeny able to differentiate in all the different cell types of the intestinal epithelium. All these findings have permitted to identify in Lgr5+ cells of the deep bottom of the crypts the characteristics of pluripotency, longevity and self-renewal typical of stem cells, and to define the Lgr5 gene as a specific marker of intestinal stem cells. To this first one, other markers were added, such as growth factors Olfm4 and Ascl2; the latter is particularly important, since the deletion of this transcription factor leads to the complete loss of Lgr5+ cells, while transgenic expression of Ascl2 gives crypt hyperplasia. Notably, BMI1 does not seem to play a significant role in Lgr5+ intestinal stem cells, since BMI1 knockout mice have a normal crypt morphology, maintain Ascl2 and Olfm4 expression and have a normal intestinal epithelium. It remains to be defined whether and how BMI1+ cells in +4 position and Lgr5+ cells are related to each other. Some recent data suggest that stem cells in +4 position are quiescent and can generate Lgr5+ stem cells, thus sustaining a hypothesis of hierarchical interaction between these two types of intestinal stem cells. Studies by Buczacki et al., for example, focused on the relationship between Lgr5+ stem cells and the cells in +4 position, characterized by a slow cell cycle and by their label-retaining ability. Thanks to a series of experiments, researchers concluded that cells in +4 position are normally destined for differentiation in neuroendocrine cells or in Paneth cells, but they maintain the ability to reacquire functional characteristics typical of stem cells after cell damage or intestinal regeneration.

13.3 Intestinal stem cells and the stem cell niche

It is believed that the stem cells of different tissues have a well-defined localization and reside in a niche made of a nest of cells and their extracellular matrix that together maintain an optimal microenvironment for stem cell function and survival. The stem cell niche gives protection to stem cells, promoting their survival and genome protection. Functionally a niche can survive even if stem cells are removed. On the opposite, if stem cells are removed from a cell niche, they lose their stemness. Moreover, if a stem cell is lost, in the niche it could be replaced by asymmetrical division of other stem cells and a niche could be colonized after stem cell transplantation or after cell migration from other niches. Thanks to experiments of labelling with BrdU or tritiated thymidine, it has been possible to identify niche structure, with stem cells anchored in the lower region of the intestinal crypts and a population of TA cells that proliferate and differentiate, migrating outside the crypt to the villus tip, where they arrive terminally differentiated. In the gastrointestinal tract the stemness niche, in the intestinal crypts, seems to be composed of epithelial cells, the underlying mesenchymal cells of the lamina propria and all the factors secreted by these cells. The mesenchymal cell layer covers the epithelium and controls its function and behaviour through to the production of paracrine growth factors and cytokines whose receptors are located on epithelial cells. This specific structure allows different signalling pathways to act, albeit with different effects, on all the cells in the niche and allows all the cells to interact with each other. The ability of niches to modulate cell behaviour suggests that they could also have an important role in transdifferentiation and in proliferation disorders.

The SEMFs, the mesenchymal population underlying the basal membrane, seem to communicate with the overhead epithelial cell layer influencing its proliferation and regeneration through an epithelial-mesenchymal cross-talk: they could ultimately determine epithelial cell fate.

In order to determine the interactions between SEMFs and epithelial cells, a feeder layer of SEMFs has been cultured with epithelial cells (T84 cell line). Normally, T84 cells proliferate as monolayer, but after this co-culture they form roundish and compact cell aggregates with small lumen. Analysis by transmission electron microscope shows the formation of lumen with differentiation towards the enterocytic phenotype, also with the appearance of organized apical microvilli. This differentiation is blocked by co-culture in the transwell system that prevents direct cell-to-cell contact. Epithelial and mesenchymal cells talk to each other through paracrine and autocrine messages (i.e. TGF-beta, PDGF secretion) in order to control different activities and cell functions, such as differentiation and the production of specific molecules as components of the extracellular matrix. Interaction between stromal and epithelial stem cells (observed in studies of co-cultures with epithelial cell lines Caco-2 and HT-29) leads to an increase in TGF-beta and PDGF release and concentration in the microenvironment, and this increase in turn stimulates fibroblasts to differentiate towards myofibroblasts (α-SMA[+], tenascin[++], increase in deposition of chondroitin sulfate and versicane) and epithelial stem cells to differentiate to epithelial lineage.

13.4 Molecular markers and the intestinal stem cell regulation mechanism

Although numerous studies have clarified different aspects of the kinetics and mechanisms of self-renewal of the intestinal epithelium, the paucity of specific markers for intestinal stem cells has slowed down the identification and localization of the stem cells themselves. Numerous markers have been recently proposed as specific for intestinal stem cells. Cycling cell express markers, such as LGR5, CD133 on the cell surface, and nuclear transcription factors, such as SOX9 and HES1. Musashi 1 (MSI1) has been identified in cells of the deepest region of the intestinal crypt (position 1-10), while HES1 is expressed principally in cycling cells that are differentiating and migrating outside the crypt. Moreover, in mice models, Msi1 and Hes have been co-localized in the crypt in the cells above Paneth cells, i.e. the region which is considered to host stem cells.

The studies focused on the identification of specific markers of intestinal stem cells have

also favoured the identification and characterization of some molecular pathways that have emerged as fundamental regulators of stem cell behaviour. It seems that some of these pathways are involved in defining and maintaining the stem cell niche, fundamental for the maintenance of stemness, and that they act as indirect regulators of stem cells. Other pathways seem to regulate the proliferation and differentiation ability of stem cells, acting on them as direct regulators. Stem cells remain in the niche and divide rarely, while TA cells receive signals for proliferation and differentiation. These molecular pathways are stringently controlled through complex interactions, used to restrict pathway activity and response to the appropriate cell compartment. Mesenchymal- and epithelial-derived pathways determine polarized gradients that regulate stemness, cell proliferation, differentiation and apoptosis as the cells proceed along the crypt-villus axis. It is important to understand whether other factors in the niche give external different signals on stem cells and on proliferating cells, or whether the different behaviour of stem and TA cells reflects innate differences between these two cell populations.

13.4.1 Wnt signalling pathway

An increasing number of genes, ligands and receptors expressed on epithelial and mesenchymal cells in the gastrointestinal tract have been identified as molecular regulators of proliferation and differentiation in intestinal epithelial cells. Of interest is the signalling pathway of Wnt, a protein that belongs to a family of secreted glycoproteins, with a central role in determining cell fate. Signal transduction starts with the formation of a complex of receptors for Wnt that is composed of a transmembrane receptor, belonging to the Frizzled family, and of a member of the receptor family of LDL, Lrp5 or Lrp6. The central molecule in this signal transduction cascade is the cytosolic β-catenin, that normally, in the absence of Wnt, is phosphoriled in Ser/Thr conserved residues of the N-terminal region and, in this way, is driven to ubiquitin-proteasome degradation by the APC-axin-GSK3β complex. In the presence of secreted Wnt, it links to Frizzled (Fzd) receptors, leading to the activation of cytoplasmic phosphoprotein Dishevelled (Dsh), that in turn inhibits the trimeric APC-axin-GSK3β complex. This situation results in cytosolic β-catenin remaining unphosphorylated and not being driven to degradation; on the contrary, it accumulates in the cells at the bottom of the intestinal crypts. The increasing amount of β-catenin results in β-catenin itself translocating to the nucleus where it interacts with Tcf4, a member of the family of T cell factor/lymphocyte enhancer factor (Tcf/LEF), changing it from transcriptional repressor to activator. In this way, the final effect is the activation of some target genes responsible for cell proliferation and for

the determination of cell fate and crypt-villus polarity. By removing Wnt, APC translocates β-catenin from the nucleus to the cytoplasm, restoring the active transcriptional repression of Tcf4 (Figure 13.4).

The Tcf/LEF family includes 4 members: TCF1, LEF1, Tcf3 and Tcf4; in particular, the last one is directly involved in Wnt signalling since it interacts with β-catenin. Cells in the crypt, both in the colon and small intestine, accumulate nuclear β-catenin and Tcf4 is expressed in the developing intestine and in the epithelium of the adult intestine. Studies with knock out mice for Tcf4 showed that the animals lacked intestinal proliferating cells, suggesting that the compartment of stem cells was absent. These observations have led to hypotheses that Wnt signalling and the transcription factor Tcf4 are essential for the determination

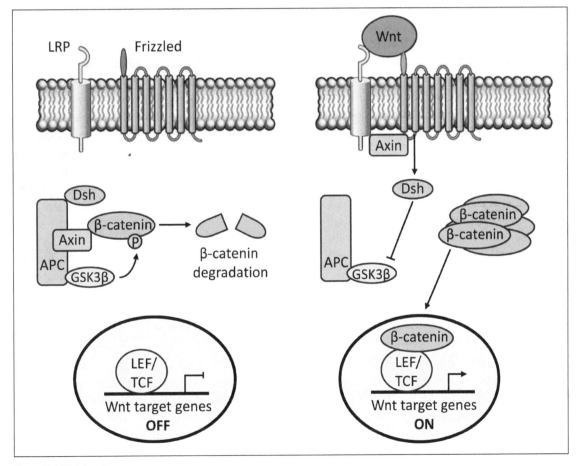

Figure 13.4. Wnt signalling.

of the stem cell population in crypts and for the maintenance of proliferating pressure in the stem cell niche during the development stages.

Tcf4 target genes include EphB2 and EphB3, which encode for two tyrosine kinase receptors, and the genes that encode their ligand Ephrin-B. Both receptor and ligand are surface molecules expressed in gradient: higher levels of EphB2 and EphB3 are at the base of the crypt and decrease going from the proliferation to the differentiation region of the epithelial progenitors. Instead the specific ligand has an opposite expression gradient, increasing from the proliferating region to the differentiation zone along the crypt-villus axis. This orderly expression of EphB and of its ligand restricts and limits the correct positioning of cells along the crypt-villus axis, resulting in a well-defined organization in the transition from the proliferation to the differentiation zone in the crypts. The absence of expression of EphB2 and EphB3 leads to the proliferating cells blending with already differentiated cells along the crypt-villus axis. This situation has been proved by studies on EphB3-/- mice in which Paneth cells do not follow the migration route to the crypt bottom, but are distributed indifferently along the crypt-villus axis.

C-myc and the cell cycle inhibitor p21 are included in the other Wnt target genes. C-myc is expressed in the nuclei of the crypt progenitors, while p21 is principally expressed in the nuclei of (Paneth cells and cells in the villus). These observations lead to suggest a role for c-myc in maintaining epithelial stem cells in a proliferating and undifferentiated state, and a central role for p21 as mediator of cell cycle arrest and of differentiation of the intestinal epithelium.

The Wnt signalling pathway is active in the normal adult intestinal epithelium and is fundamental for the formation of a normal crypt-villus axis, thanks to the ability to regulate the proliferation, position and differentiation of epithelial progenitors.

The Wnt signalling originates in the mesenchymal cells under the epithelium, coherently with the hypothesis that these cells play a role in maintaining the stem cell niche. Expression of Fzd receptors in SEMFs also suggests that secreted Wnt could act not only in a paracrine but in an autocrine way, as well. If Wnt signalling is fundamental for intestinal stem cell proliferation, on the other hand different levels of Wnt have different effects on the behaviour of stem cells in the niche. During the morphogenesis of crypts, SEMFs that secrete Wnt remain localized in the mesenchymal layer under the epithelium, near the base of the neo-formed crypts. In this way, a Wnt gradient develops all along the crypt-villus axis and has a different effect on epithelial cells, depending on the amount of Wnt received by them. The cells at the base of the crypts are influenced by high levels of Wnt, that lead to apoptosis. On the contrary, the cells at the top of the crypts, which are more distant from the Wnt source, get in touch with a low amount of protein and so go towards cell differentiation. Only the cells that are at a specific distance from the mesenchymal cells that produce Wnt receive the exact amount of protein necessary for them to be selected as the stem cells responsible for crypt maintenance. These observations show the role of Wnt signalling in the proliferation and conservation of stem cells, but it is still unclear how stem cells remain anchored to the niche despite the action of Wnt and how they escape from its signal to become TA cells and finally differentiate.

13.4.2 Notch signalling

If Wnt signalling is fundamental for cell proliferation, Notch signalling is implicated in cell fate regulation and in differentiation toward the four specialized cell lineages of the epithelium of the gastrointestinal tract. The Notch gene encodes for transmembrane receptors that interact with Delta and Jagged, the transmembrane ligands expressed by adjacent cells. This bond determines the proteolitic cut of the intracellular domain of Notch (NICD) that translocates to the nucleus and activates the transcription factor CSL, determining the specific transcription of selected genes (Figure 13.5).

Figure 13.5. Notch signalling.

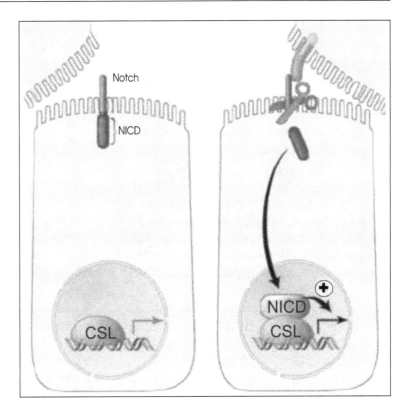

Among the well characterized Notch target genes, we must talk about those that codify for the transcription repressors of the Hes family. The nuclear helix-loop-helix proteins of the HES family regulate a series of downstream genes involved in cell fate determination. The intestine of animal models deficient for HES-1 shows an increased number of endocrine and mucosecreting cells, while the number of enterocytes is reduced. The activation of Hes-1 determines the negative regulation of the Math1 gene, a transcription activator. So, an increase of Notch gives, through activation of Hes1, a decrease in Math1 expression; it has been observed that null mice for Math1 show an inability to develop secretory lineage cells (goblet cells, Paneth and enteroendocrine cells). Anyway, the proliferating area in these mice shows an increase in cycling cell numbers, probably in an attempt to maintain crypt equilibrium, but the result is an increase in the number of enterocytes. Conversely, a decrease in Notch amounts and the subsequently increase of Delta ligands results in the block-

ing of Hes1, from which derives the increased Math1 expression that in turn leads to cell differentiation towards secretory lineages instead of enterocytes. From these observations it is clear that Notch signalling rules differentiation in the intestinal epithelium, controlling the choice between secretory or adsorbing lineage. Notch also seems to have a double function in the crypt: in addition to the control on the differentiation of the intestinal epithelium, it seems that Notch acts with Wnt in maintaining the proliferation rate and contributes to the control of crypt homeostasis in case of deletion or activation of the Wnt pathway.

13.4.3 BMP signalling

BMPs (Bone morphogenetic protein) are a group of cytokines that belong to the family of transforming growth factor β and participate to an important regulation pathway with a central role in intestinal development. Moreover, BMP signalling seems to be involved in the control of intestinal stem cell replication and in cell differentiation of the intestinal epithelium.

BMPs bind, in sequence, type II and type I serine-threonine kinase receptors, which are phosphoriled and determine the activation of SMAD transcriptional regulators. These regulators translocate to the nucleus where, interacting with transcription activators and repressors, they regulate the expression of target genes (Figure 13.6).

BMP signalling is antagonized by Noggin, an extracellular protein that binds BMP, blocking its activity. In this way there is a blocking of the signalling pathway that results in epithelial cell proliferation, a process that, if deregulated, could cause tumorigenesis. The receptors and ligands of this signalling way are expressed in the differentiated compartment of the intestine, both in epithelial and mesenchymal cells, and BMP4 is expressed in inter-villus mesenchymal cells in adult tissue. These observations together sustain a paracrine interlinking between the mesenchymal layer and the intestinal epithelium.

BMP signalling seems to negatively modulate Wnt signalling during development, preventing the self-renewal of stem cells. BMP acts by blocking β-catenin and Wnt signalling and, in this way, it can control intestinal stem cell duplication. BMP signalling, in the stemness niche at the crypt base, is strictly regulated by the expression of a gradient of antagonistic molecules (such as Noggin) that are exclusively expressed by the mesenchymal cells underlying the intestinal epithelium.

13.4.4 Hedgehog signalling

In vertebrates there are three Hedgehog genes with high homology: Sonic (Shh), Indian (Ihh) and Desert (Dhh) Hedgehog. Secreted Hedgehog proteins interact with three different transmembrane proteins localized on responsive cells: Smoothened (SMO), Patched (PTCH) and Hedgehog interacting protein (HIP). In absence of the specific ligand it seems that PTCH blocks the activity of SMO; after the binding between PTCH and one of the ligands of the Hedgehog family, SMO is released and no longer inhibited. This starts a signalling cascade that culminates in the translocation, from cytoplasm to nucleus, of proteins belonging to the GLI family of Zn-finger transcription factors. After this translocation, the members of the GLI family drive the expression of some target genes in cells that respond to the Hedgehog signalling.

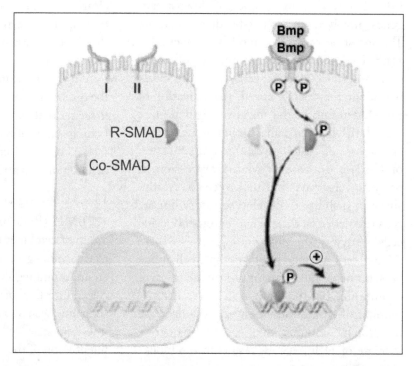

Figure 13.6. BMP signalling.

Ligands of Hedgehog act on development with a morphogenic action and control cell fate in a dose-dependent way. Shh gene encodes an important morphogenic protein with a role in regulating gastrointestinal development. Indeed, blocking Shh signalling in mice gives a pronounced increase in proliferation of gastric glandular cells; so, mice with homozygous deletion of Shh failed in developing a gastric epithelium. The exact role of Shh in intestinal epithelium is not yet completely clarified. Ihh, the principal protein of the Hedgehog family expressed in the intestine, is secreted in a paracrine way by differentiated epithelial cells and acts on the mesenchymal cells underlying the epithelium. Ihh seems to contribute to the maintenance of mesenchymal cell homeostasis and it seems to regulate the proliferation of epithelial cells, inducing the secretion of BMP by mesenchymal cells. Mice with homozygous deletion of Ihh show shortened villi and a reduced population of epithelial progenitors, suggesting a specific role for the Ihh gene in promoting cell proliferation and regeneration in the small intestine.

13.4.5 Interaction between molecular signalling and stemness niche determination

Overall, these molecular signalling cascades strictly interact with each other, taking to defining stemness niche and permitting to control the maintenance and proliferation of stem cells.

The stem cell niche is defined thanks to a strict epithelium-mesenchymal interaction, which limits Wnt expression to mesenchymal cells at the crypt base. The signals released by these Wnt expressing cells, combined with those obtained from epithelial cells in villi that express Ihh, determine the maintenance of mesenchymal BMP4 expression. BMP4 in turn has an inhibitory effect on Wnt expression, limiting it to mesenchymal cells that surround the crypt base. Ihh expression is limited to epithelial cells in the villus by a factor that is unknown, but that seems to depend on Wnt signalling.

Moreover, low levels of Wnt near the intermediate and upper region of the crypt seem to permit Notch to act on differentiation towards intestinal cell lineages and, in the same way, to suppress Wnt signals. The gradient of all these

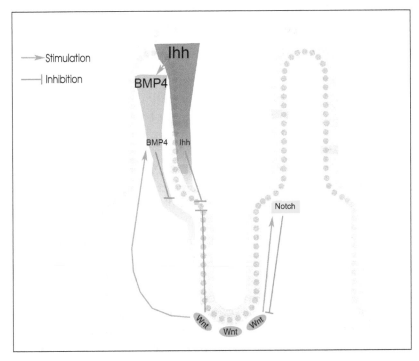

Figure 13.7. Epithelium-mesenchymal layer interaction.

factors in the crypt microenvironment seems to promote adhesion of the stem cells to the niche, proliferation of TA cells and differentiation of the epithelium. It seems that Wnt signalling represents a keystone for interaction of different molecular pathways that together participate to in the regulation of intestinal stem cells and it seems that Wnt creates the basis for different morphogenic actions in the niche microenvironment (Figure 13.7).

13.5 *In vitro* culture of intestinal stem cells

The absence of a standard method of *in vitro* cell culture for expansion of primary cells from intestinal tissue has slowed down the studies focused on the characterization of intestinal stem cells. Recently the research group of Clevers has identified a cell culture method for crypt and intestinal stem cells, both murine and human, and these have been the first of a series of studies focused on improving protocols for *in vitro* culture of intestinal stem cells.

Until the experimental work of Clevers and colleagues, no cell culture protocols had been identified that were able to maintain *in vitro* and in the long term the basal physiology of the crypt-villus system. Trying to overcome this lack of knowledge, Clevers and co-workers have tried to recreate a culture system that could consider and combine all the necessities of physiological growth previously identified for the intestinal epithelium. First, they tried to solve the principal problem that intestinal cells have to solve when they are isolated from their normal tissue: the phenomenon of *anoikis*, i.e. an apoptosis due to the absence of cell-matrix interactions. The crypt base is rich in laminin (α1 and 2) which gives support to the aforementioned cells of the intestinal epithelium; for this reason, researchers have thought to give a similar support to intestinal cells by culturing them *in vitro* on a Matrigel layer enriched with laminin, in order to support in a more physiological way the growth of intestinal epithelium *in vitro*. Second, the attention

of the researchers focused on the central role of Wnt signalling in crypt proliferation and, in particular, on the action of the Wnt agonist, R-spondin1, that *in vivo* induces a pronounced hyperplasia of crypts. Moreover, they thought that, to favour the success of the protocol of *in vitro* culture of intestinal crypts, other elements were necessary, such as the addition of EGF, which is associated with intestinal proliferation, and of Noggin, that induces expansion in the number of crypts and cell differentiation. The combination of these two factors has permitted to obtain *in vitro* stable cell cultures starting from murine intestinal crypts. Original crypts recovered from intestinal tissue, dissociated and cultured on Matrigel, have rapidly produced organized structures with a central lumen, with apoptotic cells in it, and crypts with a bottom region that hosted Paneth cells and that were involved in phenomena of "budding", reminiscent of the crypt fission process. The additional expansion of these structures has created real organoids, with more than 40 crypt-like structures that surrounded a central lumen delimited by an epithelium similar to the intestinal epithelium of villi. These organoids were weekly dissociated and re-seeded at lower cell density and gave new organoids; the organoids were cultured in this way for more than 8 months without losing any initially described characteristics. The in-depth analyses of the cell components of these organoids have shown, not only the presence of Paneth cells at the bottom of the crypts, but also the presence of Lgr5$^+$ stem cells interposed with Paneth cells.

The same research group has obtained *in vitro* cell cultures starting from single Lgr5$^+$ stem cells. The addition to the culture *medium* of an inhibitor of Rho, able to block *anoikis* and to avoid the sudden death of single cells after the seeding *in vitro*, has led to the development of organoids starting from single stem cells positive for Lgr5 expression. The organoids obtained from single stem cells were totally similar to the ones obtained from crypt cultures; in both cases, there were all the cell types of the intestinal epithelium (enterocytes, Paneth cells, enteroendocrine and goblet cells) and they were also structurally organized according to the normal crypt-villus axis, with Paneth cells at the bottom of the crypts. However, histological analysis of these organoids has showed the absence, under the epithelial cells, of mesenchymal stroma; the crypt structure and the central lumen were defined by a single layer of polarized epithelial cells directly leaned against the Matrigel layer. The absence in this culture system of subepithelial myofibroblasts (SEMF), that normally contribute in creating a specialized niche at the bottom of the crypt, demonstrates that a limited set of specific growth factors permit to stabilize *in vitro* an epithelium with normal ability of self-renewal and able of organizing structures similar to crypts, with all the intestinal cell types created *de novo* from intestinal stem cells.

The culture system used for murine crypts and intestinal stem cells has also been used for cultures of human intestinal epithelial cells. In this case, in addition to the factors used for murine cell cultures, it has been necessary to add other molecules identified through a wide screening of growth factors, hormones and vitamins. The researchers of Clevers' team have identified in nicotinamide, gastrin, Alk4/5/7 inhibitor and p38 inhibitor the ability to extend the time in culture and to expand human intestinal cells in the long term. The confirmation of these abilities has been obtained by following tests where, removing nicotinamide, p38 and R-spondin1 from the culture medium, cell proliferation was blocked, while cell differentiation to all the cell types in the intestinal epithelium was stimulated. This culture system, that led to organoids, gives the possibility to recreate *in vitro* the architecture, physiology and the full complex of interaction between the cells that are normally present in intestinal tissue *in vivo*.

Recently, Wang and colleagues have described another method of supporting the long-term culture of intestinal stem cells from human fetal and adult tissues. In this system, a single cell suspension was seeded on a feeder layer of murine fibroblast, in order to recreate *in vitro* the physiological support given by SEMFs *in vivo*. The cells grew in bi-dimensional colonies maintaining their self-renewal ability and genetic stability for the entire time and through all passages in culture. In this condition the cells were expanded as bi-dimensional colonies on the fibroblast feeder layer without differentiating and, only with the addition of the same factors used by the group of Clevers and thanks to the use of a specific air-liquid interface, did stem cells start to generate all the differentiated cell types normally present in the intestine, partially mimicking the intestinal anatomy. Thanks to this culture method, stem cells differentiated in different intestinal cell types, but it was not clear if the dynamic intestinal turnover was recreated and how it could resemble what happens *in vivo*.

The studies made by Clevers and colleagues and the many other studies made by numerous research groups that followed confirm in an increasingly incisive way the possibility of culturing in vitro intestinal stem cells and of obtaining organoids that mimic in vitro the crypt-villus structure. These cultures will make it possible to deepen the studies and the knowledge on the biology of intestinal stem cells, in the events involved in tumorigenesis of colon cancer and will also provide a useful tool for toxicology, pharmacology and microbiology studies; these studies would be able to rely on a culture system that will be more similar to the real intestinal physiology and they will give more reliable results in comparison to the *in vitro* studies made until now that generally used intestinal cell lines.

Recommended reading and references

1. Leedham SJ, et al. *Intestinal stem cells.* J Cell Mol Med 2005.

2. Brittan M, Wright NA. *Stem cell in gastrointestinal structure and neoplastic development*; Gut 2004.

3. Wong MH. *Regulation of intestinal stem cells.* J Investid Dermatol Symp Proc, 2004 Sep.

4. Mahida YR, et al. *Adult human colonic subepithelial myofibroblasts express extracellular matrix proteins and cyclooxigenase-1 and -2.* Am J Physiol 1997.

5. Powell DW, et al. *Myofibroblasts. II. Intestinal subepithelial myofibroblasts.* Am J Physiol 1999.

6. Rizvi AZ, et al. *Epithelial stem cells and their niche: there's no place like home.* Stem Cells 2005.

7. Reya T, et al. *Wnt signalling in stem cells and cancer.* Nature 2005

8. Batlle E, et al. *β-catenin and TCF mediate cell positioning in the intestinal epithelium by controlling the expression of EphB/EphrinB.* Cell 2002.

9. Radtke F, et al. *Self-renewal and cancer of the gut: two sides of a coin.* Science 2005

10. Sancho E, et al. *Signalling pathways in intestinal development and cancer.* Annu Rev Cell Dev Biol 2004.

11. Fre S, et al. *Notch signals control tha fate of immature progenitor cells in the intestine.* Nature 2005.

12. Holmberg J, et al. *EphB receptors coordinate migration and proliferation in the intestinal stem cell niche.* Cell 2006.

13. Blanpain C, et al. *Epithelial stem cells: turning over new leaves.* Cell 2007

14. Pinto D, et al. *Canonical Wnt signals are essential for homeostasis of the epithelium.* Genes and development 2003.

15. Barker N, et al. *Lgr proteins in epithelial stem cell biology.* Development 2013.

16. Barker N, et al. *The intestinal stem cell.* Genes & Development 2008.

17. Medema JP, Vermeulen L. *Microenvironmental regulation of stem cells in intestinal homeostasis and cancer.* Nature 2011.

18. Fujii M, Sato T. *Culturing intestinal stem cells: applications for colorectal cancer research.* Frontiers in Genetics 2014.

19. Biswas S, et al. *Microenvironmental control of stem cells fate in intestinal homeostasis and disease.* Journal of Pathology 2015.

20. Wang X, et al. *Cloning and variation of ground state intestinal stem cells.* Nature 2015.

Stem Cells and the Liver

14

Fabio Marongiu

14.1 Morphological and functional characteristics of the liver

The liver is a rather complex organ that performs a great number of vital functions, including the metabolism of fats and sugars, the production and secretion of bile, and the manufacture of essential proteins. The liver also acts as the main "filter" of our body, contributing to the removal of potentially toxic metabolites derived from alcohol, drugs and the environment.

All these functions are carried out by various types of cells that are strictly interconnected with one another, albeit each with their specific independent roles (Figure 14.1). These cells are:

- **hepatocytes**: they represent the main cell type in the liver and constitute the hepatic epithelial parenchyma;
- **biliary cells** or cholangiocytes: they constitute the epithelium of the bile ducts;
- **endothelial cells:** they line the interior surface of vascular structures;
- **Kupffer cells:** they are specialized macrophages that reside in the liver;
- **stellate cells:** they are localized around the hepatic capillaries and perform several functions, including the regulation of capillary blood flow;
- **mesenchymal cells:** they constitute the stroma.

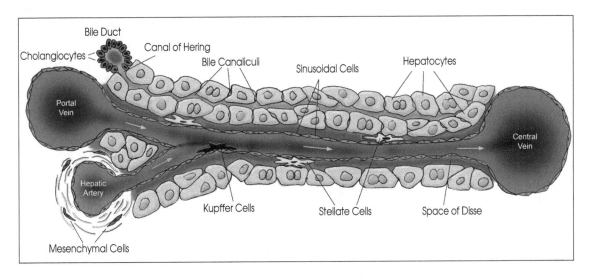

Figure 14.1. Schematic representation of the structural unit of the liver and the spatial relation between different types of liver cells.

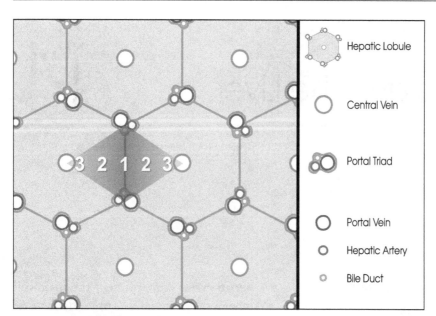

Figure 14.2.
Representative schematic representation of the microscopical organization of liver lobules.

At the microscopic level, the liver is organized into peculiar structures, called lobules (Figure 14.2). The hepatic lobule is defined as the functional unit of the liver and is constituted by strings of hepatocytes organized radially around a central vein. As depicted in Figure 1, in between two strings of hepatocytes are the blood capillaries (called sinusoids) and the bile canaliculi. At each lobule vertex, a portal space is present, which is constituted of a branch of the portal vein, a branch of the hepatic artery, a bile duct and a lymphatic vessel.

The liver receives a dual blood supply: the flow from the hepatic artery mainly provides the oxygen necessary for the maintenance of liver cells; the flow from the portal vein carries the blood drained from the spleen, the gastrointestinal tract, and its associated organs, which is poor in oxygen but rich in nutrients. Both the arterial and venous flow merge and stream along the sinusoids. Thanks to the interaction with the hepatocytes, respiratory and metabolic exchanges can occur, and the "transformed" blood can proceed towards the centrilobular veins.

Bile, which is metabolized and secreted by the hepatocytes, flows in the opposite direction: it is secreted within the space between two adjacent hepatocytes, where the bile canaliculi originate. These lead to the interlobular ducts within the portal tracts.

14.2 Embryonic development of the liver

During gastrulation and early somitogenesis, the endoderm (the germ layer from which internal organs, including the liver, originate) is patterned into the foregut, midgut, and hindgut along the anterior-posterior axis by signalling factors secreted from the adjacent mesoderm. The *fibroblast growth factor* (FGF), Wnt, *bone morphogenic protein* (BMP), and retinoic acid signalling pathways are implicated in this patterning. If foregut patterning does not occur properly, the liver that derives from the foregut endoderm does not form properly. Alteration of any of these signalling pathways during early somitogenesis, for example when Wnt/β-catenin signalling is suppressed or overactivated, results in a failure of liver formation.

The following phases of liver development lead to the so-called hepatic competence, where cells gain the ability to respond to hepatic inducing signals, thereby giving rise to hepatoblasts.

This stage is mainly regulated by transcription factors, such as FOXA and GATA, that have the ability to bind to their target sites in the compacted chromatin and locally open it, thus permitting the subsequent binding of additional factors.

At this stage, the anterior intestinal endoderm is defined as dorsal and ventral. Competent cells can now receive and respond to specific signals for hepatic differentiation. Three hepatic inducing signals have been identified so far, FGF, BMP, and Wnt, which are secreted by the cardiac mesoderm and the septum transversum mesenchyme. These tissues are adjacent to the ventral foregut endoderm. Therefore, liver specification occurs in a discrete region of the endoderm, where cells respond differentiating into hepatoblasts and originating the liver bud.

Hepatoblasts are the bipotential progenitors that will eventually become either hepatocytes or cholangiocytes. These cells have a high nucleus-to-cytoplasm ratio and are interspersed among haematopoietic cells and other non-parenchymal cells in the developing liver, although no defined tissue organization is present at this stage. Hepatoblasts express specific markers (e.g. *Delta-Like 1 Homolog*, Dlk1), together with markers of fetal (*alpha-fetoprotein*, α-FP) and of adult hepatocytes (*Albumin*, Alb; *Hepatocyte Nuclear Factor 4 alpha*, HNF4A). As liver development continues, these cells commit to being hepatocytes or cholangiocytes (which express *cytokeratin 19*, CK19), although the processes that determine their fate are far from being fully elucidated. However, it has been established that, once committed to the hepatocyte cell fate, hepatoblasts gradually acquire liver-enriched transcription factors that in turn regulate the expression of genes that make them polarized, cuboidal, and functional cells. Various growth factors and cytokines are involved in this process, together with cell-cell interactions that enable the upregulation of certain transcription factors, while others are downregulated.

Several signalling molecules are implicated in the lineage determination of hepatoblasts to cholangiocytes. A key cellular interaction guiding this process is between the hepato-blasts and the neighbouring developing portal vein. In fact, there exists a gradient of activin/TGFβ with the highest exposure limited to the cells around the portal mesenchyme which allows for the differentiation of hepatoblasts to cholangiocytes. Other important inputs for this process are those coming from the Jagged/Notch signalling pathway.

Right after they originate from hepatoblasts, hepatocytes look distinct from hepatocytes at later stages of hepatic development, where they acquire a cuboidal morphology and a clear cytoplasm due to glycogen accumulation. This indicates that hepatocytes continue to change their characteristics and functional capabilities drastically both perinatally as well as postnatally, under the control of factors such as Oncostatin M, glucorticoids, hepatocyte growth factor and Wnt.

Hepatocytes also begin to acquire characteristics and functions that are location-specific. In adult life, in fact, liver cells possess distinct properties based on their location in the hepatic lobule.

The hepatocytes located in close proximity to the hepatic inflow around the portal triad are referred to as being in the periportal zone (zone 1), while those around central vein are located in the centrizonal or pericentral zone (zone 3). Zone 2 is composed of the hepatocytes lying in between the other two zones (Figure 2). The functions of hepatocytes in the periportal, mid-, or pericentral zones are distinct and this is due, at least in part, to a gradient of nutrients, oxygen and metabolites in the blood flow.

In fact, hepatocytes in zone 1 are in contact with both portal and arterial blood flow, which is rich in substrates and oxygen, so they have a high oxidative and biosynthetic metabolism; on the other hand, pericentral hepatocytes are more active in glycolysis and ketogenesis.

Several proteins typical of hepatocytes (e.g. *cytochrome P45 enzymes*, CYP) are expressed differently in cells of different zones. A determinant role for the establishment of metabolic zonation is played by the Wnt/β-catenin signalling pathway. β-Catenin is highly expressed in the pericentral area and many of the genes downstream of this signalling are upregulated in the hepatocytes located in this zone.

Although this zonal specification is marked in adult hepatocytes, some cell transplantation experiments have shown that hepatocytes isolated from one zone or another, once transplanted in a recipient liver, acquire the phenotype of the zone in which they engraft. This suggests that adult hepatocytes retain a certain degree of plasticity, and that the microenvironment that surrounds them provides cues that are fundamental for the determination of their metabolic/functional profile.

14.3 Liver regeneration and progenitor cells

In most tissues with a high turnover or high regenerative capacity, the loss of parenchyma is followed by the genesis of new cells, thanks to the presence of adult stem cells or progenitor cells that, through well-regulated and complex mechanisms, have the ability to proliferate and differentiate into one or more cell types in order to maintain/restore tissue homeostasis. For many of these organs, there is extensive knowledge of the mechanisms that regulate the differentiation of stem cells in proliferating progenitor cells first and in terminally differentiated mature cells later, as well as of the signalling pathways that oversee these differentiation stages. However, the mechanisms that regulate these processes in the liver are yet to be fully elucidated.

14.3.1 Physiological turnover

Cell turnover in the liver is relatively slow. In the absence of damage, in fact, hepatocytes have a low proliferation index, with an average life of 200-300 days. In 1985, Zajicek and colleagues proposed the *streaming liver* hypothesis to explain the slow but steady renewal of hepatocytes. Inspired by the continuous regeneration of the intestinal epithelium, this hypothesis proposed that the hepatocytes originated

from cells present in the periportal area (zone 1), which had stem-like characteristics. From there, hepatocytes would slowly move towards the central vein where they would eventually be eliminated. This model has been intensively debated over the last 30 years. Some studies supporting this hypothesis have shown that the liver contains clonal zones of hepatocytes that share the same mitochondrial mutations and extend from the periportal spaces to the central vein. Recent studies have also shown that new hepatocytes are slowly but steadily generated from a population of periportal cells expressing the Sox-9 transcription factor. However, this conclusion was subsequently questioned by other researchers who used similar systems to trace the newly formed hepatocytes and follow their fate. None of these studies has shown a significant contribution of biliary and/or periportal cells to normal hepatocyte turnover, leaving still open the question about the real existence of a stem cell population in the liver that participates in physiological conditions.

14.3.2 Regeneration after acute damage

Despite its slow cell turnover, the adult liver retains an impressive regenerative capacity. Classic experiments on rats have shown that, following partial hepatectomy, the liver is able to restore its initial mass within a few days. Although this process takes a longer time in humans (a few weeks), the regenerative capacity of the liver forms the basis for various clinical interventions, including partial hepatectomy (e.g. to remove liver tumours) or living-donor transplants, where a considerable portion of the donor liver is removed and transplanted into a recipient: both parts will regenerate to restore the correct mass of the organ for the two different individuals.

This type of regeneration occurs exclusively through the division of mature epithelial cells (hepatocytes), which leave their normal state of replicative quiescence (G0) to enter the cell cycle and mitotically divide. With this extraordinary regenerative capacity, the hepatocytes can be unquestionably considered as the main "stem cell" of the liver, being able to divide more than 100 times without loss of function. Although this ability may seem astounding, it is certainly justified if one considers the physiological role of hepatocytes. During the normal life of each individual, they are continually exposed to a series of endogenous and exogenous elements that they have to metabolize and process. However, due to the potential toxic nature of these substances or their metabolites, a certain number of hepatocytes may undergo necrosis, the extent of which may be mild or clinically important. After acute damage caused by toxins or viral infections, the liver is able to efficiently regenerate, restoring its mass even after extensive necrosis (up to more than half its mass). The undamaged hepatocytes will be able to carry out some replication cycles until the hepatic mass is completely restored.

14.3.3 Regeneration after chronic damage

In the context of chronic liver injury, the regenerative ability of mature hepatocytes is progressively compromised. In many liver diseases, such as chronic viral hepatitis and those conditions leading to alcoholic and non-alcoholic steato-hepatitis, hepatocytes are commonly observed to acquire a senescent phenotype and are no longer able to effectively regenerate the hepatic parenchyma. In this scenario, a pool of cells, generally defined as hepatic progenitor cells (HPC), is activated. These cells are able to differentiate into both hepatocytes and biliary epithelial cells. Studies on HPCs are increasingly common, although their biology is less studied compared to progenitor cells in other adult tissues. Moreover, the identification of the quiescent and proliferating populations of these cells is still difficult, as specific markers are yet to be clearly defined.

Origin and nature of HPCs

Various studies on rodents have revealed that, in the presence of chronic damage (e.g. choline-deficient diet model) a population of small cells, with an ovoid-shaped nucleus and a high nuclear/ cytoplasmic ratio, emerges in the periportal regions. These cells have been named "oval cells" and are characterized by the simultaneous expression of hepatocyte (Alb) and biliary epithelial cell (CK19) markers. Cells with similar, though not identical, characteristics have also been described in humans and mice, and have been more generally defined as HPCs. A three-dimensional reconstruction of the human liver has shown that these cells seem to originate from the canals of Hering, i.e. from the interface region between the biliary canal system and the actual biliary tree.

Several animal models have been used to induce the appearance of HPCs in rodents. For example, in rats, combining partial hepatectomy with the chemical inhibition of differentiated hepatocyte replication (using 2-acetylaminofluorene or retrorsine) resulted in a marked proliferative response from HPCs. This phenomenon is often referred to as "ductular reaction" because, due to their characteristics and their position near the periportal regions, it has been hypothesized that these cells derive from cells of the biliary system. However, their origin has not yet been conclusively demonstrated. Moreover, there is indirect evidence in humans to suggest the existence of a link between ductular reaction and hepatocytes, thus hypothesizing that hepatocytes themselves might be "dedifferentiating" to give rise to HPCs.

Although several molecules expressed by HPCs (including CK7, αFP, OV6, Lgr5) have been proposed as a marker, none of these allows for their unambiguous identification.

Regenerative ability of HPCs

In order to restore the function of a damaged liver, bipotent HPCs must be able to differentiate into hepatocytes, the parenchymal cell of the liver, and cholangiocytes. *In vitro* studies have shown that HPCs possess a high clonogenic and proliferative capacity, and are able to differentiate both in cells with the features of hepatocytes and in cholangiocytes. Several recent studies on animal models have shown that HPCs can contribute to the regeneration of hepatocytes and cholangiocytes *in vivo*. Although HPCs have a phenotype that is largely closer to the biliary epithelial cells, it appears to be a heterogeneous population containing various sub-types of cells with characteristics ranging from the most primitive progenitors to cells with the characteristics of mature hepatocytes.

The type of damage and the so-called "niche" (i.e. the microenvironment in which HPCs are found) are fundamental in determining the fate of these cells. As a result of damage to the biliary system, for example, fibroblasts secrete Notch ligands, which lead to the activation of its signalling pathway in and around the niche, thus promoting biliary tract regeneration. On the contrary, if the damage is to the hepatocytes, macrophages increase the production of Wnt in response to the increased phagocytosis of dead cells. In turn, this seems to promote the differentiation of HPCs into hepatocytes. However, the actual contribution of HPCs to liver regeneration in the event of chronic damage is still controversial. During regeneration processes, in fact, only a small part (1-3%) of the newly formed hepatocytes seems to originate from HPCs. Although these numbers only represent a small proportion of mature hepatocytes, one must take into account the fact that most animal models present with moderate liver damage which is often short-termed when compared to chronic diseases in humans. Further experiments are needed to determine the actual regenerative capacity of HPCs in the presence of severe, prolonged or repeated damage that is able to effectively mimic what is observed in human pathology.

14.4 Stem cell transplantation for the regeneration of the liver

Liver diseases include:

a. acute injuries (i.e. due to the accumulation of toxic compounds) in which hepatic cells are unable to perform their function, thus leading to liver failure;

b. chronic insults to the liver (e.g. continuous consumption of alcohol) which lead to fibrosis and cirrhosis that prompt the emergence of hepatocellular carcinoma (HCC) in the liver;

c. metabolic diseases (inherited or acquired) where a functional deficit can lead to a variety of outcomes.

Liver transplantation is currently the only available therapeutic option for a wide range of liver diseases, including acute and chronic liver failure and a number of liver-based inborn defects. Although this is a well-established procedure and patient survival has significantly increased over the last decades, some major issues still need to be addressed. Firstly, patients are kept under immunosuppressive therapy for the rest of their life: this is often associated with severe complications due to the high toxicity of the immunosuppressive agents, which can also increase the risk of the development of cancer. Moreover, the availability of useful organs for transplantation is limited by the insufficient number of donors. Great improvement has been brought by the use of split-liver from living donors; however, a great number of patients still die while waiting for an organ to be available.

For this reason, the research field of regenerative medicine attempts to maximize the repair potential of the liver, an organ that retains significant regenerative capacity. The use of isolated cells, including stem cells, is being considered as a possible therapeutic tool for the management of human disease, including liver disease. This approach attempts to achieve two main goals:

• To favour the endogenous regeneration and remodelling of the liver architecture, by promoting the activation of physiological repair mechanisms (i.e. activation of the liver progenitor cell compartment). Ideally, this could be achieved by means of exogenous modulatory factors (such as cytokines, growth factors, etc.) or through the transplantation of a cell type that is able to produce and release such factors.

This approach would be relevant for those types of liver disease where a chronic insult is the cause of major structural alterations, such as fibrosis and cirrhosis;

- To replace a damaged cell type by repopulating the liver parenchyma with healthy counterparts. In this scenario, two options can be considered: (a) the transplantation of terminally differentiated hepatocytes, in order to provide a temporary metabolic support under conditions of acute functional failure. This could serve as a bridge to whole organ transplantation or, in the most desirable outcome, it could foster the regeneration and/or functional recovery of the endogenous liver, thereby avoiding the need for liver transplantation altogether; (b) the transplantation of a stem/progenitor cell type. In this case, the correction of a chronic functional deficit (inborn or acquired) can be achieved by long-term engraftment of the cells into the host parenchyma, provided that they are able to differentiate and/or express the defective/missing function.

14.4.1 The use of stem cells for the reduction of fibrosis

Liver fibrosis occurs in a variety of medical conditions, including chronic exposure to toxic compounds or alcohol, viral infections or metabolic disorders. In these settings, the production and deposition of collagen and other extracellular proteins, resulting from chronic parenchymal damage and the ensuing activation of hepatic stellate cells (HSC), leads to the accumulation of scar tissue within the liver. Progressive fibrosis frequently evolves towards cirrhosis, where severe scarring to the liver constrains functional hepatocytes into regenerative nodules, thus severely altering the structure and reducing the ability of this organ to carry out its normal functions. Liver cirrhosis is also a major risk factor for the emergence of HCC.

Several stem cell types, including amnion-derived mesenchymal stromal cells (hAMSC) and epithelial cells (hAEC), have been tested for their ability to modulate the progression of fibrosis in experimental animals.

AMSCs have been transplanted in a model of liver fibrosis that is based on the chronic administration of carbon tetrachloride. In this model, donor cells were able to engraft and modulate the progression of the fibrosis, with a decrease in collagen deposition and a reduction of the pro-inflammatory and pro-fibrotic cytokines typically expressed during fibrogenic processes. Moreover, it was shown that stem cell transplantation reduced the activation of the stellate cell compartment, reducing the apoptosis and senescence of hepatocytes, and favouring their proliferation.

In another study, human amniotic membrane patches were applied on the surface of the liver following bile duct ligation. These patches were able to reduce the progression of the fibrosis and decreased ductular reaction, myofibroblast activation and collagen deposition.

Based on these studies, a main consideration emerges: while hAECs and hAMSCs were shown to engraft and express some phenotypic features of hepatocytes, such as albumin production and secretion, there was no evidence of cell proliferation. Moreover, no signs of cell engraftment were reported with the use of amniotic membrane patches. It appears therefore that in all these cases there is no direct contribution of amnion-derived cells to the remodelling of the liver architecture, thus suggesting that the modulation of fibrosis progression is possibly achieved via paracrine effects that these cells exert on the surrounding tissue. hAMSCs are known to produce and release several anti-inflammatory and immunomodulatory cytokines.

Although in this context there is no direct involvement of amnion-derived cells in tissue remodelling, they retain a high regenerative potential that can hopefully be exploited in a clinical setting in the near future.

14.4.2 Differentiation of stem cells into hepatocytes and their possible applications

There are a number of diseases where the functional capability of the liver is impaired, due to either a general damage of the hepatocytes or a specific function that is lost in an otherwise efficient cell population. In both these cases, aiming at a paracrine effect of transplanted cells on resident hepatocytes would not represent a rational approach.

Based on this premise, transplantation of differentiated hepatocytes has been proposed as a method to support liver function in acute or chronic hepatic failure and as a "cell therapy" for metabolic diseases in the liver. Numerous studies in animal models clearly indicate that hepatocytes, delivered through the spleen or the portal vein, display normal hepatic function in the recipient liver. Over 100 human hepatocyte transplants have been performed worldwide in patients with a variety of liver diseases. While still preliminary, the results of these early studies are promising and suggest that hepatocyte transplantation could be a relatively inexpensive and most effective therapy for liver disease.

An important factor limiting the use of hepatocyte transplants in additional medical centres is the availability of hepatocytes. The only source of cells for hepatocyte transplants are livers that are unsuitable for whole organ transplantation. Nowadays, also livers that once were considered unideal for transplantation (e.g. extensive steatosis), can be rescued and utilized in the clinics. This further limits the source for hepatocyte isolation.

Despite their great regenerative potential *in vivo*, isolated human hepatocytes rapidly lose their ability to proliferate and their functional characteristics when cultured *in vitro*. Since their fully differentiated phenotype is largely regulated by the surrounding microenvironment, the effects of cytokines, cell-to-cell and cell-to-matrix interactions and other physical factors are being studied for the development of efficient culture systems for the expansion and maintenance of hepatocytes *in vitro*.

Table 14.1. Molecular markers of hepatocytes:

Plasma Proteins	
Albumin	
Alpha-fetoprotein (predominantly in fetal hepatocytes)	

Cytochrome P450	
CYP 1A2 (adult isoform) - CYP 1A1 (foetal isoform)	
CYP 3A4 (adult isoform) - CYP 3A7 (foetal isoform)	
CYP 2B6	
CYP 2C8	
CYP 2C9	
CYP 2C19	
CYP 2D6	
CYP 7A1	

Phase II enzymes	
UGT1A1	(UDP glucuronosyltransferase 1, A1)
UGT1A6	(UDP glucuronosyltransferase 1, A6)
UGT1A9	(UDP glucuronosyltransferase 1, A9)

Other enzymes	
A1AT	(Alpha -1 antitrypsin)
OTC	(Ornithine transcarbamylase)
G6P	(Glucose-6-phosphatase)
TAT	(Tyrosine aminotransferase)
GGT1	(Gamma-glutamyltransferase 1)
SULT2A1	(Sulfotransferase, 2A)
GLUL	(Glutamine synthetase)
CPS1	(Carbamoyl-phosphate synthetase 1)
GSTP1	(Glutathione S-transferase)
PAH	(Phenylalanine hydroxylase)

Transport Proteins	
P-gp	(P glycoprotein - ATP-binding cassette, B1 (ABCB1 - MDR1))
MDR3	(Multidrug resistant protein 3 (ABCB4))
BSEP	(Bile Salt Export Pump (ABCB11))
MRP2	(Multidrug resistant protein 2 (ABCC2))
NTCP	(Sodium/bile acid cotransporter 1 (SLC10A1))
ABST	(Sodium/bile acid cotransporter 2 (SLC10A2))

Transcription factors and nuclear receptors	
HNF4α	(Hepatic nuclear factor 4 alpha)
HNF6	(Hepatic nuclear factor 6)
C/EBPα	(CCAAT/enhancer binding protein, alpha)
C/EBPb	(CCAAT/enhancer binding protein, beta)
GATA4	(GATA binding protein 4)
AHR	(Aryl hydrocarbon receptor)
FXR	(Nuclear receptor subfamily 1, H4)
PXR	(Nuclear receptor subfamily 1, I2)
CAR	(Nuclear receptor subfamily 1, I3)
RARα	(Retinoic acid receptor, alpha)

Structural and surface proteins	
CK8	(Cytokeratin 8 (CK8))
CK18	(Cytokeratin 18 (CK18))
CX32	(Connexin 32, Gap junction prot. beta 1 (GJB1))
ASGR1	(Asialoglycoprotein receptor)
MET	(HGF receptor)
ITGB4	(Integrin, beta 4 (CD104))

For these reasons, a wider use of hepatocyte transplantation will not be possible until alternative sources of cells are found.

Considering the great plasticity of stem cells, several research groups have tested their ability to differentiate into hepatocytes, by means of different culture systems *in vitro*. Adult stem cells, embryonic stem cells (ES) and induced pluripotent stem cells (iPS) have been vastly studied as candidates for differentiation into liver cells. Contrary to hepatocytes, their great *in vitro* proliferative potential allows a substantial expansion so that sufficient numbers could be available for both cell therapy and tissue engineering.

The most common strategy for the differentiation of stem cells into hepatocytes is to take into account what is known about liver development during embryogenesis. The general idea is that the administration of several growth factors and hormones at very specific times is able to induce the expression of those transcription factors that regulate the expression of genes/proteins typical of hepatocytes. Although several encouraging results exist, the literature regarding stem cell-derived hepatocytes is rather controversial.

In order for one to claim that a stem cell has acquired the mature hepatocyte phenotype, it is necessary for the cell to fulfil a number of criteria. The first one is the concomitant expression (both at gene and protein level) of different markers typical of hepatocytes (Table 14.1). Moreover, differentiated cells should have the ability to perform several specific metabolic functions (Table 14.2).

In some reports, only a partial analysis of differentiated cells is performed. Although some claim full differentiation into hepatocytes, the analysis is often limited to the expression of albumin and a few more proteins, with a partial assessment of the metabolic capacity, if any. Moreover, comparison with an appropriate positive control, such as authentic mature hepatocytes, is often absent. All these factors make for a difficult interpretation of the actual differentiative potential of stem cells.

Differentiation of embryonic stem cells and induced pluripotent stem cells

Besides their marked proliferative capacity, ESs have the advantage, as compared to other stem cells, to differentiate into cells from all three germ layers. There are several reports on the differentiation of ESs into hepatocyte-like cells that could be used for the engineering of bioartificial livers to support the hepatic function while waiting for an organ to be available.

However, several problems still exist concerning

i.   the possible emergence of teratomas,
ii. immune-compatibility, and
iii. ethical issues, that still limit the use of ES-derived cells for transplantation.

In order to avoid the last two problems, strategies have been developed to create iPSs from fibroblasts and other adult cells, by genetic manipulation. iPSs have to ability to

Table 14.2 Metabolic assay for the assessment of hepatocyte function:		
Production and release of albumin		
Urea and ammonia metabolism		
Bile acid production and transport (e.g. Na-taurocholate)		
CYP450 function	**Substrate**	**Product**
CYP 1A1/2	*Ethoxyresorufin*	*Resorufin*
CYP 2C9	*Flurbiprofen*	*4-hydroxy-flurbiprofen*
CYP 2D6	*Dextromethorphan*	*Dextrorphan*
CYP 3A4	*Testosterone*	*6-β-hydroxy-testosterone*
Phase 2 enzyme function	**Substrate**	**Product**
UGT 1A1	*Estradiol*	*3-OH-Estradiol gluc.*
UGT 1A9/10	*Mycophenolic acid*	*MPA-G*
Sulfotransferase	*4- methylumbelliferone*	*4-MU-sulfate*

differentiate *in vitro* into hepatocyte-like cells, and they have been successfully transplanted in some animal models, thus proving their engraftment and differentiation into mature hepatocytes. Despite recent progress in gene editing techniques, concerns still exist regarding possible genomic alterations of these cells, and the ensuing risk of tumour formation upon transplantation.

Nonetheless, both ES- and iPS-derived hepatocytes could have enormous potential, particularly for pharmacological research and toxicity studies.

Differentiation of adult and placental stem cells

Stem cells derived from adult tissues are often preferable for cell therapy applications, as their use does not raise ethical concerns, nor is it associated with the risk of tumour development.

Among adult stem cells, those isolated from the bone marrow (BM) have been suggested as a possible source for differentiation into hepatocytes. Preliminary encouraging results have shown that BM-derived cells were able to efficiently repopulate the liver in a mouse model of chronic damage. However, later studies revealed that the beneficial effects of transplantation were due to fusion events between donor and recipient cells, rather than the actual transdifferentiation of BM-derived stem cells into hepatocytes, thus making them unsuitable for providing liver support in patients with liver failure.

Placental tissues are increasingly being considered as a possible resource for regenerative medicine. Several stem cell types can be isolated from term placenta, each with peculiar characteristics depending on the compartment they are isolated from. Such characteristics are discussed in detail in Chapter 18.

Particularly, hAECs possess the potential to differentiate into liver cells. The most effective approaches for hAEC differentiation involved a sandwich culture system that utilized liver-derived extracellular matrix along with specific growth factors, cytokines and hor-

mones. hAEC-derived hepatocytes expressed mature hepatocyte marker genes and activities, including some of the major metabolizing enzymes, such as CYP 3A4, 3A7, 1A1, 1A2, 2B6, 2D6, and UDP-glucuronosyltransferase 1A1. Although hAECs, just like ESs and iPSs, are able to respond to the differentiation stimuli of these culture systems and to express complex functions, typical of hepatocytes, the gene and protein expression levels obtained *in vitro* are consistently lower than those of authentic mature hepatocytes reaching, at best, levels similar to fetal hepatocytes.

On the other hand, *in vivo* studies showed that hAECs are able to engraft and differentiate into cells with the characteristics of mature adult hepatocytes. This suggests that the hepatic tissue microenvironment is able to properly stimulate stem cells and guide their differentiation much more efficiently than the *in vitro* culture systems developed so far. In a syngeneic transplant system, it was shown that rat-derived amniotic epithelial cells are able to engraft and form clusters of mature hepatocytes when transplanted in the liver of recipient animals pre-treated with retrorsine. This is a naturally occurring compound that is able to persistently block the cell cycle of resident hepatocytes, thus favouring repopulation by transplanted cells. Most importantly, no evidence of cell fusion was reported in this experimental setting. The integration of donor cells in the liver parenchyma of recipients was confirmed by the expression of the enzyme dipeptidyl-pepidase type IV, which was expressed (as expected in the adult liver) in a polarized manner, at the bile canaliculus between two adjacent hepatocytes. Moreover, donor-derived clusters expressed normal levels of Connexin 32, a gap junction protein predominantly expressed in the liver, that mediates the communication between hepatocytes. Further immunofluorescence analyses on liver sections revealed that transplanted cells acquired the expression of other proteins characteristic of mature hepatocytes, such as CYP 2E1 e 3A1, HNF 4α and β-catenin, at levels comparable to the surrounding liver tissue. Lastly, transplanted cells did not express markers of neoplastic transformation, making them safe for a potential clinical use.

A recent pre-clinical study showed that, upon transplantation in the liver of mouse model for MSUD (maple syrup urine disease), undifferentiated AECs were able to correct the high levels of plasma and brain amino acids, and to normalise the neurochemical brain unbalances typical of this disease.

These encouraging results provide further evidence on the high plasticity of AECs that, upon transplantation in the liver, are able to differentiate into functional hepatocytes and correct metabolic defects, thus representing a promising source of cells for liver-based regenerative medicine.

Recommended reading and references

1. Boulter L, Lu WY, Forbes SJ. *Differentiation of progenitors in the liver: a matter of local choice.* J Clin Invest. 2013 May;123(5):1867-73.

2. Williams MJ, Clouston AD, Forbes SJ. *Links between hepatic fibrosis, ductular reaction, and progenitor cell expansion.* Gastroenterology. 2014 Feb;146(2):349-56.

3. Huch M, Boj SF, Clevers H. Lgr5($^+$) liver stem cells, hepatic organoids and regenerative medicine. Regen Med. 2013 Jul;8(4):385-7.

4. Forbes SJ, Rosenthal N. *Preparing the ground for tissue regeneration: from mechanism to therapy.* Nat Med. 2014 Aug;20(8):857-69.

5. Zaret KS, Grompe M. *Generation and regeneration of cells of the liver and pancreas. Science.* 2008 Dec 5;322(5907):1490-4.

6. Michalopoulos GK. *Principles of liver regeneration and growth homeostasis.* Compr Physiol. 2013 Jan;3(1):485-513.

7. Shin D, Monga SP. *Cellular and molecular basis of liver development.* Compr Physiol. 2013 Apr;3(2):799-815.

8. Laconi E, Laconi S. *Principles of hepatocyte repopulation.* Semin Cell Dev Biol. 2002 Dec;13(6):433-8.

9. Fanti M, Gramignoli R, Serra M, Cadoni E, Strom SC, Marongiu F. *Differentiation of amniotic epithelial cells into various liver cell types and potential therapeutic applications.* Placenta. 2017 Nov;59:139-145.

10. Alison MR, Islam S, Lim S. *Stem cells in liver regeneration, fibrosis and cancer: the good, the bad and the ugly.* J Pathol. 2009 Jan;217(2):282-98.

Stem Cells in Kidney Injuries

Francesca Bianchi Gaetano La Manna
Andrea Angeletti Giorgia Comai

15.1. Introduction

In the last few years, kidney diseases have grown exponentially and globally, resulting in increased mortality. Renal failure results in a loss of function in the kidneys, that are no longer able to perform their regulating activities of water and saline balance, elimination of acids and waste from the body and production of hormones, such as erythropoietin. Several causes are recognized as responsible for kidney failure, often associated with different pathological conditions, such as high blood pressure, anaemia, dyslipidaemia and diabetes. Renal diseases manifest as either acute or chronic: the former may be reversible, if properly treated; the latter are irreversible conditions, whose symptoms occur late, when the disease has already advanced. Also if adequately treated, this manifestation degenerates into a clinical condition requiring renal replacement treatment, such as dialysis or kidney transplant.

Acute kidney injury (AKI) manifests with a rapid loss of renal function and may be characterized by different histological findings, depending on the aetiological factors: it is associated with numerous aetiologies and pathophysiological mechanisms.

Chronic kidney disease (CKD), by contrast, is a condition characterized by a gradual loss of kidney function over time, slowly leading to end-stage renal disease. Both AKI and CKD are associated with an increased risk of morbidity and mortality due to cardiovascular events.

The development of AKI and/or CKD is strictly related to the inability of the kidney to repair the damaged area, as neo-nephrogenesis is not preserved in the adult, but appears only in the embryo. In kidney development, only one mesenchymal metanephric embryonic stem cell can regenerate all epithelial cells of the nephron (except those of the collecting ducts that originate from the ureter), but it is not yet clear whether these progenitor cells persist during adulthood.

In recent years numerous studies have been conducted to assess the presence of renal stem/progenitor cells in adults. However, the methods used to identify the resident stem population varied considerably, often resulting in conflicting results. Methods used to identify renal stem cells are based on the identification of well-defined cell characteristics: low proliferative activity, selective culture conditions, expression of specific surface markers, such as CD133, CD24, CD106, stem cell antigen-1, 4-1 and Oct-Bml.

In any case, the studies performed to date have shown that renal cells maintain their regenerative competence even in adulthood: it appears to be related to some type of kidney cells that survived the damage, thanks to a clonogenic potential. However, these cells fail to fully activate the transcription pattern that is characteristic of the embryonic age; therefore, the repair process results ineffective and, after recurrent damage, the maladaptive response results in fibrosis and loss of renal function.

In order to define the main signalling pathways activated during nephrogenesis, several studies *in vivo* evaluated the presence of fetal renal progenitor cells, especially in murine models. The majority of the research showed how some genes (Sall1, EYA1, OSR1, CITED1) and transcription factors (PAX2 and WT1) may play a key role in this direction. In humans, Wilm's tumour represents the principal model for the investigation of progenitor cells, due to the lack of terminal differentiation of this cell population. In Wilm's tumour, renal cells express renal progenitor markers, such as Six2, Wt1, Cited1, and Sall1, CD56 Neural Cell Adhesion Molecule (NCAM), Frizzled-7-precursor (FZD7) and CD133, which is maintained in adulthood.

Renal progenitor cells give rise to nephrogenesis, which occurs only during embryonic development, until the 34th week of pregnancy. In adults, no kidney cells have a similar potential; cells that may contribute to the repair of damage and that can reactivate the pathways involved in nephrogenesis, through genes such as Pax2, BMI-1 and Six2. Although it is not possible to regenerate the entire nephron, renal homeostasis requires the involvement of cells with progenitor characteristics. In fact, physiologically, thousands of renal cells are daily lost in urine and need to be replaced; in addition, the kidney is able to replace tubular cells lost as a result of acute tubular damage. Therefore, there is a population able to perform this action. Acute toxic or ischaemic injuries are often associated with the death of tubular epithelial cells, which can lead to AKI. Cellular damage is primarily characterized by loss of cell polarity and tubular brush border and relocation of transmembrane proteins, such as sodium/potassium channels or the ATPase pump. Dead cells spill over into the tubule lumina, obstructing them. The resulting increase in intratubular pressure may contribute to the development of renal dysfunction. The kidney often manages to repair the damage by migrating surviving tubular cells in the necrotic area, where they proliferate and differentiate, restoring the basement membrane. This process involves growth factors that can promote the proliferation and differentiation of surviving kidney cells, but also pro-inflammatory factors or vasoconstrictors which can worsen the damage and lead to acute kidney failure. The normal kidney repair process cannot always restore the dead died tubular cells and restore renal function, however; so in recent years there has been a growing interest in the use of adult stem cells to improve kidney regeneration.

15.2. Renal progenitor cells

Animal studies, performed to verify the presence of progenitor cells at tubular level, showed that the regenerative process following tubular damage is related to the presence of intratubular resident cells, with a regenerative ability limited to a single segment, and with proliferative and clonogenic properties. However, many aspects regarding these theoretic cells are still the subject of debate: especially if they are to be considered as progenitor cells or if, most probably, they have plasticity properties that allow them to acquire the characteristics of transient progenitor cells. Cell populations with a low proliferative capacity and expressing stem cell markers have been identified in different portions of the tubule and in the papilla of the kidney. Contrary to what happens in the tubules, the regenerative potential of subtype cells in the glomeruli is very limited. The progenitors that are identified in Bowman's capsule, in fact, seem to contribute to the regeneration of podocytes, migrating in the glomerulus, but only until adolescence: this phenomenon has not been observed in adults.

In humans, several studies have reported positivity for CD133, a marker expressed by haematopoietic stem cells in different segments of the nephron, and in particular in Bowman's capsule, in the distal and proximal

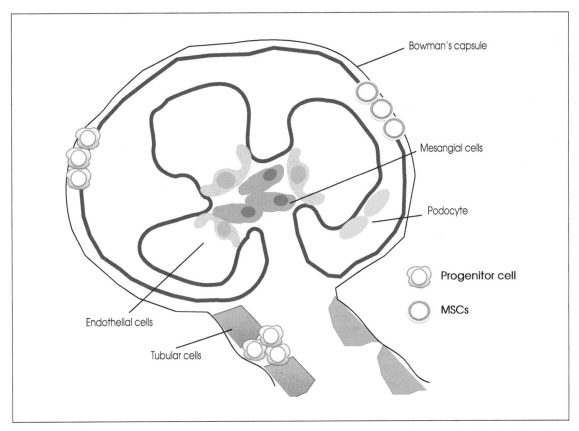

Figure 15.1. Localization of resident progenitor cells and resident mesenchymal stem cells in human glomeruli and tubules. Different populations of progenitors/stem cells have been identified in the adult kidney in humans. In particular, in human adult kidneys, the presence of resident progenitors/stem cells expressing the CD133 stem cell marker has been detected in the tubular compartment, in Bowman's capsules. The presence of an MSC population has been identified in the glomerular compartment of the human kidney.

tubules and in the internal medullary papilla, including the loop of Henle and the S3 segment. CD133 cells co-express vimentin, a mesenchymal marker, and both cytokeratins 7 and 19, not expressed by the tubular epithelial cells, a characteristic that allows the identification of this specific population. In Bowman's capsule, cells positive to CD133[+] and to CD24[+] are located at the urinary pole, while cells positive to podocalyxin, a marker of podocyte differentiation, are located at the vascular pole. CD133[+] cells have recently been identified in pre-transplant renal biopsy, indicating their presence at physiological level. Morphologically, this population is different from other cells of the proximal tubule, as they are smaller, with fewer mitochondria and devoid of the brush border.

The CD133 marker seems to be involved in the regulation of glycolytic metabolism and these cells seem to have an anaerobic metabolism, which would explain their particular resistance to injury. These observations support the hypothesis that CD133[+] cells are physiologically present and are highly resistant to injury, rather than a population induced by the damage. These cells are involved in the repair of acute kidney injury, as demonstrated in a mouse model of glycerol-induced AKI, where the injection of CD133[+]/CD24[+] attenuated tubulo-interstitial fibrosis and the clinical progression of the disease. These data were confirmed in humans: recent research showed an increase of CD133[+]/CD24[+] cells in patients receiving a kidney transplant with delayed graft function due to acute tubular necrosis, compared to pre-transplant or to patients with good organ function. The involvement of these cells in kidney repair mechanisms is supported by evidence that almost all proliferating cells in acute tubular injury biopsies are CD133+/CD24+. The number of CD133+ cells in these patients seems to be predictive of regeneration.

CD133+ cells have been found in patients with CKD too. However, in this case, they are not able to repair the damage, probably because of cellular senescence, although the cause has to be clarified. These cells are also involved in those diseases associated with hyperproliferation, such as glomerulonephritis or polycystic kidney disease. In both cases, a large number of CD133+ cells has been found in the kidney. These results support the hypothesis that CD133+ cells represent the progenitor population, able to proliferate, participate in tissue repair and homeostasis, matching the population previously described in mice as ancestor segment-specific. In addition, looking at the phenotype, they are not differentiated and express stem cell markers. It is still unclear if these cells are present at physiological level or consequent to damage, but it seems that cell plasticity plays a key role, as happens in other organs, such as the lungs, the bone marrow and the pancreas.

Cell reprogramming could be induced by stimuli from the surrounding microenvironment. Discovery of the mechanisms involved in this phenomenon would allow, on one hand, the modulation of cell reprogramming in situ by adding specific molecules, and, on the other hand, the treatment of cells *ex vivo* before using them *in vivo*.

15.2.1 Renal progenitor cells in renal injury

Animal studies show that, although these cells cannot generate new nephrons, they can contribute to the repair of acute and chronic renal damage. CD133+/CD24+ cells isolated from human fetal kidneys improve renal function in a mouse model of AKI. Similar results were obtained with human fetal progenitor cells in a model of CKD obtained by kidney resection. Progenitor cells obtained through differentiation of iPS and transplanted into a mouse model of AKI migrated to the damaged tubules. But the action is not limited to those fetal progenitor cells; in fact, even adult ones have a potential therapeutic effect. This action was highlighted both with animal and human cells. CD133+/CD24+ cells transplanted into mice with AKI improved renal function, showing an effect similar to that achieved by using MSCs. Unlike MSCs, CD133+ cells are localized especially in the kidney even at 48 hours after injection. CD133+/CD24+ cells have proved effective even in a model of focal segmental glomerulosclerosis characterized by damage of podocytes, in reducing proteinuria and improving chronic glomerular damage.

The mechanisms underlying the observed effects seem to be, unlike MSCs, not only the release of paracrine factors, but also the integration into the tissue and transdifferentiation. In fact, cells derived from the CD133+/CD24+ population and expressing renal tubular markers were found at the level of the proximal and distal tubules in an AKI model, and the same population was able to differentiate in podocytes in a podocytic damage model.

Fetal progenitor cells showed a high rate of tissue integration in a murine model of CKD with resection of 5/6 of the kidney. In this case the cells, injected directly into the parenchyma, initially accumulated in the surviving renal tubules or in the interstitium, while, after 3 months, they organized themselves in generating tubules with a lumen.

Renal progenitor cells produce growth factors and vesicles able to support kidney regeneration. In particular, they produce IL-15, a cytokine involved in renal differentiation, while their vesicles promote *in vitro* survival and proliferation of epithelial cells. The action of progenitor cells seems to be due to the association of paracrine factors and transdifferentiation.

15.3. MSCs in the treatment of renal disease

Ischaemia/reperfusion injury

Ischaemia/reperfusion (I/R) represents the most common mechanism of endothelial damage, expecially in the kidney, with consequent kidney failure. I/R is frequently the result of an arterial clamp during surgical procedures, such as cardiological surgery or renal transplantation. The reduced oxygenation due to the decrease of blood flow causes a decrease of the available ATP, metabolic disorders, apoptosis, ROS production, a situation worsened by reperfusion, causing inflammation, vasoconstriction and oxidative damage. This type of damage has been extensively studied in animals, in which it is induced by clamping the renal artery for a given period of time. Studies with bone marrow mesenchymal stem cells identified that the optimal timing for cell transplantation is immediately after ischemia to 1 h after reperfusion. The best concentration to be used is from 5×10^5 to 1×10^6 cells; higher concentrations may result in the formation of blood clots.

MSCs (bone marrow-derived, from Wharton's jelly in the umbilical cord, from amniotic fluid or adipose tissue) act on multiple aspects involved in I/R injury. First of all, they reduce oxidative stress by inducing a decrease in the amount of malondialdehyde, superoxide dismutase and glutathione peroxidase in kidneys exposed to ischaemia, but they also have an anti-inflammatory action, reducing inflammatory cytokines, such as IL-6, TNF-α, IL-1β, IFN-g, CXCL-2 and increasing anti-inflammatory cytokines, such as IL-10.

In vitro, pretreatment with chemical or natural molecules can increase the regenerative potential of MSCs. In rat models of AKI, the *in vivo* infusion of human MSCs derived from fetal membranes, pretreated with hyaluronic and butyric acid, reduced inflammation and increased the recovery of renal function.

MSC action also induces a reduction of the number of macrophages and their migra-tion, by the downregulation of MCP-1 and CX3CL1, which are chemoattractant factors for macrophages. Furthermore, MSCs reduce renal interstitial fibrosis and the formation of myofibroblasts.

MSCs and related extracellular vesicles play a positive action on the pathophysiological events of I/R, even if the mechanism at the basis of such effects has not yet been completely clarified.

Chemotherapy

One of the most used nephrotoxic drugs is cisplatin, a chemotherapeutic drug used for the treatment of many solid tumours. Its nephrotoxicity is associated with accumulation in the renal tubules, causing death of tubular cells by apoptosis. *In vivo*, cisplatin is used in models of both AKI and CKD, depending on dose and way of administration. Cisplatin predominantly induces apoptosis; the administration of MSCs isolated from various sources (bone marrow, amniotic fluid, umbilical cord blood, adipose tissue) or their conditioned culture medium, promotes renal regeneration, through the activation of the p38, MAPK, Bax and Bcl-2 pathways. The regenerative potential of MSCs seems to be related to the secretion of renal protective factors, such as HIF-1a or VEGF, more than to a transdifferentiation activity, because of the limited cell numbers found in the injured kidney. This also explains the effect observed with the administration of conditioned culture media. A trial with the aim of evaluating the safety and efficacy of treatment with MSCs in patients with solid tumours treated with cisplatin is currently ongoing. The treatment involves a single infusion of allogeneic bone marrow-derived MSCs and a follow-up to 1 month.

Diabetic Kidney Disease

Diabetic kidney disease develops very slowly and is characterized by the deposition of extracellular matrix on the tubular and glomerular basement membrane. In animal models, streptozotocin injection is the most common method used to obtain a representative type 1 diabetes, while genetic deletion of leptin receptor represents the model of diabetes type 2. Positive effects in the treatment of this disease were found both with MSCs or with their conditioned culture medium, confirming once again the importance of secreted chemokines and of extracellular vesicles. The effect is mainly due to a reduction of glomerulosclerosis and deposition of extracellular matrix, but also to a reduction in proinflammatory cytokines and macrophage infiltration, caused by a decreased expression of tissue level of MCP-1.

Two clinical trials, that aim to evaluate the feasibility, safety and tolerability of allogeneic MSCs, as well as their effectiveness in patients with diabetic kidney disease, are in the enrolling phase. Squillaro et al. have reported no side effects in administrating MSCs to patients with diabetic kidney disease, but the authors did not demonstrate a significant improvement of clinical conditions; it will be necessary to conduct further studies to increase the number of patients and to prolong follow-up times.

Polycystic kidney disease

Polycystic kidney disease (PKD) is a genetic disease characterized by the development of numerous cysts in the kidneys, which affect the functionality of the organ. This pathology is a major cause of CKD, so patients in whom the disease has progressed to end-stage renal disease need dialysis or transplant.

The formation of cysts is caused by an alteration of the protein signalling function within the cells and in the primary cilia. Therefore, the cells that line the tubules grow and divide abnormally, causing the growth of numerous cysts. Few preclinical studies have reported MSC administration for the treatment of PKD with consequent improvement of renal function. Also in this case it has been shown that the activity is mainly due to trophic factors released from stem cells, such as SDF-1, VEGF, and HGF. Once injected, MSCs can acquire an endothelial phenotype, suggesting a possible process of transdifferentiation. Despite the low number of preclinical studies, a phase I clinical trial was conducted: autologous bone marrow-derived MSCs were administered to patients with polycystic kidney disease, followed for 18 months. Due to the low number of patients involved, the study did not reach significant results; however, it proved the safety and tolerability of MSC administration.

Kidney transplantation

Kidney transplantation is the treatment of choice for patients with end-stage renal disease (1). It guarantees higher survival rates than haemodialysis or peritoneal dialysis for all patients, including the elderly. Surgical techniques and advanced immunosuppressive treatments have significantly improved, but long-term graft survival is still a clinical challenge and patients are at risk of developing fibrosis and tubular atrophy often associated with glomerulosclerosis and vascular occlusion. The use of stem cells in this field is justified by their immunomodulatory properties: they can be used in combination with immunosuppressive treatments allowing to reduce the drug dose and related adverse events.

In vivo studies in rats have shown the effectiveness of bone marrow-derived MSCs, specifically in preserving renal function, reducing tubular atrophy and interstitial fibrosis by a decreased activation of T-cells and macrophages, at 24 weeks from transplant. The time of administration was found to be key. In rat kidney transplantation models with mismatch between donor and recipient the infusion of bone marrow two days from MSC transplantation worsened the outcome of transplantation, resulting in organ failure and rejection within 20 days. Under the same conditions, if MSCs were administered between 1 and 7 days before the transplant, they exerted their regenerative action that extended the functionality of the organ. These cells indeed migrate in the spleen, where they induce an expansion of Treg cells. The improvement of the survival of the organ is correlated with the reduction of the percentage of CD8$^+$, MHCII$^+$, CD80$^+$, CD86$^+$

cells caused by MSCs, as well as with their antifibrotic action and the down-regulation of pro-inflammatory cytokines, such as TGF-β1.

In vivo studies were performed to test the association of MSCs and immunosuppressive drugs, in particular Cyclosporin-A. The results showed that the use of cells and drugs together was less effective than Cyclosporin-A alone in improving animal survival, suggesting a potential interaction between this drug and the MSCs. To date, four clinical trials that involved the use of MSCs in combination with immunosuppressive agents have been concluded. One study evaluated the use of autologous peripheral blood-derived stem cells in paediatric patients who received a kidney transplant treated with Cyclosporine-A and prednisone. At 18 months of follow-up, 100% of graft survival was observed, with good kidney function and low incidence of opportunistic infections. In another study, a double infusion of autologous bone marrow MSCs to transplanted patients with subclinical rejection was performed. Five of the six patients showed an inhibition of donor-specific immunity at 6 months of treatment. In a third study, the infusion of MSCs in combination with calcineurin inhibitors was compared to the administration of inhibitors administered together with antibody anti-IL2 receptor. Patients who received MSCs showed lower incidence of acute rejection, a reduced risk of opportunistic infections, and improved renal function at one year, compared to the other group. Finally, in the fourth study, MSCs were administered to patients who received a living-donor kidney transplant. The MSCs were isolated from the bone marrow of the kidney donor. Patients were treated with alemtuzumab, a humanized monoclonal antibody against the lympho-B membrane protein CD52. In this case, the addition of MSCs did not induce tolerance and graft survival was suboptimal. Other studies are still in progress and have not yet been completed, and will help to answer the questions that are still open, allowing to determine the best timing of administration, and whether co-adminis-

tration with immunosuppressive drugs that are commonly used can have a synergistic or antagonistic effect.

15.3.1 Mode of action of MSCs

MSCs have proved to be promising candidates for the treatment of renal failure. Studies conducted until now, as we mentioned above, have shown that these cells carry on their action not by their transdifferentiation, but rather through the release of immune-modulating factors, microvesicles, microRNAs, exosomes and mitochondrial transfer.

MSCs and the immune system

In vitro studies have shown that intercellular interaction between renal epithelial cells takes place through the exchange of cytoplasmic material, while MSCs are able to transfer mitochondrial material to tubular cells through intercellular connections, as demonstrated by a study in which tubular rat cells were cultured with human MSCs. Their immunomodulatory capacity is of particular importance, due to the lack of MHC Class II molecules and co-stimulatory molecules CD80 (B7-1), CD86 (B7-2), CD40, or CD40L. Several studies *in vitro* showed that both undifferentiated and differentiated MSCs are not recognized by T cells, nor are they lysed by cytotoxic T lymphocytes or natural killer cells, but rather that MSCs inhibit the growth of T cells in culture. MSCs exert their action on all cells of the immune system: they suppress the function of activated T cells, induce regulatory T cells, denditric cells, alter the maturation of B and NK cells, and polarize the phenotype of monocytes to anti-inflammatory type M2. M2 macrophages secrete factors that mediate wound healing, support angiogenesis, extracellular matrix deposition and tissue remodelling. In the case of renal transplantation, secretion of 2.3-dioxygenase and generation of Treg cells induced by MSCs prevents acute rejection and induces tolerance, prolonging survival. MSCs suppress the tyrosine kinase receptor expression on monocytes and macrophages, preventing monocyte infiltration and acute rejection. These cells also change the pattern of cytokines to a tolerogenic setting, increasing IL10 levels and reducing those of IFNg and IL6. These data are underpinning the reasons that led to transplant the MSCs in MHC-incompatible individuals without immunosuppression, and to use them to prevent rejection in organ transplant (Gregorini MBF et al., 2014).

Extracellular vesicles (Stem cell extracellular vesicles)

Extracellular vesicles represent a promising new therapy for the treatment of acute and chronic renal failure, which does not Figure the administration of cells. Indeed, extracellular vesicles preserve the characteristics of source cells, and those derived from stem cells will mimic their regenerative properties. Vesicles are composed of a phospholipid bilayer membrane, and differ in size, settling velocity and density. They may contain proteins, lipids or nucleic acids, such as mRNA and non-coding RNAs (e.g. miRNAs or other small RNA), and act on target cells through different mechanisms: by interacting with cell surface receptors, through direct stimulation or by transferring protein and/or genetic material. It is through these mechanisms that they exert their action, which ranges from stimulation of cell proliferation and angiogenesis to apoptosis and inflammation reduction. Unlike stem cells that do not need to accumulate at the site of the injury to exert their action, the ligand-receptor interaction is fundamental for extracellular vesicles. Treatment with trypsin, commonly used to destroy surface molecules, stops their effect.

Under physiological conditions, vesicles, upon being intravenously injected, mostly accumulate in the liver and spleen, rather than in the kidney. However, in the case of kidney injury, the increased permeability and cell loss promote localization even in the kidney, passing through the peritubular capillaries or glomeruli. The regenerative potential of extracellular vesicles from mesenchymal cells has been con-

firmed by numerous studies that have tested the feasibility in different models of kidney failure. Given the regenerative capacities of MSCs, extracellular vesicles derived from MSCs isolated from various sources, such as bone marrow, adipose tissue, cord blood, Wharton's jelly, or from MSCs isolated from the kidney or the liver were tested to assess their regenerative potential. In animal models of AKI induced by the use of toxic substances, intravenous administration of extracellular vesicles induced an improvement in survival, associated with a protection from oxidative stress, an increase in cell proliferation and a reduction of apoptosis in the kidney. In all models, the use of vesicles led to a reduction of histological lesions, such as debris in the tubular lumen or necrosis of the proximal and distal tubular cells. In the case of AKI induced by ischaemia reperfusion, in most studies the vesicles were administered intravenously immediately after ischaemia. Regardless of the source tissue used to isolate MSCs, their vesicles were effective in inducing regeneration, albeit with different mechanisms: if cells were isolated from cord blood, their vesicles promoted a dedifferentiation of tubular cells through induction of HGF; if isolated from Wharton's jelly, they promoted cell proliferation and reduced inflammation and apoptosis through a mitochondrial protection. A reduction in inflammation was observed even if the vesicles, obtained from bone marrow-derived MSCs, were injected under the kidney capsule.

Several studies have analyzed the action of extracellular vesicles produced by renal MSCs; they were able to improve kidney function and to reduce ischaemic injury by promoting tubular proliferation. If MSCs were grown under hypoxic conditions, their vesicles were effective in promoting angiogenesis *in vitro* and *in vivo*, and in improving microvascular peritubular rarefaction. The use of CD133[+] cells sited at tubular level, with progenitor characteristics, has proved effective in improving kidney function, while their vesicles did not show the same effect in this case.

The data obtained from the studies conducted up to date have shown a marked improvement in renal function after acute kidney injury, following a single administration of extracellular vesicles derived from mesenchymal stem cells. Their mechanisms are different and range from induction of resident cell proliferation and survival, reducing inflammation, vascular oxidation and rarefaction.

Extracellular vesicles have also been tested in animal models of CKD. In an animal model of type I diabetes (induced by Streptozotocin injection), which represents one of the main causes of CKD, urine MSC-derived vesicles were administered intravenously for 12 weeks starting from the appearance of the disease. These have proved effective in preventing the progression of diabetic kidney disease, probably through the action of TGF-b, angiogenin or BMP-7. Even a single administration through intra-renal injection may lead to kidney regeneration by suppressing cellular infiltration and reducing interstitial fibrosis and glomerular alterations. The action is mediated by IL-10. The regenerative potential of extracellular vesicles was confirmed in different models of CKD, obtained by renal 5/6 resection, that caused a rapid decline in the glomerular filtration rate, leading to glomerulosclerosis and fibrosis. In this case, the administration of vesicles was repeated several times, proving effective in preventing kidney failure. In a similar pattern, administration of conditioned culture medium obtained from embryonic MSCs, administered twice a day for four consecutive days, improved kidney function. After 6 weeks of treatment, glomerular filtration rate and renal plasma flow were restored, indicating a possible use of vesicles also in advance phases of CKD, and not only as a preventive measure. Another promising approach involved the use of vesicles in combination with perfusion solution used in graft before kidney transplant. An animal study showed that the addition of extracellular vesicles to the liquid leads to a significant reduction of renal impairment compared with controls, with a greater effect compared to the same MSCs used to produce vesicles. Which factors contained in vesicles may play a key role in renal protection remains to be established.

15.4. Conclusions

Several studies have been conducted to evaluate the clinical use of MSCs or renal progenitors for kidney regeneration. Based on the results obtained so far, it can be assumed that the therapeutic effects in case of AKI could be due to the paracrine mechanism, because it activates resident cells that can support kidney regeneration. In this disease, then, it is easier to use MSCs, because renal progenitor cells are difficult to isolate, cultivate and expand. In CKD, on the contrary, resident cells responsible for regeneration are depleted and an integration of new cells to reacquire lost functionality is required. In this case, therefore, renal progenitor cells may represent the ideal cell type to get positive clinical effects. These cells can be isolated from the patient's own tissue biopsies or from urine, thus avoiding the need for immunosuppressive therapy.

It is very important to consider the mode of administration: if cells are injected intravenously, they will remain trapped, especially in the lungs and liver and must overcome two tubular basement membranes to reach the kidneys. This kind of administration can be chosen in case of AKI, where barriers are partially damaged. In the case of CKD, on the contrary, an intraparenchymal injection will be preferable, which requires fewer cells and prevents their dispersion in organs other than the kidney. This kind of administration, however, has the disadvantage of being associated with local necrosis, thrombosis and limited distribution of cells in the kidney.

Further studies are needed for more information regarding the nature of this population and of this mechanism of action. Understanding the factors that modulate the plasticity of renal cells will allow us, in the future, to improve their regenerative potential in kidney damage.

Recommended reading and references

1. Bonventre JV. *Dedifferentiation and proliferation of surviving epithelial cells in acute renal failure.* J Am Soc Nephrol. 2003;14 Suppl 1:S55–S61.

2. Bussolati B, Camussi G. *Therapeutic use of human renal progenitor cells for kidney regeneration.* Nat Rev Nephrol. 2015 Dec;11(12):695-706.

3. Bussolati B, Collino F. & Camussi G. *CD133⁺ cells as a therapeutic target for kidney diseases.* Expert Opin. Ther. Targets. 16, 157-65 (2012).

4. Carden DL, Granger DN. *Pathophysiology of ischaemia-reperfusion injury.* J Pathol. (2000) 190:255–66.

5. Casiraghi F, Azzollini N, Todeschini M, Caroline RA, Cassis P, Salary S, et al. *Mesenchymal stromal cells dictates immune or localization of proinflammatory effects in their kidney transplantation.* Am J Transplant. (2012) 12:2373 – 83.

6. Franchi F, Peterson KM, Xu R, Miller B, Psaltis PJ, Harris PC, et al. *Mesenchymal stromal cells improve renovascular function in polycystic kidney disease.* Cell Transplant. (2015) 24:1687–98.

7. Franquesa M, Herrero and, Torras J, Ripoll and Flaquer M, Goma M, et al. *Mesenchymal stem cell therapy prevents interstitial fibrosis and tubular atrophy in a rat kidney allograft model.* Stem Cells Dev. (2012) 21:3125 – 135

8. Grange C, Iampietro C, Bussolati B. *Stem cell extracellular vesicles and kidney injury.* Stem Cell Investig. 2017 Nov 16;4:90.

9. Gregorini MBF, Rocca C, Corradetti V, Valsania T, Pattonieri EF, Esposito P, et al. *Mesenchymal stromal cells reset the scatter factor system and cytokine network in experimental kidney transplantation.* BMC Immunol. (2014) 15:44.

10. Kale S, Karihaloo A, Clark PR, Kashgarian M, Krause DS, Cantley LG. *Bone marrow stem cells contribute to repair of the ischemically injured renal tubule.* J Clin Invest 2003; 112: 42–49.

11. La Manna G, Bianchi F, Cappuccilli M, Cenacchi G, Tarantino L, Pasquinelli G, Valente S, Della Bella E, Cantoni S, Claudia C, Neri F, Tsivian M, Nardo B, Ventura C, Stefoni S. *Mesenchymal stem cells in renal function recovery after acute kidney injury: use of a differentiating agent in a rat model.* Cell Transplant. 2011;20(8):1193-208.

12. Liu X, Cai J, Jiao X, Yu X, Ding X. *Therapeutic potential of mesenchymal stem cells in acute kidney injury is affected by administration timing.* Acta Biochim Biophys Sin (2017) 49:338–48.

13. Maeshima, A. et al. *Involvement of Pax-2 in the action of activin A on tubular cell regeneration.* J. Am. Soc. Nephrol. 13, 2850–59 (2002)

14. Makhlough A, Shekarchian S, Moghadasali R, Einollahi B, Hosseini SE, Jaroughi N, et al. *Safety and tolerability of autologous bone marrow mesenchymal stromal cells in ADPKD patients.* Stem Cell Res Ther. (2017) 8:116.

15. Metsuyanim S, Harari-Steinberg O, Buzhor E, Omer D, Pode-Shakked N, Ben-Hur H, Halperin R, Schneider D, Dekel B. *Expression of stem cell markers in the human fetal kidney.* PLoS One 14 4, e6709 (2009).

16. Meyer-Schwesinger C. *The Role of Renal Progenitors in Renal Regeneration.* Nephron. 2016;132(2):101-9.

17. Nagaishi K, Mizue Y, Chikenji T, Otani M, Nakano M, Konari N, et al. *Mesenchymal stem cell therapy ameliorates diabetic nephropathy via the paracrine effect of renal trophic factors including exosomes.* Sci Rep. (2016) 6:34842.

18. O'Brien LL, Guo Q, Bahrami-Samani E, Park JS, Hasso SM, Lee YJ, Fang A, Kim AD, Guo J, Hong TM, Peterson KA, Lozanoff S, Raviram R, Ren B, Fogelgren B, Smith AD, Valouev A, McMahon AP. *Transcriptional regulatory control of mammalian nephron progenitors revealed by multi-factor cistromic analysis and genetic studies.* PLoS Genet. 2018 Jan 29;14(1):e1007181

19. Plotnikov EY, et al. *Cytoplasm and organelle transfer between mesenchymal multipotent stromal cells and renal tubular cells in co-culture.* Exp Cell Res. 2010;316(15):2447–55.

20. Rinkevich Y, et al. *In vivo clonal analysis reveals lineage-restricted progenitor characteristics in mammalian kidney development, maintenance, and regeneration.* Cell Rep. 7, 1270-83 10 (2014)

21. Sagrinati C, Netti GS, Mazzinghi B, Lazzeri E, Liotta F, Frosali F, Ronconi E, Meini C, Gacci M, Squecco R, Carini M, Gesualdo L, Francini F, Maggi E, Annunziato F, Lasagni L, Serio M, Romagnani S, Romagnani P. *Isolation and characterization of multipotent progenitor cells from the Bowman's capsule of adult human kidneys.* J Am Soc Nephrol. 2006 Sep;17(9):2443-56.

22. Squillaro T, Peluso G, Galderisi U. *Clinical Trials With Mesenchymal Stem Cells: An Update.* Cell Transplant. 2016;25(5):829-48.

23. Večerić-Haler Ž, Perše A, M (Cerar Mesenchymal) *Stem Cell-Based Therapy in Cispla-*

tin-Induced Acute Kidney Injury Animal Model: Risk of Immunogenicity and Tumorigenicity. Stem Cells Int. 2017.

24. Yao W, Hu Q, Ma Y, Xiong W, Wu T, Cao J, et al. *Human adipose derived mesenchymal stem cells repair cisplatin-induced acute kidney injury* *through antiapoptotic pathways.* Exp Ther Med. (2015) 10:468–76.

25. Zhuo W, Liao L, Xu T, Wu W, Yang S, Tan J. *Mesenchymal stem cells ameliorate ischemia-reperfusion-induced renal dysfunction by improving the antioxidant/oxidant balance in the ischemic kidney.* Urol Int. (2011) 86:191–96.

Neurogenesis in the adult brain 16

Vito Antonio Baldassarro

Luciana Giardino   Laura Calzà

16.1 The end of a dogma: nervous tissue is not composed by "permanent" cells only

Our knowledge of the histology of the nervous system has been extraordinarily enriched in recent years and new discoveries have conceptually modified the vision of its structural organization. To a large extent, this knowledge has been made possible by the definition of the molecular properties of the different cell types, leading to the development of identification tools based not only on their morphology but, first of all, on the antigenic properties recognized by specific antibodies used for *in situ* studies.

We know that the cell types composing the nervous tissue are not limited to neurons, astrocytes and oligodendrocytes. For example, the extraordinary properties of microglia, the population of glia cells responsible for immune recognition in the central nervous system (CNS), have been recognized. This cell population, which has been estimated to account for about 20% of CNS glial cells, is endowed with great motility, proliferative capability and great structural plasticity in response to environmental stimuli. Microglia morphology in resting conditions, i.e. a very small cell body and a dense network of thin, short and highly-ramified extensions, switches in a few minutes to a phagocyte shape, i.e. a large and rounded cell body without extensions. Two different microglia phenotypes, called M1 and M2, have been also identified. They produce different cytokines and play

opposite roles: in particular M1 is seen as detrimental and M2 as neuroprotective phenotype. A new glial cell population was also identified, estimated to be 10-15% of the total non-neural CNS cells, defined as oligodendrocyte precursor cells (OPCs). These cells are the precursors of the oligodendrocytes, the CNS myelinating cells. Different roles have also been attributed to the OPCs, such as being able to form functional interactions with astrocytes, pericytes and neurons, receive presynaptic inputs and respond to neurotransmitter release, thus contributing to regulate blood flow and synaptic function.

Until the middle of the last century it was thought that the structure of the adult CNS, neurons and connections was defined at birth, fixed and immutable. Furthermore, it was thought that degenerating neurons cannot be replaced.

Raymon y Cajal wrote that "*in the adult centres the nerve paths are something fixed, ended and immutable, everything might die, nothing might be regenerated*". In the 1950s–1960s important discoveries and brilliant intuitions revolutionized this way of interpreting the anatomo-physiology of the CNS. First, the hypotheses regarding "synaptic plasticity" began to be formulated, referring to the ability of the CNS to modify the structure and the functional effectiveness of its connections in relation to the circuits' activity. In the meantime, the dogma of the "permanent" nervous tissue began to be dismantled. The 1960s, Altman and colleagues carried out a series of pioneering studies using [3H]-timidine to mark dividing cells and trace their fate, also in the adult rodent CNS. This approach demonstrated a constitutive production (i.e. in physiological conditions) of new neurons in the hippocampus and olfactory bulb (OB). These observations generated initial scepticism and were not willingly accepted by most biologists. In the 1980s, the studies of Nottebohm and colleagues confirmed the continuous production of new neurons in the brain of several vertebrates, first of all birds and mammals. They suggested that neurogenesis could be demonstrated in several ways: (i) through the use of tritiated thymidine (or bromodeoxyuridine, BrdU), which integrates into the chromosomes of replicating cells; (ii) by showing the characteristic morphology of neurons and the expression of neuronal markers in cells marked in the proliferative phase; (iii) through the study of the electrophysiological properties and functional connectivity of these neo-formed cells. In the 1990s, Weiss and Bartlett demonstrated that the precursors isolated from the basal forebrain can differentiate *in vitro* into neurons, thus supporting the view that adult neurogenesis occurs

in at least two areas of the CNS, i.e. the OB and the dentate gyrus of the hippocampus (DG).

16.2 Constitutive neurogenesis in the adult brain

It is now accepted that new neurons with a specific phenotype are generated during adulthood in the adult brain of vertebrates, including mammals (and thus humans). These findings are based on studies in the normal animal or in experimental CNS lesions, performed by *in vivo* administration of cell proliferation markers, like BrdU, different survival times related to cell cycle length, and double *in situ* staining using different neural lineage markers. Moreover, the possibility to isolate precursors from specific brain areas growing them in suspension in the presence of mitogens, maintaining them for several generations and then differentiating them by adherent cultures without mitogens is a well-established procedure. Figure 16.1 shows the cerebral areas that have been shown to be involved in the constitutive neurogenesis and which has served as proof of the *in vitro* production of precursors and adult

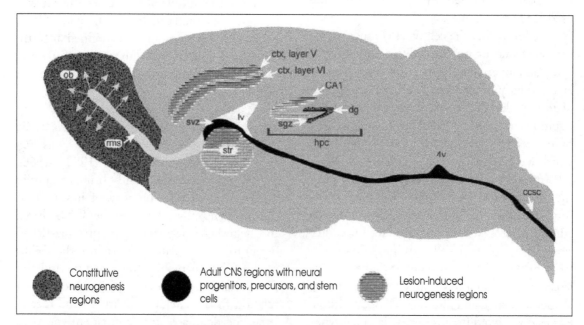

Figure 16.1. Schematic representation of constitutive neurogenesis regions (punctuation on a dark gray background), lesion-induced neurogenesis regions (squaring on a light grid) and areas of the central nervous system from which adult CNS with neural progenitors, precursors, and stem cells can be isolated (modified from Emsley et al., 2005).

neurons. The subventricular zone of the lateral ventricles (SVZ), the olfactory bulbs (OB) and the dentate gyrus of the hippocampus (DG) are the areas of so-called "constitutive neurogenesis", where neurogenesis represents a physiological event. The cerebral cortex, the dorsal basal ganglia and the hippocampal CA1 area are the regions in which neurogenesis has been described following injuries, usually acute lesions (ischaemia or trauma).

This picture is rapidly changing. For example, evidence has accumulated that neurogenesis can occur in both the juvenile and adult mammalian hypothalamus, being regulated by dietary, environmental and hormonal signals (Yoo and Blackshaw, 2018). Moreover, in other brain areas, including the substantia nigra, the *locus coeruleus* and the nucleus of the solitary tract, neurogenesis has been described in case of injury or experimental pathology, even if these data are not considered definitive. There are inter-specific differences: for example, adult neurogenesis seems to be well established in mice in the hypothalamus while, in humans, it takes place in the striatum. Finally, it is possible to isolate cells that, in suitable *in vitro* situations, behave like stem cells, generating neurons and glial cells, as well as other cell types from all peri-ventricular areas.

Quantitative studies have attempted to estimate the number of nerve cells generated daily in the adult mammal brain, using injection with high doses of BrdU. In the adult rat DG, about 9,400 proliferating cells are labeled with a 25-hour cell cycle, which generate about 9,000 new cells every day and more than 250,000 per month. In adult humans, it has been estimated that 700 new neurons are added daily to the hippocampus, with an annual turnover covering 1.75% of the entire population. Not all of these cells persist in the tissue: a highly controlled process of integration and/or apoptosis ensures the constancy of the number of neurons that constitutes the hippocampus. The migration time from the place of production to the final destination is 3 days, while the maturation of the neural

phenotype and its integration into the existing circuits requires about 60 days. This neurogenesis is believed to contribute to about 3.3% of the total population of granule cells per month, thus providing an extraordinary potential for replacing degenerated neurons. In the SVZ, 10-30,000 cells per day duplicate. The migration speed toward the definitive site (OB) is 70/80 microns per hour and, in this case too, adult neurogenesis guarantees the turnover of 3% of granule cells, for the most part, but also of periglomerular cells of the OB.

Neurogenesis is an age-dependent phenomenon, decreasing with ageing. The age-dependent reduction of the neurogenesis rate may be due to a progressive slowing of the cell cycle of the precursors (NPC) and, therefore, to a general ageing process of all tissues, but it can also be linked to the exposure and accumulation of environmental factors throughout life, including stress and the consequent increase in corticosteroid levels.

A fundamental question remains open: which cell do these new cells originate from and how is it generated in the course of development? Some definitions would be useful: neural stem cell (NSC): a multipotent cell, capable of *in vitro* generation of all nervous tissue cell types; neural and glia restricted precursors (NPC): precursors already committed towards the relative lineage; neural stem and progenitor cell (NSPC): this definition reflects the uncertainty still present about the *in vitro* longevity of these cells.

We know that nervous tissue is generated by the ectoderm, through the mesodermal induction that determines the formation of the neuroectoderm. The neuroectoderm is rapidly organized into the neural tube, originally a cellular monolayer with an epithelial-like morphology, then a multilayer with a layer of cells that remains attached to the neural tube wall (lateral ventricular system) and which constitutes the "germinative layer", and the other layers, progressively more complex, designed to generate nervous tissue. It is therefore evident that "ectodermal" morphology, characterized by junctional systems among the cells, will evolve into extremely complex cell morphology and will be characterized by the substantial absence of physical junctions between cells (in mammals, with few exceptions).

Nowadays it is believed that the "stem cell" of the adult brain is of astrocytic nature (the B1 of the SVZ), as demonstrated through studies on the development of the mammalian cortex and the role of the radial glia, a precursor of both neurons and glia in the embryonic brain. It appears at the beginning of the neurogenesis process, as an evolution of neuroectodermal epithelial cells, with progressive appearance of astroglial molecular markers, such as the astrocyte specific glutamate transporter, brain lipid-binding protein and tenascin C. The stem cell's cytoplasm contains abundant smooth endoplasmic reticulum and abundant intermediate filaments that are found at the base of the cell. The cell body, orthogonally elongated towards the ventricle, remains localized in the ventricular zone (VZ). The nuclei of these cells are perpendicularly stretched to the ventricular lumen surface and contain lightly-packed chromatin and one or two nucleoli. Two long processes emerge from the cell body, extending towards the pial surface on one side, and towards the parenchyma on the other side. These processes serve as a guide for the migration of young neurons from their generation site to the ventricular zone. All cells are in contact with the lumen, where a single primary cilium extends. The transformation of the tight junctions, typical of neuroepithelial cells, into adherent junctions, and the appearance of contacts of astrocytic types with endothelial cells, mark the transition from epithelial cells to radial glia.

The radial glia, in turn, give rise to stem cells present in the adult brain, with astrocytic morphology. These cells maintain a defined polarity, that guarantees the regulation of the asymmetric division at the base of the correct function of the stem cell also in the adult brain. The regulation of the NUMB and NUMBL expression is a key molecular mechanism in cell polarity and asymmetric division. Initially these cells divide symmetrically to increase the stem cell pool and then divide asymmetrically, generating a stem cell that remains in the VZ and a daughter cell that migrates to the final destination. In accordance with the definition developed by Alvarez-Buylla for the SVZ (see also 16.2.2), adult neural stem cells correspond to astrocytes (type B cells) derived from radial glia. Type B cells, usually quiescent (and nestin-negative), generate "transit-amplifying cells" (type C, nestin-positive) in the presence of "niche"-derived stimuli, which in turn become migratory neuroblasts (type A cells, doublecortin- and PSA-NCAM-positive) after about 3 cell cycles of symmetric division.

The stem cells that we find in the adult brain are therefore formed during development and seem to "retain" a trace of this origin, in particular a sort of "regional identity" that affects the differentiation capability of the various CNS neurogenesis areas.

16.2.1 The neurovascular niche

Stem/progenitor cells in the constitutive neurogenesis areas of the adult brain reside in a highly specialized microenvironment, called "niche", that regulates cellular interaction and the spreading of soluble substances. This microenvironment regulates the self-maintenance of the undifferentiated precursor pool, the stem cell activation and differentiation, as well as start-of-migration signals.

The niche consists of several components, which also keep a stable architecture. There is a close association with blood vessels, extensive cell-cell interaction, a specific composition of the extracellular matrix that modulates the adhesion ability and the activity of both signal molecules and basal lamina for cell anchoring. In addition, the epigenetic status of the cells determines their ability to respond to signals. The vascularization of the niche plays a fundamental role in the regulation of adult neurogenesis, both by the intrinsic cells of the vascular system and by the circulating molecules that can converge in the niche. Endothelial cells and pericytes surrounding the lumen of the vessels are separated from the brain by the basal lamina which facilitates the activation of regulatory factors specific for neurogenesis and angiogenesis processes, including betacellulin (BTC), stromal cell-derived factor 1 (SDF1) and pigment epithelium-derived factor (PEDF). The ependymal cells that cover the lateral ventricles also provide a massive supply of nutrients, supporting the high proliferative rate in this region. Moreover, their destruction eliminates neurogenesis. The possible role of circulating factors is more blurred; however, it is demonstrated by the strengthening of neurogenesis in an old animal through the transfusion of blood from a young one. Several hormones could be implicated, like insulin and IGF, steroids, thyroid hormones.

The molecular signalling that operates in the niche, regulating cell division, lineage specification and cell migration, is extremely varied and complex. Epidermal growth factor (EGF) and basic fibroblast growth factor (bFGF) are the main mitogens, which also maintain cells in the undifferentiated state. Among other soluble factors, vascular endothelial growth factor (VEGF) and brain derived neurotrophic factor (BDNF) seem to work in a coordinated way for neural differentiation. The Wnt/GSK3b/b-catenin pathway, operating in an autocrine manner, supports proliferation and multipotency of NSCs also in the hippocampus, as does Sonic Hedgehog (Shh). Among the intrinsic mechanisms, the family of Sox genes should be mentioned: Sox2 is believed to repress the expression of GFAP, thus maintaining the undifferentiated state, and Sox9, which interacts with microRNA (among which mir-124), regulating the production of neuroblasts from C cells. Helix-loop-helix (bHLH) transcription factors are a group of "pro-neural" proteins: the expression of Mash1 is essential for the appearance of new GABAergic neurons, while Neurog2 is necessary for the paroxysm of new glutamatergic neurons. Neutral D1, Pax6, Gsx2, Sp8, Prox1, Ascl1, TLX are the other transcription factors involved.

The role of epigenetic regulation, i.e. histone acetylation/methylation, DNA methylation, chromatin-remodeling complexes and non-coding RNA, is also emerging.

Lastly, the neurotransmitter-mediated regulation of the adult brain stem cell niche is of great interest, even if difficult to study and with contrasting and partial data. All cell types (A, B and C) constituting the niche express dopaminergic receptors and the activation of serotoninergic receptors, 5HT1A, 1B and 2C, modifies the proliferative rate in the SVZ, probably through dense synaptic contacts on ependymal and B1 cells. GABA, spontaneously released by the young neuroblasts, exerts an inhibitory tonic control on astrocyte proliferation in the SVZ, while the glutamate released by B cells probably regulates neuroblasts. Neurotransmitter signals are also critical in the integration of neo-formed neurons in existing circuits, and the neurotransmitter regulation of the niche is under observation in order to explain the regulation of neurogenesis operated by environmental conditions and lifestyles (see 16.3).

16.2.2 SVZ-OB system

The SVZ is an important germinal layer of the adult brain, which is formed during development adjacent to the wall of lateral ventricles at the telencephalic level, and maintains the ability to generate neurons and glia, including oligodendrocytes. It is a complex structure, containing different cell types, and in close contact with blood vessels. In the embryo, the SVZ progenitors are derived from VZ terminal cells. These two zones, apart from their cellular morphology, can be distinguished by the expression of two peptides: *noggin* and *distal less homeobox 2* (DLX2). *Noggin* binds *Bone Morphogenetic Proteins* (BMP) to prevent receptor activation, while DLX2 is a transcription factor expressed in neural progenitors. At time zero (P0) *noggin* is expressed primarily by cells in the VZ while DLX2 is expressed in the SVZ. In the adult brain, *noggin* protein is expressed in the ependymal cells and DLX2 continues to be expressed throughout life by C cells in the SVZ and by the neuroblasts in the migratory stream.

Cells with undifferentiated morphology, glial cells and cells with transitional morphology are present in the adult SVZ. As already mentioned, three different types of cells have been highlighted: neuroblasts (type A), astrocytes (NSC/NPC; type B1 and B2) and undifferentiated cells (type C) (Figure 16.2).

Type A cells form tangentially oriented chains enveloped by type B cells, while clusters of type C proliferating cells are associated with neuroblast chains. Type A cells are combined with other type A cells through small circular junctional complexes distributed on the cell's surface. At the level of these complexes there are endocytic vesicles that could suggest the exchange of molecular signals between cells or could be related to the removal of the complexes themselves.

Type B cells show irregular contours filling the spaces between neighbouring cells: they have irregular nuclei and many intermediate filaments and dense bodies in the cytoplasm. There are two subtypes: B1 and B2. Type B1 astrocytes are clearer and wider, with more

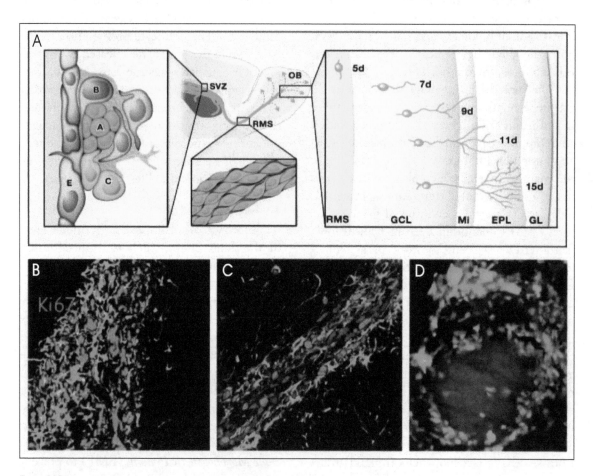

Figure 16.2
Neurogenesis in the telencephalic subventricular zone (SVZ).
A. Progenitors (A-C) in the subventricular zone (SVZ) are adjacent to the ependymal cells (E), which delimitate the lateral ventricles and interact with basal lamina and local microvessels. Neo-formed neurons reach the olfactory bulb (OB) through a line well defined by astrocytes ("migratory stream"), they undergo morphological and physiological development before that part of them integrates as granular neurons in the granular cell layer (GCL) and periglomerular neurons (not shown) in the glomerular layer (GL).
Abbreviations: Mi, mitral cell layer; EPL, external plessiform layer; RMS, rostral migratory stream. From Zhao et al., 2008.
B-D: immunohistochemical visualization of proliferating cells marked for a proliferation marker (B, C: Ki67, red) or after in vivo BrdU administration (D: green), in the SVZ (A), RMS (B) and OB (C), in the astrocytic niche (marked in B and C through GFAP immunohistochemistry).

cytoplasm than those of type B2. Further-more, in B1 cells chromatin is relatively dis-persed while in B2 it is more compacted. B1 cells are found mainly adjacent to the ependy-mal cells, creating an area rich in extracellular matrix, or they form the tubes within which the neuroblasts migrate. B2 cells are instead located more frequently at the interface with the striatal parenchyma. Type C cells are larger and more spherical, their nuclei have deep invaginations and lots of loose chroma-tin, with a large and cross-linked nucleolus, while the cytoplasm contains an extensive Golgi apparatus and few ribosomes compared to type A cells and no bundles of interme-diate filaments typical of type B cells. Their contours are smooth and they frequently con-tact type A cells with which the formation of small junctional complexes is occasionally observed.

Type E epithelial cells form an epithelial monolayer that separates the SVZ from the ventricular cavity. The lateral processes of adja-cent ependymal cells are strongly interdigi-tated and contain apical junctional complexes. The surface exposed to the ventricular cavity contains microvilli, the cytoplasm has many mitochondria, the nuclei are spherical, and the chromatin is not aggregated. Ependymal cells play an extremely important role in adult neu-rogenesis, which is normally inhibited in the SVZ by BMPs produced by SVZ astrocytes. Ependymal cells secrete *noggin*, which neu-tralizes the inhibitory effect of BMPs (mem-bers of the *transforming growth factor beta fam-ily* - TGFβ), determining the mobilization of stem cells from the niche.

Neuroblasts generated in the SVZ begin a longitudinal rostral migration along the migratory stream (RMS) towards the OB, at the level of which, after having left the RMS by tangential migration, they differentiate into granules and periglomerular neurons. These cells migrate in aggregates also called "chains" due to their topographic arrangement.

Type B1 cells are not a homogeneous population and are characterized by regional

specification, already established during early embryo development. In fact, the position of B1 cells throughout the walls of lateral ven-tricles determines the type of OB neuron. In particular, NSCs sited in the ventral side pro-duce deep granule neurons and calbindin-pos-itive neurons, but not tyrosine hydroxylase (TH)-positive perigromerular cells. On the other hand, dorsal NSCs generate TH-posi-tive cells, superficial granule cells but not cal-bindin-positive perigromerular cells. Moreo-ver, OB interneurons are generated not only from the lateral wall of the lateral ventricle, but also from the dorsal, medial walls and within the RMS, generating a variety of interneurons with specific structural and physiological prop-erties. This regional specification seems to be cell-intrinsic and it remains unclear how many sub-regions exist in the SVZ.

A single-cell transcriptional analysis in mice revealed that the SVZ exhibits regional and cell type heterogeneity at anatomical scale: the lateral wall is more enriched in neurogen-esis while the septal wall is more enriched in gliogenesis. Moreover, sex differences in these regions were also detected, mostly in OPCs enriched in the septal wall of male animals.

Like rodents and primates, also the human brain contains progenitors that can give rise to new neurons and glial cells. The ultrastruc-tural study of human brains has indicated that astrocytes of the SVZ are separated from the ependyma by a side containing *glial fibrillary acid protein* (GFAP)-expressing processes. These processes appear to extend into the ependymal layer towards the lumen of the ven-tricle, but the presence of any neuronal migra-tory chain in the SVZ has not been observed. Thus, unlike the other species taken into con-sideration, it has been hypothesized that there is a lack of migration from the SVZ to the OB, or that if this happens, the precursors migrate as individual cells.

16.2.3 SGZ-DG system

The dentate gyrus of the hippocampus is the second brain region in which adult neurogenesis is a constitutive phenomenon in several animal species (reptiles, birds, rodents and primates, including humans). Cells addressed to become neurons are generated in the innermost part of the granule cell layer, the subgranular zone (SGZ) of the dentate gyrus, which is the boundary zone between the granule cell layer and the hilum. From this area, cells migrate for a short distance, sending the dendrites into the molecular layer of the hippocampus and the axons in the CA3 region. The SGZ is a highly vascularized area and a close spatial relationship was observed between the blood vessels and the dividing precursors. Based on their morphological criteria and antigenic properties, three types of proliferative cells have been identified in this zone: precursors of the radial glia (B cells, or type 1 cells); type 2 cells expressing nestin and lacking glial characteristics; type 3 cells, doublecortin positive and nestin negative (Figure 16.3).

Cells with radial glia characteristics, which contain multiple processes with intermediate filaments rich in GFAP, have been identified as "stem cells" also in this region (even if they do not seem to be able to generate oligodendrocytes). Two types of GFAP-positive cells were characterized in the SGZ of the DG: horizontal cells, quiescent, and radial cells, active. Horizontal cells extend highly branched processes along the edge of the SGZ and do not express nestin (the marker of immature cells). Radial cells, instead, send projections into the granule cell layer and thin lateral processes interposed

Figure 16.3. Neurogenesis in the hippocampus.
A: type 1 and 2 progenitors in the subgranular zone (SGZ) can be identified by their morphology and expression of specific markers. The neo-generated neurons in the dentate gyrus go through several morphological and functional maturative stages. In particular, during the third week of life of these neurons, corresponding to the dendritic spines development, a transition from GABAergic (blue) to excitatory glutamatergic neurons is observed. Other regulations in the niche derive from astrocytes (not shown) and from vascularization (red).
Abbreviations: GCL, granular cells layer; Mol, molecular layer. From Zhao et al., 2008.
B: immunohistochemical visualization of neuroblasts in the dentate gyrus of the hippocampus, marked by doublecortin; C: double staining of BrdU (red) after *in vivo* administration and doublecortin, which show the differentiation toward neural lineage of this new-born cell. From Sivilia et al., 2008.

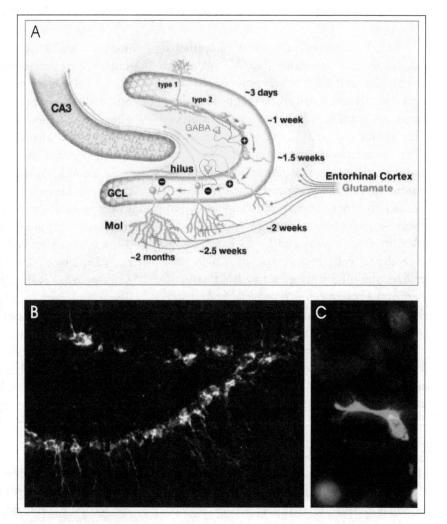

near the granule neurons. Moreover, they also express nestin. At electron microscopy observation, these cells have similar characteristics to SVZ astrocytes. Following treatment with antimitotic substance (Ara-C), in order to eliminate the dividing cells, the disappearance of type D cells and many astrocytes was noted; however, the cells that survive resume dividing and the type D cells finally reappear.

These experiments have shown that SGL astrocytes are the primary precursors that give rise to new granule neurons in the adult DG (excitatory) through the intermediation of D cells. Compared to SVZ cells, type D cells divide less frequently and are more differentiated with respect to type C cells. They have a cytoplasm rich in organelles containing many mitochondria, lysosomes, abundant rough endoplasmic reticulum and a distinct Golgi apparatus. These cells are also small, negative for GFAP and appear to divide as transient precursors in the formation of new neurons.

Also in the DG, the capillary is a niche constitutive element, as the astrocytes are intimately connected to the endothelial cells. It should be noted that these contacts increase in physiological conditions that increase hippocampal neurogenesis (see 16.3). Vascular endothelial growth factor (VEGF) is considered a mediator of this effect.

It should be noted that the granule layer of the DG, where the hippocampal "niche" is located, contains a strong concentration of microglia cells, which are thought to play a fundamental role in regulating neurogenesis under physiological conditions, mediating apoptosis of the precursors and for their phagocytic activity. Cytokines and chemokines are considered the mediators of this very delicate balance between proliferation and death in new cells, in which "mature" astrocytes also participate, and include tumour necrosis factor-α (TNF-α), interleukin-6 (IL-6), transforming growth factor-β (TGF- β). Microglia are investigated in order to explain changes in neurogenesis both in a positive and negative sense, in different systemic and environmental situations, such as physical exercise and ageing, and in all acute or chronic conditions that lead to an inflammatory response (see 16.3).

Even if methodological challenges make human studies difficult to perform and interpret, there is a general consensus that the hippocampus is one region in which adult neurogenesis occurs in humans as it does in other animals. Different studies from different research groups have shown the presence of neurogenesis in the hippocampus by BrdU staining or using post-mortem samples. In a recent study, brains from autopsy samples were analyzed, covering a range from 14 to 79 years of age. In medication-free subjects with no-brain diseases and no reported cognitive impairment, good global functioning and low recent life event-related stress, hippocampal neurogenesis was detected into eight decades of life and stable DG volume over a life span of 65 years.

However, a recent study from Sorrells and colleagues totally confuted these data. They used specific markers in order to analyze neuronal precursor cells, proliferating cells and immature neurons in 59 human subjects, from fetal development to old age. Their findings set the limit for hippocampal neurogenesis to 13-year-old subjects and they also explain how a wrong use of markers or BrdU staining in humans can lead to wrongly interpreted results.

The biggest issue of human neurogenesis studies is that no clear notions on the stability of markers in human samples are reported, given that in rodents it is known that PSA-NCAM is quickly modified and DCX easily degrades after tissue manipulation. Moreover, the identity of hippocampal precursors in the well-known rodent brain is still debated, while in humans it is possible that we simply do not know what to look for.

In 2005, Frisen's group at Karolinska Institutet proposed a novel method for the retrospective birth dating of cells in humans, based on levels of the isotope ^{14}C in the atmosphere following nuclear weapon testing and exponential decrease. Although these studies are not easy to reproduce, they further supported the existence of human neurogenesis in several brain areas, including the hippocampus, athough differences with other mammalian species are present.

16.2.4 Other areas

It has been observed that cell populations with stem cell characteristics are also present in other non-classically neurogenic areas of the adult brain. In particular, in the hypothalamus, where the niche is located in the ventral part of the third ventricle wall, a brain area that connects the CNS and the endocrine system through the hypophysis peduncle and, in particular, its ventral portion called "the median eminence". Here the hypothalamus floor and the hypophysis portal system meet a vascular system that conveys hypothalamic regulation factors towards the anterior pituitary lobe. A different population of glial cells, the tanycytes, constitute a physical bridge between the wall of the third ventricle and the capillaries of the median eminence. The new neurons migrate from the niche to the adjacent hypothalamic parenchyma, integrating in particular in the dorsomedial, ventromedial and arcuate nuclei. Hypothalamic neurogenesis is believed to play an important physiological role, participating in the regulation of food intake (including control of energy consumption and body weight), at the regulated seasonal rhythms of the hypothalamus.

The vagal complex, the substantia nigra, the cerebral cortex and the spinal cord are other areas for which the persistence of neurogenesis/gliogenesis in the adult has been hypothesized.

The dorsal vagal complex (DVC) is located in the floor of the fourth ventricle and includes the nucleus of the solitary tract (NST) and the dorsal motor nucleus of the vagus nerve (dmnX). The NST is the nucleus that receives the axons of visceral-sensory afferent neurons of the vagus nerve, while the dmnX contains the cell bodies of the efferent fibres of the vagus nerve. The area postrema (AP), instead, is a circumventricular organ located dorsally at

the level of the third half of the rostro-caudal extension of the DVC. These nuclei constitute the main integrative centre of cardiovascular, respiratory and gastrointestinal reflexes and play a modulatory role in the functions of the autonomous system. In adult rats, the DVC has a high expression of the growth-associated Gap-43 protein, which is expressed exclusively by axonal growth cones and the polysialylated neural cell adhesion molecule, i.e. the isotype expressed in development (PSA-NCAM). These two molecules are expressed ubiquitously throughout the period of embryonic development and they seem to disappear in the adult phase, except in structures showing synaptic plasticity and structural reorganization in response to afferent activity. Since, among the adult neural substrates, PSA-NCAM is most closely associated with neurogenesis, the observation of its presence at the level of the DVC, co-distributed with neural markers and BrdU, has led to hypothesize the presence also here of a neurogenesis area. It was found that the neurogenic potential is lower than in areas such as the SVZ or the SGZ, 75% at the NST level and 16% in the AP, with a positivity of 9.2% for mature neurons and 7.2% for astrocytes.

The substantia nigra (SN) is found in the ventral tegmental area of the midbrain and is subdivided into the pars compacta (SNpc) and the pars reticulata (SNpr) of the SN. SNpc consists of dopaminergic neurons located above the SNpr which in turn is composed of typically multipolar GABAergic neurons of a rounded or triangular shape. Since nigro-striatal dopaminergic neurons, whose loss is typical of Parkinson's disease and involves the manifestation of highly disabling motor dysfunctions, is located in the SN, a potential neurogenesis at the level of this area would therefore be of extreme interest. Here, the existence of progenitors able to generate the three expected lineages was hypothesized, even if in a more limited way than in the SVZ or the SGZ. Most of the positive BrdU cells were observed in the middle-rostral part of the SNpc, where neuronal density was higher, while no cells were observed at the level of the most caudal portion. The neuronal phenotype was confirmed using immunocytochemical techniques. According to the authors who have described this phenomenon, new dopaminergic neurons are generated continuously in the SN, starting from the subependymal layer of the lateral ventricle and after migration along the ventral medial-line to the SN, where they differentiate into dopaminergic cells. This process is thought to be stimulated as a result of injury. It should also be noted that neurogenesis in the SN is a rather controversial subject, since all the results described above have been refuted by other authors who have not obtained any results from the same experiments.

The possibility of neurogenesis in the cerebral cortex after an ischaemic lesion, studied in rodents and primates, remains a subject on which a consensus has not yet been reached; the same is true for spinal neurogenesis, where the localization of the stem cell/precursor remains obscure. The main hypothesis is that immature glial progenitors play this role in this area, as well. Unlike glial progenitors described for the brain, these cells express mature astrocyte and oligendendrocyte markers four weeks after administration of BrdU *in vivo*. After this time, 5% of the dividing cells express mature or immature markers associated with oligodendrocytes and 3-5% of the total cells labeled with BrdU express mature astrocyte markers. To date, two models have been proposed for neurogenesis in the spinal cord. The first involves the presence of a stem cell at the level of the ependymal layer that divides asymmetrically. The daughter cell is believed to migrate to the outermost circumference of the spinal cord where it appears as a glial progenitor that begins to divide rapidly. The second model predicts that a stem cell population is present in the outermost part of the spinal cord where cell division is more common.

On the contrary, the study of neurogenesis in the human cerebral cortex using the ^{14}C method to date cell age reveals that occipi-

tal neurons in human cortex are as old as the individual, while glial cells are continuously exchanged, corroborating the hypothesis that neurogenesis is not present in this region.

16.3 Endogenous neurogenesis: possible meaning and regulation

The presence of NSCs in the CNS, with the ability to proliferate and differentiate in the main neural lineages and to functionally integrate into neuronal circuits, has raised great hopes for potential therapeutic use. It has also stimulated numerous studies aiming to verify the possibility of regulating this phenomenon through environmental factors and lifestyles, with drugs or other therapeutic treatments. At the same time, numerous studies have attempted to understand if alterations of endogenous neurogenesis are part of the pathological process in neurological and psychiatric diseases, to verify the possibility of intervention (e.g. pharmacological) to correct any defects, or to influence their fate in order to enhance a possible reparative intervention.

The possibility of regulating neurogenesis in adulthood depends on the region (SVZ or SGZ), and the phase of the neurogenesis process (proliferation, differentiation, integration in existing circuits and survival). There are two functions with respect to which neurogenesis in adulthood seems to have a physiological role: learning and memory, and mood regulation. Conversely, cognitive training is believed to have a positive impact on adult neurogenesis.

Data obtained with neurogenesis suppression studies have given rise to controversial conclusions, but neurogenesis is important for at least some of the hippocampus-dependent memory forms. It seems that neurons generated in adulthood are activated during learning and there is also a regional specificity. For example, after a single learning experience, the percentage of activated granule cells is higher in the ventral dentate gyrus than in the dorsal dentate gyrus. Because the ventral hippocampus is closely related to emotional memory and the dorsal hippocampus to spatial memory, these data suggest that granule cells generated in adulthood can be involved in the emotional, rather than spatial, aspects of hippocampal behaviour.

With reference to mood regulation, the salient data derived from the pharmacological regulation of endogenous neurogenesis were obtained with three classes of drugs: glucocorticoids, lithium (used as a mood stabilizer) and the antidepressant drugs acting as selective serotonin re-uptake inhibitors, namely fluoxetine, which is the most used tool for the study of DG neurogenesis. Many studies have shown that acute and/or chronic glucocorticoid administration decreases neurogenesis, in particular the proliferation of type 1 cells. On the contrary, lithium increases neurogenesis, as do antidepressants of the SSRI class.

Moreover, behavioural strategies that, in the absence of drugs, regulate endogenous neurogenesis should be mentioned: on the one hand stress, which reduces it significantly, and, on the other, the housing of laboratory animals in "enriched" environments, including the possibility of voluntary physical exercise (running), which instead enhances endogenous neurogenesis. Stress is the best known negative regulator of adult hippocampal neurogenesis. Conditions of acute stress, such as the smell of predators, immobilization or electric shock, drastically reduce the proliferation of adult cells in the DG. Even mild chronic stress, which summarizes the behavioural characteristics of depression, reduces adult hippocampal neurogenesis. As seen above, it is hypothesized that glucocorticoids, which increase in case of stress, are one of the cellular mediators of this effect. On the contrary, an enriched environment and exercise (animals raised in large communities, in large cages, always provided with new games and with the possibility of practising physical exercise on a voluntary basis) improve neurogenesis both in healthy and in pathological animals and, although the results of these experiments are still the subject of heated debate, it seems that this has posi-

tive feedback on performance in learning and memory. These effects appear to be mediated by BDNF and VEGF, perhaps also through a different regulation of the blood-brain barrier mediated in particular by intense physical exercise, which would allow the exposure of the neurogenic niche to a greater concentration of circulating blood factors, among which VEGF itself (of muscle production) and insulin growth factor-1 (IGF-1).

Among the negative physiological regulators of neurogenesis, we must mention ageing as probably the most powerful factor which decreases the proliferation, differentiation and survival of new neurons. The age-dependent reduction of neurogenesis is not linear, and it is believed that this is related to a progressive "exhaustion" of the stemness of the niche, in turn due to both the intrinsic properties of these cells and to external, local and systemic regulators.

However, the question of the function of neurogenesis in adulthood remains open, also fuelled by the difficulty of performing studies in primates, including humans. To date, hippocampal neurogenesis has been proven to be involved in 3 key processes of the hippocampal function, on hypotheses derived in particular from computational models of learning and memory: (i) "pattern separation", through which similar patterns of neural activity generate different responses; (ii) encoding of the temporal context of the events; (iii) "memory resolution", i.e. the ability to integrate "what, where and when" in a unitary memory. In addition to learning and memory, neurogenesis in adulthood seems to be involved in emotional conditioning, exploratory capacity, olfactory recognition, spatial orientation and memory, anxiety and related responses, attention and, in general, in emotional response and events that are very different from each other. Finally, the contribution of adult neurogenesis to the "cognitive reserve" is also discussed, namely the capacity of the brain to maintain a normal function when confronted with neurodegenerative diseases, injury, and/or ageing.

In fact, another very important and vibrant field of study is related to the possible role of endogenous neural stem cells in neurodegenerative diseases (or, in general, diseases characterized by a cognitive decline) and traumatic events involving the CNS. The first include diseases such as Alzheimer's dementia (AD), Parkinson's disease (PD), multiple sclerosis (MS), amyotrophic lateral sclerosis (ALS), Huntington's chorea (HD); among the latter we can mention stroke and trauma.

In these conditions, a pre-eminent and abrupt inflammatory condition is often present, as in acute events, or a subtle and minimal one in chronic events. A regulation of neurogenesis has been also described, both as an increase and a decrease, or as an increase followed by a decrease. It is possible that inflammatory molecules, both humoral and microglia-derived, play a fundamental and differentiated role in the phases of neurogenesis (proliferation, differentiation, integration and survival). Soluble factors that include interleukins (including: interleukin-6, tumour necrosis factor alpha, interferon gamma, interleukin-1b, interleukin-18) and chemokines (including: SDF-1α, MCP-1), as well as inflammatory cells, like the previously mentioned microglia and astrocytes (see also 16.2.3), immune T and B cells, can both stimulate or inhibit the different phases of neurogenesis.

Post-mortem studies performed so far in the brain of patients suffering from chronic neurodegenerative diseases, such as PD, AD and HD, have led to conflicting results on possible alterations in neurogenesis, also due to the great diversity of the patients analyzed, to disease duration, age, and type and timing of pharmacological and non-pharmacological treatments. In contrast, in the brain of MS patients, an inflammatory/demyelinating disease characterized by the inability to generate oligodendrocytes capable of repairing the myelin sheath, there is a marked increase in the proliferation of NSCs in the SVZ, but newly formed cells are unable to differentiate in mature and effective reparative cells. Endogenous neurogenesis is also stimulated during neurodegenerative diseases, such as HD. One hypothesis is that during this disease there are stimuli that promote the latent proliferative potential of NSCs in the SVZ in an attempt to repair the damage by recruiting new neurons, but, until now, only a transient increase in cellular proliferation has been identified and there is no evidence of the functional integration of NSCs in neuronal circuits compromised by the pathology.

Acute events in the CNS, such as an ischaemic attack (stroke) and trauma, but also seizures in epilepsy, stimulate the proliferation of endogenous NSCs and promote the migration of "new" cells to the site of damage. Neurogenesis increases in the areas of constitutive neurogenesis, from which the new neurons migrate to the lesion areas, but new neurons also appear in the ischaemic penumbra surrounding the lesion site, preferentially located near blood vessels, thus suggesting a possible neurogenesis-angiogenesis relation.

However, when the inflammatory condition goes on, the neurogenesis decreases until it goes out. This is what probably happens in epilepsy, a disease characterized by acute attacks and remission (usually pharmacological) phases. Epileptic attacks are a situation characterized by an inflammatory component of the brain; we cannot exclude the possibility that factors recruited in inflammation during epilepsy can act by stimulating endogenous neurogenesis. Several studies on animal models indicate that, on the contrary, a long-lasting epileptic status inhibits neurogenesis. It has been demonstrated that the proliferative capability of cells derived from human hippocampal DG of patients suffering from pharmacoresistant epilepsy decreases the longer the disease lasts and is absent in patients with mesial temporal sclerosis. However, the role of neurogenesis in the brain affected by epilepsy has not yet been clarified; in particular, it has not yet been established whether newly generated cells can fit into functional or aberrant circuits. In fact, it seems that the new granule cells induced by an epileptic attack can show morphological and migratory characteristics aberrant towards the hilus in which they persist for a long time.

16.4 Neurosphere system (*in vitro* neural stem cells): possibilities and limitations

In recent years, neural stem cell research has been greatly expanded by the *in vitro* study of NSCs/NPCs, thanks to improvements in isolation and expansion techniques. Currently, NSCs can be obtained with clonal selection from fetal and adult brains, next to *in vitro* derivation of embryonic stem cells and cells obtained with genetic reprogramming. Like all biological systems, neurospheres are a model of great interest for the study *in vitro* of the potential of NSCs, but the limitations of this system should be well known and taken into account. In any case, these techniques have allowed a strong advancement in the knowledge of the genetic and molecular mechanisms of regulation of these cells, even with the limitations of a cellular system deprived of its natural microenvironment composed by the niche.

As already mentioned, neural cell precursors can be isolated from different regions of the adult central nervous system. The adult brain neurosphere system offers some very interesting opportunities: first of all the possibility of deriving these cells from pathological brains subjected to treatment, pharmacological or not. When grown in suspension, in the presence of mitogens such as EGF and bFGF, they give rise to spherical aggregates of cells called "neurospheres". Neurospheres are a heterogeneous population, comprising stem cells, precursors already directed towards specific lineages (neural or glial) and a rich extra-cellular matrix component (ECM). When maintained in the presence of mitogens, these aggregates increase in size, and it is possible to produce successive generations of cells; while, when the mitogens are removed, and the cells are allowed to adhere to the substrate, a rapid process of differentiation begins, leading to the formation of neurons (which will mature showing the antigenic, neurotransmitter and electrolyte characteristics typical of mature neurons, even *in vitro*), astrocytes and oligodendrocytes (Figure 16.4). Using different protocols, it is possible to obtain "enriched" cultures for each lineage, even if it is not yet possible to obtain populations composed by 100% one single lineage.

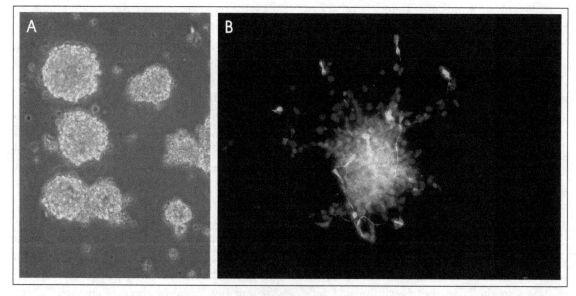

Figure 16.4. Neurospheres obtained from the SVZ of adult rats. A: when cultured in suspension and in the presence of mitogens, NSCs/NPCs grow as rounded aggregates increasing their size with time; B: these aggregates show intense proliferating activity (nuclei incorporating BrdU) and part of these cells already expresses neural lineage markers (doublecortin), the white brilliant spots.

Neurospheres and derived cells may be characterized on the antigenic level by microarray, cytofluorimetry, immunocytochemistry. The advantage of the latter technique lies in the fact that it allows to also describe the morphology of the cells. It should be immediately noted that, to date, there is no neural stem cell marker, and that only the use of combinations of markers (such as intermediate filaments, nestin, transcription factors, cell cycle regulation proteins, and molecules involved in the signalling previously mentioned) allows an adequate characterization of the system and the possible derivation of purified populations. Moreover, quiescent stem cells (B1) are not present in the neurospheres, isolated precisely because of their response to mitogens (EGF and bFGF). For these ($GFAP^+/CD133^+$), an isolation protocol based on a combination of markers, both in isolation and sorting, has recently been proposed.

This *in vitro* system has also been used to characterize the cellular population derived from the SVZ and the SGZ in pathological brains (pathologies induced in laboratory animals and spontaneous pathologies in humans), and its potential role for drug-screening in CNS pathologies is of great interest.

Recommended reading and references

Remember that the field is continuously updated, therefore it is necessary to constantly update your readings.

Historical

1. Allen E. *The cessation of mitosis in the central nervous system of the albino rat.* J Comp Neurol 1912 22:547-568
2. Altman J, et al. *Autoradiographic and histological evidence of postnatal hippocampal neurogenesis in rats.* J Comp Neurol 1965 124:319-336
3. Alvarez-Buylla A, et al. *Neuronal stem cells in the brain of adult vertebrates.* Stem Cells 1995 13:263-272
4. Cajal S, et al. *Histologie du système nerveux de l'homme et desvertébrés.* Paris: Maloine 1911.
5. Lois C and Alvarez-Buylla A. *Long-distance neuronal migration in the adult mammalian brain.* Science 1994; 264:1145-1148

General

1. Aimone JB et al. *Regulation and function of adult neurogenesis: from genes to cognition.* Physiol Rev 2014 94:991- 1026.
2. Braun SM and Jessberger S. *Adult neurogenesis: mechanisms and functional significance.* Development 2014 141:1983-6.
3. Brus M, et al. *Temporal features of adult neurogenesis: differences and similarities across mammalian species.* Front Neuro- sci 2013; 7:135.
4. Cameron HA, et al. *Adult neurogenesis produces a large pool of new granule cells in the dentate gyrus.* J Comp Neurol 2001; 435:406-417
5. Cheng MF. *Hypothalamic neurogenesis in the adult brain.* Front Neuroendocrinol 2013;34:167-78.
6. Crawford AH, et al. *Oligodendrocyte progenitors: adult stem cells of the central nervous system?* Exp Neurol 2014; 260:50-5.
7. Dimou L and Götz M. *Glial cells as progenitors and stem cells: new roles in the healthy and diseased brain.* Physiol Rev. 2014;94:709-37.
8. Doetsch F, et al. *Subventricular zone astrocytes are neural stem cells in the adult mammalian brain.* Cell 1999; 97:703- 71627.
9. Horner PJ, et al. *Proliferation and differentiation of progenitor cells trough out the intact adult rat spinal cord.* J Neurosci 200; 20:2218-2228.
10. Ihrie RA, et al. *Cells in the astroglial lineage are neural stem cells.* Cell Tissue Res 2008; 331:179:191
11. Migaud M, et al. *Seasonal regulation of structural plasticity and neurogenesis in the adult mammalian brain: Focus on the sheep hypothalamus.* Front Neuroendocrinol 2015; 37:146-157.
12. Ming GL and Song H. *Adult neurogenesis in the mammalian brain: significant answers and significant questions.* Neuron 2011; 70:687-702.
13. Moe MC, et al. *Multipotent progenitor cells from the adult human brain: neurophysiological differentiation to mature neurons.* Brain 2005; 128:2189-2199
14. Morrison BE. *Discovery of nigral dopaminergic neurogenesis in adult mice.* Neural Regen Res. 2016, 11:878-81.
15. Mu Y, et al. *Signaling in adult neurogenesis.* Curr Opin Neurobiol 2010; 20(4):416-23.
16. Sanai N, et al. *Unique astrocyte ribbon in adult human brain contains neural stem cells but lacks chain migration.* Nature 2004; 427:740-744
17. Snyder JS. *Recalibrating the Relevance of Adult Neurogenesis.* Trends Neurosci. 2019, 42:164-178.

18. Spalding KL, et al. *Dynamics of hippocampal neurogenesis in adult humans.* Cell 2013; 153:1219-1227
19. Whitman MC and Greer CA. *Adult neurogenesis and the olfactory system.* Prog Neurobiol 2009; 89:162-75.
20. Yoo S and Blackshaw S. *Regulation and function of neurogenesis in the adult mammalian hypothalamus.* Prog Neurobiol. 2018;170:53-66.

Niche

1. Alvarez-Buylla A and Lim DA. *For the long run: maintaining germinal niches in the adult brain.* Neuron 2004; 41:683- 686
2. Bond AM, et al. *Adult mammalian neural stem cells and neurogenesis: five decades later.* Cell Stem Cell 2015; 17: 385-395.
3. Faigle R and Song H. *Signaling mechanisms regulating adult neural stem cells and neurogenesis.* Biochim Biophys Acta 2013; 1830: 2435-48.
4. He Z, et al. *Estrogen Selectively Mobilizes Neural Stem Cells in the Third Ventricle Stem Cell Niche of Postnatal Day 21 Rats.* Mol Neurobiol. 2015; 52:927-33.
5. Kazanis I. *The subependymal zone neurogenic niche: a beating heart in the centre of brain.* Brain 2009; 132: 2909-2921.
6. Lim DA and Alvarez-Buylla A. *Adult neural stem cells stake their ground.* Trends Neurosci 2014; 37:563-71.
7. Lim DA and Alcarez-Buylla A. *The adult ventricular-Subventricular Zone (V-SVZ) and Olfactory Bulb (OB) neurogenesis.* Cold Spring Harb Perspect Biol 2016; 8:a018820.
8. López-Juárez A, et al. *Thyroid hormone signaling acts as a neurogenic switch by repressing Sox2 in the adult neural stem cell niche.* Cell Stem Cell. 2012; 10:531-43.
9. Madri JA. *Modeling the neurovascu- lar niche: implications for recovery from CNS injury.* J Physiol Pharmacol 2009; Suppl 4:95-104.
10. Mizrak D, et al. *Single-cell analysis of regional differences in adult V-SVZ neural stem lineages.* Cell Rep 2019; 26:394-406.
11. Porlan E, et al. *Paracrine regulation of neural stem cells in the subependymal zone.* Arch Biochem Biophys 2013; 534:11-9.
12. Ziegler AN, et al. *Insulin and IGF receptor signalling in neural-stem-cell homeostasis.* Nat Rev Endocrinol. 2015 Mar;11(3):161-70.

Human neurogenesis

1. Bergmann O, et al. *Adult Neurogenesis in Humans.* Cold Spring Harb Perspect Biol. 2015 7(7)
2. Boldrini M, et al. *Human hippocampal neurogenesis persists throughout aging.* Cell Stem Cell 2018; 22:589-599.
3. Kempermann G, et al., *Human Adult Neurogenesis: Evidence and Remaining Questions.* Cell Stem Cell. 2018, 23:25-30.
4. Snyder JS. *Questioning human neurogenesis.* Nature 2018; 555:315-316.
5. Sorrells SF, et al. *Human hippocampal neurogenesis drops sharply in children to undetectable levels in adults.* Nature 2018; 555:377-381.
6. Spalding KL, et al. *Retrospective birth dating of cells in humans.* Cell 2005; 122:133-143.

Physiologic, pharmacologic and pathologic regulation.

1. Aboody K, et al. *Translating stem cell studies to the clinic for CNS repair: current state of the art and the need for a Rosetta Stone.* Neuron 2011; 70:597-613.
2. Boku S, et al. *Glucocorticoids and lithium in adult hippocampal neurogenesis.* Vitam Horm 2010; 82:421-31.
3. Calzà L, et al. *Cellular approaches to cen- tral nervous system remyelination stimulation: thyroid hormone to promote myelin repair via endogenous stem and precursor cells.* J Mol Endocrinol 2010; 44:13-23.
4. Cameron HA and Glover LR. *Adult neurogenesis: beyond learning and memory.* Annu Rev Psychol 2015; 66:53-81.
5. Christian KM, et al. *Functions and dysfunctions of adult hippocampal neurogenesis.* Annu Rev Neurosci; 2014 37:243-62.
6. Christie KJ and Turnley AM. *Regulation of endogenous neural stem/progenitor cells for neural repair-factors that promote neurogenesis and gliogenesis in the normal and damaged brain.* Front Cell Neurosci 2012; 6:70.
7. Giusto E, et al. *Neuro-immune interactions of neural stem cell transplants: From animal disease models to human trials.* Exp Neurol 2014; 260:19-32.
8. Hattiangady B et al. *Implications of decreased hippocampal neurogenesis in chronic temporal lobe epilepsy.* Epilepsia 2008; 49(suppl 5): 26-41
9. Katsimpardi L and Lledo PM. *Regulation of neurogenesis in the adult and aging brain.* Curr Opin Neurobiol. 2018; 53:131-138.

10. Kempermann G. *Activity Dependency and Aging in the Regulation of Adult Neurogenesis.* Cold Spring Harb Perspect Biol. 2015;7(11)

11. Kohman RA and Rhodes JS. *Neurogenesis, inflammation and behavior.* Brain Behav Immun 2013; 27:22-32.

12. Ji F, et al. *The role of microRNAs in neural stem cells and neurogenesis.* J Genet Genomics 2013; 40:61-6.

13. Jin K, et al. *Evidence for stroke-induced neurogenesis in the human brain.* Proc Natl Acad Sci USA 2006; 103:13198- 13202.

14. Magnus T, et al. *Neural stem cells in inflammatory CNS diseases: mechanisms and therapy.* J Cell Mol Med 2005; 9:303-319

15. Ruan L, et al. *Neurogenesis in neurological and psychiatric diseases and brain injury: from bench to bedside.* Prog Neu- robiol 2014; 115:116-37.

16. Seib DR and Martin-Villalba A. *Neurogenesis in the Normal Ageing Hippocampus: A Mini-Review.* Gerontology 2014; Nov 29.

17. Sousa-Ferreira L, et al. *Role of hypothalamic neurogenesis in feeding regulation.* Trends Endocrinol Metab 2014; 25:80-8.

18. Snyder JS, et al. *Anatomical gradients of adult neurogenesis and activity: young neurons in the ventral dentate gyrus are activated by water maze training.* Hip- pocampus 2009; 19:360-70.

19. Wang B and Jin K. *Current perspecti- ves on the link between neuroinflamma- tion and neurogenesis.* Metab Brain Dis 2015; 30:355-65.

20. Winner B and Winkler J. *Adult neu- rogenesis in neurodegenerative diseases.* Cold Spring Harb Perspect Biol 2015; 7:a021287.

Neurospheres

1. Ahmed S. *The culture of neural stem cells.* J Cell Biochem 2009; 106:1-6.

2. Bez A, et al. *Neurosphere and neurosphere-forming cells: morphological and ultrastructural characterization.* Brain Res 2003; 993:18-29.

3. Codega P, et al. *Prospective identification and purification of quiescent adult neural stem cells from their in vivo niche.* Neuron 2014; 82: 545-59.

4. Conti L, et al. *Neural stem cell systems: physiological players or in vitro entities?* Nat Rev Neurosci 2010; 11:176-87.

5. Pastrana E, et al. *Eyes wide open: a criti- cal review of sphere-formation as an assay for stem cells.* Cell Stem Cell 2011; 8:486-98.

Placental stem cells

Anna Cargnoni Marta Magatti Antonietta Rosa Silini
Francesco Alviano Ornella Parolini

17.1 Structure and cells isolated from human term placenta

17.1.1 Structure

The human term placenta is an oval- or round-shaped organ with a diameter that

Figure 17.1. Human term the placental. Fetal membranes protrude from the fetal side of the placental disc and stretch out from the border of the chorionic plate and from the umbilical cord.

ranges from 15 to 20 cm and a thickness of between 2 and 3 cm. The placenta is a feto-maternal organ; the fetal part is made of the amniotic and chorionic membranes, the umbilical cord, and the placental disc. The maternal part is made of the decidua, which derives from the maternal endometrium (Figure 17.1).

The placental disc consists of the chorionic plate and the basal plate, which together form a base and a cover, respectively, to enclose the intervillous space, and is surrounded by the fetal membranes, which closely adhere to each other and form the amniotic sac (Figure 17.2). The amniotic membrane is a thin, avascular sheet where epithelial and stromal layers can be distinguished. The ectodermally-derived amniotic epithelium is composed of a single layer of flat, cuboidal, or columnar epithelial cells uniformly arranged on a base-

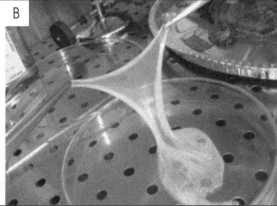

Figure 17.2. (A) Manual separation of the fetal membranes to obtain the amnion and chorion. In (B) a section of the amniotic membrane is shown prior to mechanical dissociation and enzymatic digestion.

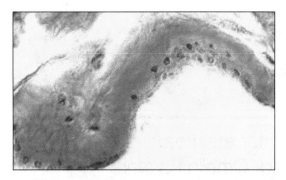

Figure 17.3. Human amniotic membrane stained with Mallory's trichrome as seen by light microscopy. Epithelial cells have a cuboid morphology and form a monolayer facing the amniotic cavity. The blue colour shows the mesenchymal region where single cells (mesenchymal cells) are visible in the extracellular matrix.

ment membrane (Figure 17.3). The amniotic epithelium also covers the umbilical cord, which is composed of one umbilical vein and two umbilical arteries embedded in a gelatinous proteoglycan-rich matrix, called Wharton's jelly (WJ) (Figure 17.4). The amniotic stroma derived from mesoderm is a collagen-rich acellular compact layer with widely dispersed fibroblast-like cells and rare macrophages. The chorion, which is the outer membrane surrounding the fetus, is comprised of chorionic stromal and trophoblastic layers, which include extravillous cytotrophoblast cells.

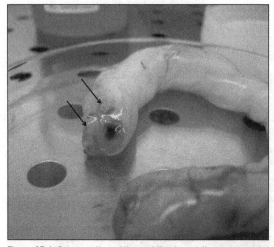

Figure 17.4. Cross-section of the umbilical cord: the arrows point to the two arteries and the vein is located where the blood clot is seen.

17.1.2 Cells isolated from the human placenta

A variety of cells can be isolated from different birth-related tissues, including different regions of the placenta and the amniotic fluid. Besides haematopoietic stem cells, other tissue-specific cells with stem/progenitor characteristics have been identified. According to the *First International Workshop on Placenta-Derived Stem Cells* held in Brescia (Italy) in 2007 (Parolini et al., 2008), different cells with stem/progenitor properties can be isolated from amniotic epithelial, amniotic mesenchymal stromal, chorionic mesenchymal stromal, and chorionic trophoblastic tissues, named human amniotic epithelial cells (hAEC) (Figure 17.5), human amniotic mesenchymal stromal cells (hAMSC)

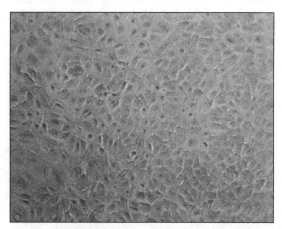

Figure 17.5. Epithelial cells isolated from the amniotic membrane are shown after one culture passage.

(Figure 17.6), human chorionic mesenchymal stromal cells (hCMSC), and human chorionic trophoblastic cells (hCTC), respectively. MSCs can be isolated from other placental tissues, such as chorionic villi, and different components of the umbilical cord, such as Wharton's Jelly (hWJ-MSC) (Figure 17.7) and the maternal side of the placenta, referred to as the decidua.

Generally, cells can be identified by their phenotype, a term defined as cell surface antigen expression. Indeed, different cell types, such as haematopoietic cells, endothelial cells,

Figure 17.6. Mesenchymal cells isolated from the amniotic membrane are shown after one culture passage.

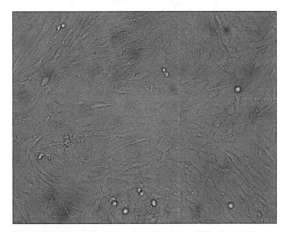

Figure 17.7. Fibroblast-like cells isolated from Wharton's jelly are shown after one culture passage.

epithelial cells, and mesenchymal cells, express characteristic markers. For example, haematopoietic cells express markers such as CD45 and CD34, endothelial cells express CD31, CD105 (endoglin), and vascular endothelial growth factor receptor (VEGFR), epithelial cells express cell adhesion molecules such as CD324 (E-Cadherin) and CD326 (Epithelial cell adhesion molecule (EpCAM)), and mesenchymal cells express CD90, CD13, and CD44.

The consensus from the *First International Workshop on Placenta-Derived Stem Cells* established a phenotype for mesenchymal cells isolated from the amniotic membrane (hAMSC), namely the positive (≥95%) expression of CD90, CD73, and CD105, and

the lack of (≤2%) CD45, CD34, CD14 and HLA-DR (Parolini et al., 2008). After cell isolation (P0), there may be a percentage of cells (ranging from 5% to 15%) expressing CD45, CD14 and HLA-DR; however after cell culture, the percentage of cells expressing CD45, CD14 and HLA-DR is greatly reduced (<2%). On the other hand, hAECs express markers including CD324 (E-cadherin), CD326 (EpCAM), CD73, CD166 (ALCAM), and the stage specific embryonic antigen SSEA-4, but do not express CD14 and CD45.

17.2 Cell differentiation

According to the consensus set out by the International Society for Cellular Therapy (ISTC) (Dominici et al., 2006), and to the consensus specifically referring to placenta-derived MSCs (Parolini et al., 2008), one of the minimum criteria required to define human MSCs is that *in vitro* they must differentiate into osteoblasts, adipocytes and chondroblasts under standard *in vitro* differentiating conditions. Indeed, several research groups have demonstrated that placenta-derived cells, when cultured in media supplemented with specific growth factors and/or hormones, can differentiate towards classical mesodermal lineages, such as osteogenic, adipogenic and chondrogenic lineages, but also towards other mesodermal cell types. For example, when cultured in neural differentiating medium, placental cells have been shown to take on an elongated neuronal morphology and express or up-regulate the expression of neuron-specific genes, such as nestin and glutamic acid decarboxylase. Moreover, upon culture in hepatic differentiation conditions, placental cells can express hepatocyte-related genes, including transthyretin, tyrosin aminotransferase, and transcription factors, such as hepatocyte nuclear factor 3γ and enhancer-binding protein (CEBP α and β), as well as several drug metabolizing genes (cytochrome

P450). In addition, under specific culture conditions, placental cells have also been shown to express cardiac-specific genes and transcription factors, such as GATA4, myosin light chain 2a and 2v, and cardiac troponin I and T.

Even though placenta-derived cells have been reported to differentiate towards cells of different lineages *in vitro*, their differentiation properties *in vivo* are still widely debated. An important point to consider is that *in vitro* multi-lineage differentiation is stimulated with media supplemented with specific growth factors, hormones and/or other additives; a condition that is likely not often reproduced in the *in vivo* setting. In fact, very few groups have suggested the cells' capacity to commit to functional phenotypes *in vivo*. For example, hAECs transplanted into immunodeficient mice livers have been shown to adopt a hepatic phenotype, including secretion of albumin or α-1 antitrypsin, as well as the metabolic features of functional hepatocytes (Marongiu et al., 2011; Sakuragawa et al., 2000). Pancreatic differentiation has also been suggested for hAECs after transplantation in the spleens of diabetic immunodeficient mice (Wei et al., 2003).

17.3 Immunological properties

The placenta not only plays a fundamental role in fetal development and nutrition, but also plays a crucial part in allowing the maternal acceptance of the fetus: an organism/individual immunologically distinct from the recipient organism, the mother. Indeed, the zygote is composed of half paternal and half maternal DNA, so the fetus has "semi-allogeneic" antigens that could theoretically be recognized by the mother's immune system and drive the immunological rejection of the fetus. Despite this, the majority of pregnancies are taken to term without rejection phenomena. In this context, the placenta and fetal membranes, which represent the interface between mother and fetus, very likely participate in the creation of an environment of mutual immunological tolerance. Therefore, it can be hypothesized that cells isolated from these tissues could modulate immune cell functions.

17.3.1 Immunogenicity

An important immunological feature of placenta-derived cells is their low immunogenicity. Immunogenicity is defined as the ability of a molecule or, in general, of a "foreign/exogenous" cellular component (antigen) to stimulate the immune response. Immunogenicity is induced by distinct molecular signals. The antigen is first taken up by antigen-presenting cells (APCs); these cells process the antigen and, through their major histocompatibility complex (MHC), present the antigen to T cells through their interaction with the T cell receptor (TCR). The interaction between APCs and T cells also requires the binding of co-stimulatory molecules (found on the surface of APCs) with their receptors located on T cells (co-stimulator signal). Then, cytokines produced by immune cells are required to favour the expansion of T and B cells.

Almost all cells in the human body express class I and class II MHC molecules (named HLA - Human Leukocyte Antigens- in humans). These molecules are able to present antigens, thus initiating immune responses. The particular feature of cells isolated from the different regions of the placenta is that these cells have low levels of HLA class Ia antigens (HLA-A, HLA-B and HLA-C) and lack the class II HLA antigens (HLA-DP, HLA-DQ, HLA-DR) and co-stimulatory molecules (CD40, CD80, CD86, CD275).

In addition, placenta-derived cells express molecules known for their ability to modulate the immune response, such as the HLA-G antigen, PD-L1 and PD-L2, and B7-H3. Placental cells, therefore, have a reduced ability to induce an immune response both *in vitro* and *in vivo*. Indeed, placental cells are poor stimulators of T cells *in vitro*, and their low immunogenicity is thought to contribute to the survival of placenta-derived cells for prolonged periods of time after transplantation into immune competent animals without the use of immunosuppressants. However, several studies have highlighted the heterogeneity of placental cell preparations and how culture conditions (passage number, culture media, INF-γ activation) influence their immunogenicity.

17.3.2 Immunomodulation

Various *in vitro* studies have demonstrated that placenta-derived cells exhibit immunomodulatory actions on immune cells of innate (macrophages, dendritic cells, neutrophils, natural killer cells) and adaptive (T and B cells) immunity. They are able to suppress the proliferation and cytotoxic activity of immune cells and the production of inflammatory cytokines. Furthermore, they induce the differentiation of T cells and monocytes towards immune cells with anti-inflammatory and regulatory functions. Placenta-derived cells exert their immunomodulatory action both through a direct interaction with immune cells (cell-to-cell contact) and also through an indirect action, mediated by the secretion of specific factors (Figure 17.8)

Indeed, experiments conducted using transwell systems (which prevent direct contact between placenta derived and immune cells) or using the conditioned medium (CM), containing factors secreted from placental cells during *in vitro* culture, have shown the same ability to inhibit the immune response. Placental cells and their CM have been shown to suppress T-lymphocyte proliferation when stimulated either by mitogens (Concanavalin A and phytohemagglutinin), T-cell receptor cross-linking (anti-CD3/anti-CD28), allo-antigens (in mixed lymphocyte cultures, MLC), or by the recall antigen (CMV). They suppress the proliferation of activated CD4 and CD8 T cells, and reduce T-cell subsets and related cytokines, such as Th1 (IFNγ, TNFα, IL-1β, IL-12p70), Th2 (IL-5, IL-6, IL-13), Th9 (IL-9), and Th17 (IL-17A, IL-22). In addition to their actions on T cells, placental cells and their CM block the maturation of monocytes to dendritic cells (DC) or to inflammatory M1-macrophages, and skew monocyte differentiation towards anti-inflammatory M2 macrophages. Interestingly, hAMSCs have been described as modulating the activation of resident brain macrophages (microglia) and as promoting polarization towards anti-inflammatory M2 microglia. Furthermore, placental cells and their CM can suppress NK cell cytotoxicity, inhibit the migration of murine neutrophils *in vitro*, and accelerate their apoptosis. Many factors secreted by placenta-derived cells have been described as being involved in the immunosuppressive action of these cells, such as transforming growth factor β (TGF-β), interleukin 10 (IL-10), prostaglandin E-2 (PGE-2), the soluble form of the HLA-G antigen, Fas ligand (CD95L), migration inhibiting factor (MIF), and the enzyme IDO (indoleamine 2,3-dioxygenase). IDO is an enzyme that catabolizes tryptophan, an essential amino acid required for T-cell proliferation, that leads to a decrease in tryptophan levels thus ultimately reducing T-cell proliferation. The soluble form of the HLA-G antigen induces apoptosis in CD8+ activated T lymphocytes and inhibits the proliferation of CD4+ T lymphocytes; moreover, HLA-G expressed by trophoblast and amniotic cells inhibits the activity of NK cells. TGF-β also plays a role in modulating the immune response; it is involved in mechanisms that lead to a block in the development and function of T lymphocytes, acting on DNA synthesis and consequently on the proliferation of activated T lymphocytes. PGE-2 is able to suppress the activation of T lymphocytes, the maturation of macrophages and dendritic cells, and to stimulate the production of anti-inflammatory cytokines, including IL-10. Furthermore, cells derived from the placenta express Fas ligand which induces apoptosis of lymphocytes that express the

Fas receptor on their surface. Lastly, hAECs express MIF, which inhibits the migration of neutrophils and macrophages to the inflammation site.

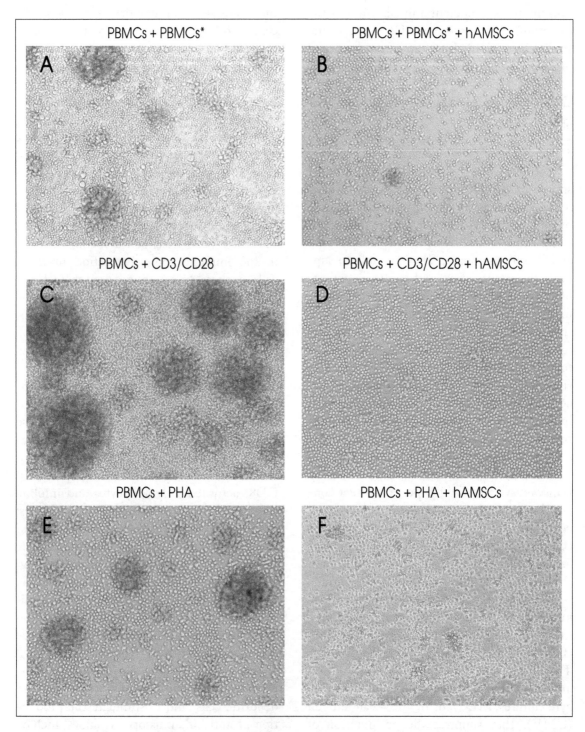

Figure 17.8. Suppression of lymphocyte proliferation by hAMSCs. Human PBMCs were stimulated with irradiated allogeneic PBMCs* (upper panels), or with anti-CD3 plus anti-CD28 (middle panels), or with PHA (lower panels), either alone (A , C, E) or in the presence of hAMSCs (B, D, and F, respectively), which were added in transwell chambers. After culture, the presence or absence of cell clusters indicates intense or poor lymphocyte proliferation, respectively. Original magnification, 10X.

17.4 Potential therapeutic effects: preclinical studies and clinical trials

17.4.1 Preclinical studies

Their unique *in vitro* biological properties, including low immunogenicity, their ability to differentiate towards a variety of cellular lineages, and their capacity to repress the inflammatory immune response make placental cells suitable as treatment for a number of diseases.

Some *in vivo* studies have reported that human placental cells are not rejected and survive for prolonged periods of time in host tissues when implanted into immune competent animals; a feature likely due to their low immunogenicity. However, other studies observed that, after transplantation, placental cells migrate to injured tissues, and that, two weeks after transplantation, their numbers were reduced and negligible. These findings suggested that the reparative action of placental cells does not rely on their ability to engraft, differentiate, and replace host damaged cells. Indeed, very few studies have documented the potential ability of placenta-derived cells to differentiate towards functional cardiomyocyte and hepatocyte-like cells *in vivo* and to improve cardiac and liver function in animal models of related diseases. Instead, increasing experimental evidence demonstrates that the reparative actions exerted by placental cells are mediated by bioactive factors, secreted by these cells, which induce tissue repair by favouring the resolution of inflammation activated by injury, and by promoting the survival of host cells and the differentiation of host progenitor cells.

A number of studies have demonstrated the beneficial effects of placental cells when transplanted in various animal disease models, such as neurological, hepatic, pulmonary, cardiac, diabetic and degenerative joint.

Placental cells have been shown to exert anti-inflammatory and anti-fibrotic effects in models of chronic liver and lung diseases. Specifically, hAECs transplanted in mice with CCl_4-induced liver fibrosis, and hAECs and hAMSCs implanted in mice with bleomy-cin-induced lung fibrosis, on the one hand, reduced parenchymal infiltration of T lymphocytes, reduced the levels of pro-inflammatory cytokines (TNF-α, IL-6, IL-1, INF-γ) and of pro-fibrotic factors (TGF-β, PDGF) and, on the other hand, increased levels of the anti-inflammatory molecules (such as IL-10) and reduced fibrosis (Figure 17.9). Other studies, performed in models of lung and liver fibrosis, renal ischaemia/reperfusion, and multiple sclerosis have correlated the beneficial effects exerted by placental cells with their ability to reduce the recruitment of macrophages into injured tissues and to promote macrophage differentiation towards M2-type macrophages which exhibit an anti-inflammatory function and play a fundamental role in inflammation resolution, in contrast with M1-type macrophages which display a pro-inflammatory activity.

The therapeutic actions of amniotic membrane-derived cells have also been observed when such cells were transplanted in inflammatory/autoimmune disorders, such as experimental collagen-induced arthritis, sepsis, inflammatory bowel disease, experimental autoimmune encephalomyelitis (an animal model for multiple sclerosis) and diabetes. Even in these studies, the benefits observed after placental cell treatment have been associated with their ability to modulate T-cell proliferation or with their ability in limiting the maturation of pro-inflammatory T-cell subtypes (Th1 and Th17) while favouring the expansion of T cells with immunosuppressive functions (T regulatory cells). A reduction of inflammatory microglia/macrophage cells in the central nervous system has also been observed after placental cell infusion into models of brain injury induced by LPS or by trauma.

Besides modulating inflammation, placental cells produce factors with anti-apoptotic, neurogenic, and angiogenic effects. Placental cell administration in mice with traumatic brain injury or ischaemic stroke increased neuronal survival and vascular density in the injured cortex; and in models of Parkinson's

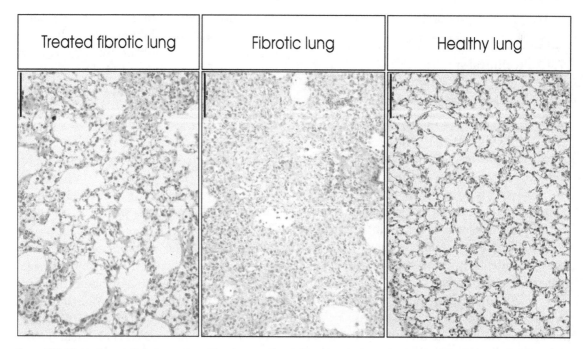

Figure 17.9. Effect of amniotic cells on mice with pulmonary fibrosis. The microphotographs show lung tissues from a healthy mouse, a mouse with pulmonary fibrosis induced by intra-tracheal instillation of bleomycin, and a mouse with pulmonary fibrosis treated with amniotic cells.
Lung tissues are stained with Masson's trichrome staining: green areas represent collagen deposition, an indicator of fibrosis. Scale bars: 100 μm.

disease, they improved locomotor function, prevented nigral dopamine neuron degeneration, and promoted endogenous neurogenesis.

In favour of the secretory action of placental cells, several studies have demonstrated that the beneficial effects were also achieved with cell-free treatments, and specifically with conditioned media containing factors secreted by placental cells during *in vitro* culture. Conditioned media generated from placental cells have been demonstrated to promote recovery in models of lung fibrosis and cardiac ischaemia. They also accelerate the healing of ulcers in diabetic mice and corneal ulcers in dogs and the resolution of tendon and ligament injuries in horses and corneal alkali injuries in rabbits.

The promising findings obtained from pre-clinical studies after transplantation of placental cells in animal models of different diseases provide a strong rationale for investigating their use in humans affected with different types of pathologies.

17.4.2 Clinical trials

The first documented use of the amniotic membrane in medicine was for skin transplantation in 1910. Subsequently, the amnion was used to favour the healing of various types of wounds (derived from burns, skin lesions, and ulcerations), in urogenital and orofacial reconstructive surgery, and in ocular surface reconstruction.

The amniotic membrane's efficacy in promoting rapid and complete healing, controlling excessive fibrosis and reducing pain, together with recent advances in tissue preservation techniques, such as cryopreservation, lyophilization, freeze-drying, irradiation and decellularization, resulted in the development of commercially available amniotic membrane products for use in patients. These products are mostly applied for ocular pathologies, including corneal epithelial defects, corneal ulcers, glaucoma, pterygium, conjunctival surface reconstruction, bullous keratopathy, limbal stem cell deficiency, and Stevens-Johnson syndrome.

More recent clinical interest has focused on the use of cells isolated from different placental regions, from either fetal placental tissues (such as the amnion and chorion, the umbilical cord), or from maternal tissues (such as the decidua). The clinical potential of placenta-derived cells essentially relies on their ability to produce and secrete bioactive factors able to reduce injury-induced inflammation, and to favor re-epithelialization and angiogenesis.

Many clinical trials carried out by academic groups and by the industry have investigated and are currently investigating the feasibility and efficacy of placental cell-based therapy for the treatment of a variety of diseases. These include autoimmune diseases, such as Crohn's disease, rheumatoid arthritis, types II diabetes; ischaemic diseases, such as critical limb ischaemia, intermittent claudication, ischaemic stroke, cardiac ischaemia, diabetic foot ulcers with peripheral arterial disease; and other diseases, such as pulmonary arterial hypertension, pulmonary sarcoidosis, idiopathic pulmonary fibrosis, haemorrhagic cystitis.

Other than placental cells, some clinical trials are applying derivatives from placental cells and specifically: i) Amnion-derived Cellular Cytokine Solution (ACCS), obtained from amniotic cell culture and containing factors relevant for wound healing (platelet-derived growth factor, vascular endothelial growth factor, angiogenin, TGF-β2, TIMP-1, and TIMP-2); ii) amniotic membrane extract, based on lyophilized human amniotic membrane, and iii) hAEC-conditioned medium, generated from the *in vitro* culture of epithelial amniotic cells. These derivatives have been developed mainly for topical treatment and used to treat radiation-induced dermatitis, gingivitis, dry eye syndrome, and persistent corneal epithelial defects.

Although promising results have been obtained after placental cell transplantation in humans, the clinical trials until now performed have been carried out on a low number of patients; they do not, therefore, yet provide unequivocal evidence of a robust clinical benefit. In addition, the safety of these cells and their derived products remains an important point to be considered. There are crucial aspects which have to be addressed in order to ensure a safe placenta-derived product: i) the development of standardized protocols of cell isolation from each placental tissue; ii) the purity of the cell product in order to avoid engraftment of undesired cell types into recipient tissue; iii) the optimization of *in vitro* culture conditions in order to avoid the use of reagents of animal origin, such as fetal bovine serum, usually added to cell culture medium, which can vehicle pathogen microorganisms in humans; iv) the improvement of *in vitro* expansion conditions which better maintain the physiological microenvironment and cell growth conditions (for example, the development of 3D cell culture systems which, in contrast with monolayer (2D) culture, allow a more physiological spatial organization of the cell surface receptors engaged in interactions with surrounding cells and influence cell proliferation and gene/protein expression profiles); v) the development of long-term culture conditions which avoid cell genetic changes and chromosomal aberrations (which possibly lead to malignant transformation); vi) the development of methods to control cellular replicative senescence during *in vitro* expansion, since cellular senescence can affect the therapeutic potential of the transplanted cells.

Recommended reading and references

Placenta structure

Placenta: The Tree of Life. Edited by O. Parolini. First ed. Boca Raton, FL: CRC Press, Taylor & Francis Group 2016.

(This book includes various chapters focused on the human term placenta, and can be reviewed for placental cell phenotype, differentiation, immunomodulatory properties, preclinical studies, and human and veterinary clinical trials).

Phenotype and Differentiation

Alviano F et al. Term Amniotic membrane is a high throughput source for multipotent Mesenchymal Stem Cells with the ability to differentiate into endothelial cells *in vitro*. BMC Dev Biol 2007;21:7-11.

Parolini, O., F. Alviano, G. P. Bagnara, G. Bilic, H. J. Buhring, M. Evangelista, S. Hennerbichler, B. Liu, M. Magatti, N. Mao, T. Miki, F. Marongiu, H. Nakajima, T. Nikaido, C. B. Portmann-Lanz, V. Sankar, M. Soncini, G. Stadler, D. Surbek, T. A. Takahashi, H. Redl, N. Sakuragawa, S. Wolbank, S. Zeisberger, A. Zisch, and S. C. Strom. 2008. "Concise review: isolation and characterization of cells from human term placenta: outcome of the first international Workshop on Placenta Derived Stem Cells." *Stem Cells* no. 26 (2):300-11. doi: 10.1634/stemcells.2007-0594.

Marongiu, F., R. Gramignoli, K. Dorko, T. Miki, A. R. Ranade, M. Paola Serra, S. Doratiotto, M. Sini, S. Sharma, K. Mitamura, T. L. Sellaro, V. Tahan, K. J. Skvorak, E. C. Ellis, S. F. Badylak, J. C. Davila, R. Hines, E. Laconi, and S. C. Strom. 2011. "Hepatic differentiation of amniotic epithelial cells." *Hepatology* no. 53 (5):1719-29. doi: 10.1002/hep.24255.

Sakuragawa, N., S. Enosawa, T. Ishii, R. Thangavel, T. Tashiro, T. Okuyama, and S. Suzuki. 2000. "Human amniotic epithelial cells are promising transgene carriers for allogeneic cell transplantation into liver." *J Hum Genet* no. 45 (3):171-6. doi: 10.1007/s100380050205.

Wei, J. P., T. S. Zhang, S. Kawa, T. Aizawa, M. Ota, T. Akaike, K. Kato, I. Konishi, and T. Nikaido. 2003. "Human amnion-isolated cells normalize blood glucose in streptozotocin-induced diabetic mice." *Cell Transplant* no. 12 (5):545-52.

Immunomodulatory properties

Abumaree MH, Abomaray FM, Alshabibi MA, AlAskar AS, Kalionis B. Immunomodulatory properties of human placental mesenchymal stem/stromal cells. Placenta. 2017;59:87-95.

Insausti CL, Blanquer M, Garcia-Hernandez AM, Castellanos G, Moraleda JM. Amniotic membrane-derived stem cells: immunomodulatory properties and potential clinical application. Stem Cells Cloning. 2014;7:53-63.

Preclinical studies

Debashree, D., G. Kmiecik, A. Cargnoni, and O Parolini. 2015. "Placenta-Derived Cells and Their Therapeutic Applications." In *Gene and Cell Therapy: Therapeutic Mechanisms and Strategies*, edited by Nancy Smyth Templeton. CRC Press.

Clinical Studies

https://clinicaltrials.gov/

Fierabracci, A., L. Lazzari, M. Muraca, and O. Parolini. 2015. "How far are we from the clinical use of placental-derived mesenchymal stem cells?" *Expert Opin Biol Ther* no. 15 (5):613-7. doi: 10.1517/14712598.2015.1000856.

Other

Dominici, M., K. Le Blanc, I. Mueller, I. Slaper-Cortenbach, F. Marini, D. Krause, R. Deans, A. Keating, Dj Prockop, and E. Horwitz. 2006. "Minimal criteria for defining multipotent mesenchymal stromal cells. The International Society for Cellular Therapy position statement." Cytotherapy no. 8 (4):315-7. doi: 10.1080/14653240600855905.

Clinical applications of mesenchymal stromal cells in stem cell transplantation

18

Roberta Rizzo   Diana Campioni
Daria Bortolotti   Francesco Lanza

18.1 Mesenchymal stromal cells: functional and immunophenotypic characteristics

Mesenchymal stromal cells (MSCs) are non-haematopoietic stem cells derived from bone marrow and other tissues. MSCs, originally described as bone marrow derived-non hematopoietic stromal cells are characterized by their capacity to sustain haematopoiesis and by their clonogenic potential *in vitro*. MSCs are a plastic population with multilineage potential. They can differentiate towards different lineages, such as osteoblastic, chondroblastic and adipocytic cell populations. Recent studies demonstrated that MSCs display myogenic potential and that they can also differentiate into other type of tissues of non-mesodermal origin, such as skin, nervous tissue, hepatocytes, etc. The multilineage potential of MSCs appears to be very interesting and possibly useful in different clinical applications.

MSCs were identified by their immunophenotypic profile, since they resulted positive for the CD90, CD105, and CD73, and negative for the CD45, CD34, CD14 and CD19 haematopoietic surface antigens, as described by the ISCT guidelines. An analytical approach to the study of the MSCs' immunophenotypic profile is needed in order to understand which are the most specific markers that could be used to select MSCs from non-expanded tissues, as well as after *in vitro* culture. The study of the different MSC immunophenotypic subsets from different tissues could have implications for the *in vivo* use of MSCs.

The heterogeneity of the different methodological approaches for isolation of MSCs from primary tissues, such as magnetic or enzymatic immune selection or cell sorting, have limited their clinical use, since no standardized systems are yet available.

For example, recent studies reveal that the MSCs' "naive" immunophenotypic pattern could be different from species to species and, in particular in humans, could vary in relation to tissue sources as well as its localization. Most of the MSC-associated immunophenotypic markers are not specific, since they be also expressed by other cell types (haematopoietic cells, endothelial cells, fibroblasts), while others could be more specific, even though they are expressed in fresh samples, while they are downregulated or are absent after expansion.

Actually the most used antigens to recognize and select MSCs before expansion are: CD271, CD146, CD56, MSCA-1, SSEA-4, fizzled-9 (FZD-9, Wnt receptor), GD2, and some others. For example, new monoclonal antibodies not yet classified in the cluster of differentiation (CD) terminology have been used in this setting, namely W8B2 and W4A5 antibodies. Based on these considerations, the immunophenotypic characterization of human MSCs is becoming an interesting field of investigation with clinical implications.

The existence of different immunophenotypic subsets in relation to the different origin tissues, as well as to the methodological approach used for MSC selection, could correlate with a different clonogenic and plastic MSC potential thus obtaining possibly different MSC populations.

Despite the homogeneous fibroblast-like aspect that they assume after *ex vivo* expansion, MSCs display an heterogeneous phenotype. Cultured MSCs express CD90, CD105, and CD73, as mentioned above, but they could be also positive for other markers, such as CD146, CD29, CD106, CD105, CD166, CD36, CD44 (different adhesion molecules), as well as some markers considered haematopoietic, such as CD10, CD13 and CD34, and moreover positive for the complement regulatory protein (CD59), for histocompatibility complex antigens (HLA-ABC-class I, HLA-DR class II), for some interleukin receptors, such as CD210 (IL-10 receptor) and for the CD184-CXCR4 (SDF-1 receptor).

Nevertheless, these markers used to identify the "standard" MSC immunophenotypic profile, after *in vitro* expansion, are not specific enough to distinguish MSCs from other cells, such as fibroblasts. Based on these data, we sustained that the MSCs' heterogeneity in relation to their tissue origin could be extremely relevant because MSC immunophenotypic heterogeneity could reflect different functional properties that could be potentially useful in different clinical settings.

On the other hand, recent studies have demonstrated that the MSCs' immunophenotypic profile could be different and vary in relation to their origin (normal vs pathologic), tissue source, culture expansion conditions, such as the presence of fetal bovine serum or platelet lysate in culture medium, the number of MSC passages in culture, and finally to the fact that the MSCs were fresh or frozen.

Recent data on the MSC gene expression array support the evidence on MSC immunophenotypic heterogeneity. The comparison of the gene expression pattern of different MSCs demonstrated the influence of microenvironmental conditions on the functional and immunophenotypic MSC characteristics and properties.

Based on these data, the concept is emerging that the microenvironmental conditions could determine the prevalence of some MSC immunophenotypic subsets with different specific functional capacities, thus creating a possible particular "MSC niche". For example, the control of the T-lymphocyte response could be differently modulated by MSCs in relation to the variable microenvironmental conditions, thus demonstrating that the different stimuli determine the immunological properties of MSCs.

For example, it has been shown that resting MSCs with low antigenic response capacity display low expression of the HLA-class I antigen, are lacking the HLA-class II (inducible after INF-gamma treatment) and do not express other co-stimulatory molecules, such as CD80 (B7-1), CD86 (B7-2) and CD40. Furthermore, MSCs share the expression of several surface markers with the thymic epithelium and further express molecules that are fundamental for MSC/T lymphocyte interaction. Moreover, MSC subsets coexpressing the CD200 or CD274/PD-L1/B7-H1 molecules have predominantly immunomodulating characteristics.

Activated MSCs could increase the expression of different cytokine receptors, such as the CXC3, CXCR4, CXCR5, CCR7, CD119/INF-gamma receptor, or can enhance the expression of other markers (CD54, CD106, DNAM ligand, such as CD112, CD155, NKG2D) that can mediate the immune response. Based on this emerging evidence, an *ad hoc* ISCT expert panel group has established some standardized GMP-graded MSC expansion protocols usable for different clinical applications. In particular, it has been demonstrated that MSCs isolated from adipose tissue under GMP conditions and expanded with platelet lysate in the presence of potent soluble activator molecules, such as CD40L and VCAM, display a particular immunophenotypic profile characterized by expression for CD274low/CD200low, which are correlated to an enhanced immunomodulating activity.

The main mechanisms of the immunomodulating capacities of MSCs will be explained in the next paragraph.

18.2 Immunological functions of MSCs

In recent years, numerous studies have demonstrated the peculiar immunological characteristics of MSCs, such as reduced antigenicity and high immune-modulatory capacity, which may have clinical applications, such as their use to improve graft versus host disease (GVHD), the most frequent and severe complication in allogeneic bone marrow transplants. The interest of MSCs is therefore related to their ability to suppress the proliferation of T lymphocytes induced by both drugs and alloantigens that regulate transplant rejection. In addition, MSCs are resistant to cytotoxicity mediated by CD8+ T lymphocytes and inhibit the differentiation of dendritic cells responsible for antigenic presentation, the proliferation of B lymphocytes, limiting antibody production and favouring the formation of regulatory T cells. As a whole they are haematopoietic precursors that are capable of innate rather than adaptive immune responses.

The evaluation of the mechanisms responsible for their tolerogenic activity has demonstrated the need for a contact between the mesenchymal cell and the activated lymphocyte and the secretion of soluble factors not expressed constitutively by the MSCs but induced by the microenvironment. Several soluble molecules have been associated with the inhibitory activity of MSCs, such as hepatocyte growth factor (HGF), transforming the growth factor beta (TGF-beta), interleukin-10 and -2, tumour necrosis factor alpha (TNF-alpha), prostaglandin E2 (PGE2), indoleamine 2,3-dioxygenase (IDO) and soluble HLA-G antigens. The intrinsic variability of the MSCs themselves is one of the causes of the different culture conditions, of the kinetics of the lymphocyte population, of the dose of MSCs used. However, a positive consensus was obtained with respect to the modulatory capacity mediated by the IDO and HLA-G molecules (Figure 18.1).

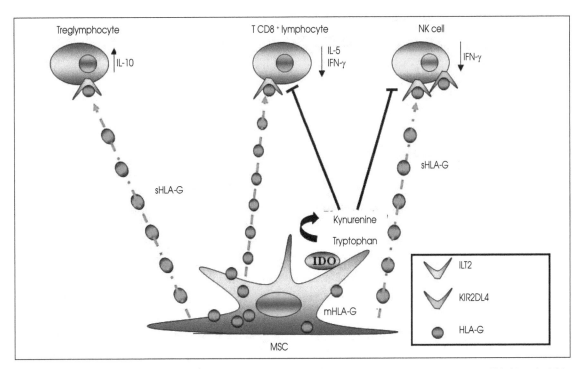

Figure 18.1. MSC effect on immune cells mediated by IDO and HLA-G molecules. MSCs, expressing membrane (mHLA-G) and soluble HLA-G (sHLA-G), inhibit the lytic activity of natural killer cells (NK) and their secretion of interferon-gamma (IFN-γ), the cytotoxic activity of T CD8+ lymphocytes and their secretion of interferon-gamma (IFN-γ) and interleukin-5 (IL-5), induce the formation and expansion of regulatory T lymphocytes (T reg) and their secretion of interleukin-10 (IL-10). Indoleamine 2,3-dioxygenase (IDO) produced by MSCs creates an immunosuppressive microenvironment that allows the inhibition of the lytic activity of NK cells, of the cytotoxic activity of T CD8+ cells and the production of cytokines.

18.3 Indoleamine 2,3-dioxygenase (IDO)

IDO is a protein that, together with the hepatic enzyme tryptophan 2,3 dioxigenase, catalyzes the conversion of tryptophan into kynurenine. The physiological role of IDO is not yet fully understood but its ubiquitous distribution and its production by cytokines, such as interferon-gamma, make this enzyme able to modulate the levels of tryptophan, a vital amino acid for cell growth. The degradative action of IDO against tryptophan induces cell death. In the antigen-presenting cells (APC), IFN-gamma-induced IDO expression and other pro-inflammatory cytokines catalyze the conversion of tryptophan into kynurenine and have an immunosuppressive effect on T-cell response by inducing the inhibition of cell proliferation and apoptosis. Mesenchymal cells do not constitutively express IDO which is induced by IFN-gamma, suggesting a functional role. IDO is detectable in mixed lymphocyte responses in which the presence of MSCs inhibits lymphocyte proliferation, which is partially reactivated following the administration of tryptophan to cultures. The partial lymphoproliferative response obtained following tryptophan treatment is due to the activity of IDO, which also induces the formation of metabolites that directly inhibit the proliferation of T cells and whose effect is not reversible. The role of IDO is confirmed by the abrogation of the implantation of heart transplants in rats following the administration of 1-methyl tryptophan (1-MT) that blocks IDO activity. These data suggest that IDO is one of the important soluble factors in the complex immune system that is established *in vitro*. Spaggiari et al. have demonstrated that MSCs are capable of inhibiting the proliferation of natural killer cells, the expression of NK activator receptors (NKp44, NKp30, NKG2D) and the induction of effector functions, such as cytotoxic activity and the production of cytokines through IDO. Recently, a study of MSCs in which the expression of the receptor 1 for interferon-gamma (IFN-gamma R1) was inhibited, showed that the inhibition of the lymphoproliferation can occur also independently from IDO. In these IFN-gamma R1-deficient MSCs, 1-methyltryptophan administration does not reactivate lymphocyte proliferation. The activation of a different immunomodulatory pathway is therefore hypothesized. The integrity of the insulin-like growth factor binding protein (IGFBP3) proposes the IGF / IGFBP system in the inhibition of cell proliferation. Furthermore, MSCs are able to suppress the expression of the NKG2D receptor (natural killer group 2, member D protein) on the surface of CD8$^+$ T cells, causing a blockage of cell proliferation. The role of IDO and the exact nature of its role in the inhibitory mechanism of MSCs against T-cell proliferation are not yet clear and require confirmation with studies performed on IDO-deficient MSCs.

18.4 The HLA-G antigen

The HLA-G antigen is a non-classical class I HLA molecule that presents inhibitory properties against the cells of the immune system. The HLA-G antigen, characterized by 7 protein isoforms, four membrane-bound (HLA-G1, G2, G3, G4) and three soluble (HLA-G5, G6, G7), obtained by alternative splicing of mRNA, is able to inhibit various immune functions, such as the lytic and cytotoxic activity of natural killer cells and CD8$^+$ T lymphocytes, the maturation of dendritic cells, the alloproliferation of CD4$^+$ T lymphocytes and to induce the formation of regulatory T lymphocytes and suppressors. HLA-G molecules differ from classical antigens due to their low allelic polymorphism and the restricted expression by the cytotrophoblast and the thymic epithelium under physiological conditions. The expression of HLA-G can be induced in pathological conditions, such as tumours, organ transplants and viral infections. Considering the tolerogenic properties of HLA-G, in particular the ability to inhibit the lymphoproliferative response, we hypothesized the involvement of these molecules in the immune modulatory activity of MSCs. The presence of HLA-G-specific mRNA has been demonstrated in both fetal and adult MSCs. Subsequent studies have confirmed the modulation of HLA-G antigens on the MSC membrane and the ability of such cells to produce, in the presence of a specific microenvironment, soluble HLA-G molecules. Numerous studies have confirmed that contact between MSCs and T lymphocytes induces the secretion of HLA-G and interleukin-10 (IL-10), a cytokine capable of stimulating HLA-G production. Neutralization experiments with antibodies specific for HLA-G and IL-10 have shown how the contribution of soluble HLA-G, induced by IL-10, is indispensable for the suppressive effect of MSCs on the proliferation of activated T cells, on the cytolytic activity, on the secretion of interferon-gamma (IFN-gamma) by natural killer cells and on the expansion of regulatory CD4$^+$/ CD25high/ FoxP3$^+$ T cells. These data suggest a fundamental role for HLA-G antigens in MSC-mediated tolerance induction. The observation of a possible correlation between the co-transplantation of MSCs and the increase in the frequency of relapse of the haematological pathology should be emphasized. As we know, the modulation of HLA-G molecules is considered a favourable event in pregnancy and in organ transplants in which the regulation of cell-mediated immune response is an essential event for a positive outcome. On the contrary, the expression of HLA-G molecules is associated with negative clinical consequences in neoplasms and viral infections, in which the tolerogenic function of HLA-G allows the mutated / infected cells to "escape" the immune response. The association between co-transplantation of MSCs and the development of neoplasia may depend on the functional capacity of HLA-G molecules to counteract GVHD while allowing the flare-up of the disease. These considerations further increase the need to *a priori* determine the immunomodulatory activity of MSCs and the expression of sHLA-G could be a good bio-

logical marker for this evaluation. It has been observed that the treatment of MSCs with modulators of the epigenetic regulation (methylation, acetylation) is able to induce HLA-G expression and increase the immunoregulatory activity of such cells. Furthermore, the induction of stable HLA-G expression via lentiviral systems is able to increase the immunosuppressive effect of MSCs. These data suggest a possible use of HLA-G expression by MSCs in therapeutic applications, in which it is necessary to establish a tolerance condition.

18.5 Clinical use of MSCs

Recently, MSCs have been proposed in different clinical settings (**Table 1**). The lack of randomized clinical trials exploring the role of MSCs and their clinical application suggests a possible potential ability of these cells to manage some pathological conditions. The paucity of clinical data in humans is strictly correlated to the evolving regulatory framework that imposes the isolation and manipulation of MSCs for clinical purposes in accredited laboratories, working in GMP (Good Manufacturing Practice) facilities. There are very few such GMP laboratories in Europe and in North America, but their number has increased in recent years. In the past few years, several clinical trials focused on MSC isolation and their *ex vivo* expansion in "GMP clinical grade" conditions that are necessary for clinical use. These protocols permit and can guarantee the maintenance of MSC characteristics, such as plasticity and immunomodulatory properties, that are necessary for clinical applications.

Nowadays most clinical applications for MSCs concern 1) regenerative medicine ("tissue repair"); 2) immunomodulating therapy. MSCs have also been found, *in vitro* and *in vivo*, to have anti-inflammatory and anti-proliferative properties, a discovery that has led to the evolution of new clinical protocols. Nevertheless, the positive effects of MSC clinical applications are not due to only one of these MSC functional mechanism but the final result

Table 18.1. Main clinical application related to the use of mesenchymal stem cells (MSC).

To treat acute and chronic *Graft versus host disease* (GVHD)
To prevent GVHD and improve the kinetic of neutrophil and platelet engraftment after combined HSC and MSC transplantation
To treat the acute and chronic rejection process after organ transplantation
To treat skin ulcers
To treat autoimmune diseases and immune-mediated diseases
To treat congenital and acquired genetic diseases
To treat myocardial infarction
To treat vascular diseases
To treat "osteogenesis imperfecta "
To treat solid tumors (mainly in murine models)

is based on the integrations of all MSC biological properties. For example, one of the most promising use of MSCs is correlated to the prevention and treatment of graft versus host disease (GVHD) in patients after allogeneic bone marrow transplantation. It is known that GVHD is a pathological condition with an elevated incidence (90%) and mortality (20%) in allo-transplanted patients. In 2004, a group of clinicians from Stockolm with K. Leblanc published the first paper in *Lancet* in which they demonstrated that *ex vitro* expanded immunomodulating MSCs were able to restore the clinical manifestations of severe (grade III and IV) GVHD after reinfusion in patients who did not respond to traditional treatment, since they observed improvement of skin lesions, hepatic and gastric damage. Nevertheless, some cases of minimal improvement of the disease after treatment with MSCs were reported, thus suggesting that it is necessary to define some important steps during MSC management before their clinical use, such as the number of *in vitro* MSC passages, cryopreservation, infusion protocols (single or multiple infusions, absolute numbers of MSCs employed), the modality of reinfusion, namely systemic or local. All these characteristic should be considered because they can potentially affect the immunomodulating capacity of MSCs after *in vivo* infusion.

For example, in preclinical studies based on animal models, the co-transplantation of MSCs and haematopoietic cells had the capacity to reduce the incidence and severity of GVHD and were able to ameliorate the timing of granulocyte and platelet engraftment after allogeneic bone marrow transplantation. Nevertheless, the immunotolerant status after MSC injection should be better controlled and examined in order to assess the incidence of secondary neoplasms. Another interesting application of MSCs is the modulation of inflammation by secreting cytokines or other anti-apoptotic molecules (secretome) that can promote the repair of the damaged tissue and protect neighbouring tissues by restoring their trophic status. Moreover their immunomodulating properties can block the lymphocyte response and induce immunotolerance.

In conclusion, MSCs could be used in different clinical applications due to their positive effects but the scarcity of clinical studies does not permit to draw definitive conclusions: further randomized clinical trials are necessary.

18.6 Anti-microbial role of MSCs

Following haematopoietic stem cell (HSCs) transplantation, a prolonged neutropenia associated with damage to the muco-cutaneous barrier may cause an increased risk of bacterial and fungal infections, sometimes related to species of Candida or Aspergillus. Moreover, after HSC transplantation, a reactivation of herpesvirus type 6 and cytomegalovirus (CMV) may occur quite frequently. In the later phases following HSC transplantation, infections are mainly due to the perturbation of the cellular-mediated immunity. The frequency and severity of infections is strictly dependent on the patient's immunocompetence status and the type and dosage of immunosuppressive drugs used after HSC transplantation. Other infections observed in this setting are related to Pneumocystis jiroveci. Furthermore, these patients are at high risk of respiratory viruses causing a large variety of infectious diseases.

Despite the promising preliminary results derived from early studies on the use of MSCs in several diseases, the potential immunosuppressive properties of MSCs on the host, which may be associated with an increased susceptibility to infections especially in patients who received HSCs or solid transplantation, are not sufficiently known.

Recent experimental and *in vivo* human data have shown that MSCs exert an inhibitory activity on the growth of gram-negative bacteria, such as *Escherichia coli* and *Pseudomonas aeruginosa*, as well as of gram-positive bacteria, such as *Staphylococcus aureus*. This activity seems to be related to LL-37 cathelicidin, a compound known for its ability to kill both Gram-neg and Gram⁺ bacteria.

A few data have been reported in the literature concerning the clinical role of MSCs on the development of viral and fungal infections.

Some data showed a reduced intracellular proliferation of CMV and herpesvirus type 1 when co-incubated with MSCs, thus suggesting the involvement of IDO in the control of virus replication.

However, it must be said that MSCs are not capable of suppressing the proliferation and production of IFN-gamma from virus-specific T-cells against CMV and EBV.

Furthermore, it has been shown that a subset of MSCs producing IL-17 may have an anti-fungal activity possibly inducing a growth inhibition of *Candida Albicans*.

Based on these considerations, it can be postulated that MSCs may exert an anti-mi-

crobial activity, and are characterized by the capacity to regulate the immune response against several pathogens, particularly in regulating the balance between pro- and anti-inflammatory pathways.

As far as *in vivo* data are concerned, the results so far published in the literature are sometimes conflicting; for example, CMV-infected MSCs induced a loss of their immunosuppressive properties and capacity to inhibit microbial growth, possibly due to a reduction in the expression of IDO on MSCs.

Current studies are trying to identify a biological compound which may correlate with the risk of infection in the immune compromised host who received either an organ or HSC transplantation. This marker may be helpful for a better assessment of the role played by MSCs in these clinical settings.

Recommended reading and references

1. Wuchter P et al. *Standardization of Good Manufacturing practice-compliant production of bone marrow-derived human mesenchymal stromal cells for immunotherapeutic applications*. Cytotherapy 2015; 17: 128-139

2. Krampera M et al. *Immunological characterization of multipotent mesenchymal stromal cells-The international Society for Cellular Therapy (ISCT) working proposal*. Cytotherapy 2013; 15:1054-1061.

3. Bourin P et al. *Stromal cells from the adipose tissue-derived stromal vascular fraction and culture expanded adipose tissue-derived stromal/stem cells : a joint statement of the International Federation for adipose therapeutics and Science (IFATS) and the Internationl Society for Cellular Therapy (ISCT)*. Cytotherapy 2013; 15:641-648.

4. Menard C et al. *Clinical-grade mesenchymal stromal cells produced under various good manufacturing practice processes differ in their immunomodulatory properties: standardization of immunomodulatory properties: standardization of immune quality controls*. Stem Cells Dev 2013; 22(12): 1789-1801.

5. Harichandan A and Buhring HJ. *Prospective isolation of human MSC*. Best Practice

& Research Clinical Haematology 2011; 24:25-36.

6. Murphy MB et al. *Mesenchymal stem cells: environmentally responsive therapeutics for regenerative medicine.* Experimental & Molecular Medicine 2013; 45: e54.

7. Keating A. *Mesenchymal stromal cells: new directions.* Cell Stem Cell 2012; 10:709-716.

8. Vaes B et al. *Application of MultiStem allogeneic cells for immunomodulatory therapy: clinical progress and preclinical challenges in prophylaxis for graft versus host disease.* Frontiers in Immunology 2012; 3:1-5.

9. Montespan F et al. *Osteodifferentiated mesenchymal stem cells from bone marrow and adipose tissue express HLA-G and display immunomodulatory properties in HLA-mismatched settings: implications in bone repair therapy.* J Immunol Res 2014; 230346.

10. Tse WT et al. *Suppression of allogeneic T-cell proliferation by human marrow stromal cells: implications in transplantation.* Transplantation 2003; 75: 389–397.

11. Spaggiari GM et al. *Mesenchymal stem cells inhibit natural killer-cell proliferation, cytotoxicity, and cytokine production: role of indoleamine 2,3-dioxygenase and prostaglandin E2.* Blood 2008; 111(3): 1327-1333.

12. Li M, Sun X et al. *Mesenchymal stem cells suppress CD8$^+$ T cell-mediated activation by suppressing natural killer group 2, member D protein receptor expression and secretion of prostaglandin E2, indoleamine 2, 3-dioxygenase and transforming growth factor-β.* Clin Exp Immunol 2014; 178(3):516-524.

13. Roemeling-van Rhijn M et al. *Human Bone Marrow- and Adipose Tissue-derived Mesenchymal Stromal Cells are Immunosuppressive In vitro and in a Humanized Allograft Rejection Model.* J Stem Cell Res Ther 2013; Suppl 6(1):20780.

14. Rizzo R et al. *New insights into HLA-G and inflammatory diseases.* Inflamm Allergy Drug Targets 2012;11(6):448-463.

15. Nasef A et al. *Immunosuppressive effects of mesenchymal stem cells: involvement of HLA-G.* Transplantation 2007; 84(2): 231-237.

16. Rizzo R et al. *A functional role for soluble HLA-G antigens in immune modulation mediated by mesenchymal stromal cells.* Cytotherapy 2008; 10(4): 364-375.

17. Rizzo R et al. *A simple method for identifying bone marrow mesenchymal stromal cells with a high immunosuppressive potential.* Cytotherapy 2011; 13(5): 523-527.

18. Le Blanc K et al. *Treatment of severe acute graft versus host disease with third partry haploidentical mesenchymal stem cells.* Lancet 2004; 363 (9419): 1410-1421.

19. Uccelli A et al. *Mesenchymal stem cells in health and disease.* Nature reviews: Immunology 2008; 8: 726-736.

20. Le Blanc K. *Mesenchymal stromal cells : tissue repair and immune modulation.* Cythotherapy 2006, 8: 559-561.

21. Campioni D et al. *A decreased positivity for CD90 on human mesenchymal stromal cells (MSCs) is associate with a loss of immune suppressive activity by MSCs.* Cytometry 2009; 76: 225-230.

22. Teklemariam T et al. *Inhibition of DNA methylation enhances HLA-G expression in human mesenchymal stem cells.* Biochem Biophys Res Commun 2014; 452(3):753-759.

23. Naji A et al. *Concise review: combining human leukocyte antigen G and mesenchymal stem cells for immunosuppressant biotherapy.* Stem Cells 2013; 31(11):2296-2303.

24. Calkoen FG et al. *Mesenchymal stromal cell therapy is associated with increased adenovirus-associated but not cytomegalovirus-associated mortality in children with severe acute graft-versus-host disease.* Stem Cells Transl Med 2014; 3(8): 899-910.

25. Balan A et al. *Mesenchymal stromal cells in the antimicrobial host response of hematopoietic stem cell recipients with graft-versus-host disease--friends or foes?* Leukemia 2014; 28(10):1941-1948.

26. Meisel R et al. *Cytomegalovirus infection impairs immunosuppressive and antimicrobial effector functions of human multipotent mesenchymal stromal cells.* Mediators Inflamm 2014; 2014:898630.

Cancer stem cells

19

Massimiliano Bonafè Gianluca Storci

19.1 Introduction

Renewable adult tissues harbour a compartment of cells called "*stem cells*". The word "stem" recalls the latin "*stamen-minis*", which identifies the warp of a tissue, as well as the thread of destiny. In German, the scientific language of the 19th century, the term "*Stamm*" means strain or jamb, as well as a grammatical root. The word "cancer" derives from the Greek word "*karkinos*", a mythical monstrous crustacean. Cancer depicts the uncontrolled growth of new tissue (neo-plasia from the Greek "neos" and "plàsis", new formation) that invades the surrounding tissues and spreads at distant sites (i.e. metastatic process). Ultimately, cancer debars the physiological function of tissues, organs and systems. The existence of cancer stem cells (CSC) was first hypothesized at the beginning of the last century, but the experimental verification of this hypothesis began in the late 20th century. The CSC model of cancer envisages that a minor pool of cancer cells is endowed with unlimited self-renewal that supports the growth of the tumour mass and allows metastatic dissemination at distant organs. Following this reasoning, CSCs are the ultimate targets of innovative diagnostics and therapeutics. In spite of this huge effort in CSC research, we can still refer to CSCs as a model that allows us to understand some features of the neoplastic growth. In fact, the hierarchical CSC model does not fully account for tumour heterogeneity, unless phenomena such as epithelial-mesenchymal transition and cellular plasticity are taken into account.

19.2 CSCs: from theory to cellular identification

The CSC model of cancer maintains that the neoplastic tissue is hierarchically organized: a small number of CSCs "mimic" the behaviour of normal stem cells. The normal stem cell pool spends most of its lifespan in a quiescent state, undergoes asymmetric cell division, and gives rise to a large number of "daughter" (progenitor) proliferating cells. To experimentally verify the presence of CSCs in a solid or a liquid (leukaemia) tumour, it is necessary to demonstrate the presence of a minor subpopulation of cells endowed with high tumorigenic potential that can be identified by a specific and reproducible immune-phenotype. The tumorigenic potential of CSCs is then assayed by means of the xenograft transplantation procedure (i.e. the injection of human cancer cells into an immune-deficient mouse). CSCs are highly enriched in cells capable of initiating a tumour xenograft in the mice (1/10, 1/100 cells) compared to the whole tumour population (1/10,000, 1/1,000,000). In human breast, brain cancer and leukaemia, CSCs occur at a frequency ranging from 1 out of 10^3 up to 1 out of 10^5. A major effort has been devoted at identifying the immunophenotype of CSCs in different types of neoplasia. The CSCs' immunophenotype is studied by using antibodies against membrane glycoproteins (identified by the abbreviation Cluster Designation or CD followed by a number). Membrane markers are more useful than intracellular ones, because specific antibodies can be exploited (without any fixation and permeabilization steps) on living cells, thus allowing subsequent *in vitro* or *in vivo* functional studies. Indeed, antibodies linked to fluorescent molecules allow us to count and separate CSCs by cytofluorimetric or immunofluorescent analysis. Furthermore, the same antibodies conjugated with magnetic beads allow sorting CSCs out of the bulk of cancer cells. The first evidence of a specific CSC immunophenotype dates back to 1994, when John Dick's group of the University of Toronto isolated a rare population (about 1 in 250,000) cells from human leukaemia blasts, expressing the CD34 marker but missing the CD38 one. These rare cells were able to generate leukaemia in immunodeficient mice. Conversely, the majority of CD34- cells or CD34-/CD38+ cells were not able to establish a xenograft in the same murine model. With a similar strategy, a few years later, Peter Dirks' group of the University of Toronto and Michael Clarke of the University of Ann Arbor in Michigan were able to identify CD133+ CSCs in human brain tumours and CD44+/CD24- CSCs (i.e. expressing CD44 but missing CD24) in human breast cancer. Subsequently, CSCs with both phenotypes have been identified in other types of solid tumours, such as pancreatic adenocarcinoma, colon and lung cancer with a frequency ranging from 1 out of 10^3 to 1 out of 10^5. It is worth mentioning that "CSC markers" are not exclusive to CSCs. For instance, CD133 is expressed by normal stem cells, as well as by mature intestinal epithelial cells and immature endothelial cells. Similarly, CD34 expression is present in immature endothelial cells. This is not surprising, owing to the fact that CD133 and CD34 antigens are membrane proteins that perform many functions in different cell types. Similar reasoning can be extended to the CD44 protein, which identifies breast cancer CSCs, but is also expressed by a variety of

tumour and non-tumour cells, including cancer-associated fibroblasts. The enzyme aldehyde dehydrogenase 1 (ALDH1) is a marker of CSCs in various cancers. The obstacle to a large-scale exploitation of this biomarker is the necessity of an enzymatic reaction for its detection, compared to common membrane CDs, which require only an antigen-antibody reaction. Nevertheless, ALDH1 seems to be able to identify, at least in breast cancer, a population of CSCs bearing peculiar characteristics, namely growth in conditions of low oxygen tension and the ability to undergo epithelial-mesenchymal transition (see following paragraphs). Some authors have argued that the above-mentioned CSCs could simply represent the most aggressive populations (clones) that are present in the tumour mass and that may originate from the evolution of cancer cells, without any need of being considered the true mother cells of the entire neoplasia. As arguably suggested by some authors, some cells with high tumorigenic power could represent populations of cancer cells that adapt better than others to grow in immune-compromised mice, rather than representing the original CSC population. As far as the most important property of CSCs is concerned, such as asymmetric cell division, which is the most difficult property to prove, the experiment required is the following: once the putative CSCs have been identified by the aforementioned characteristics (minor population, recognizable phenotype), the histological examination of the xenotransplant in mice should allow to replicate the features of the original tumour mass. Indeed, not only are the transplanted/injected cells expected to generate a neoplastic mass, but the xenograft is expected to replicate the cellular makeup and the heterogeneity of the original one. Moreover, such features should be reproducible across serial transplant passages. In other words, a CD44+/CD24- xenotransplant is expected to be populated by putative daughter cells (i.e. CD44-/CD24+) and to maintain this heterogeneity across serial transplants. This phenomenon entails the notion that the isolated CD44⁺/CD24⁻ CSCs are able to perform asymmetric division, i.e. to generate the subpopulation of CD44⁺/CD24⁻ CSC within the tumour mass, while giving rise to the CD44⁻/CD24⁻ daughter cell population. Notably, at least two CSC populations can be isolated in human breast cancer: one carrying the CD44⁺/CD24⁻ immune-phenotype, the other expressing the ALDH1⁺ marker (Figure 19.1). It is worth noting that, in some types of cancer, the presence of CSCs remains to be demonstrated. Nevertheless, in other tumours, such as melanomas and lymphomas, cells with high tumorigenic capability (putative CSCs) are present in the order of 1 out of 10 cells and even 1 out of 2 cells. Hence, the CSC model does not currently properly describe all kinds of cancers.

19.3 CSCs: from the primary tumour mass to the *in vitro* model

Although *in vivo* studies are of pivotal importance to demonstrate the existence of CSCs, reproducible *in vitro* models are fundamental for gaining an insight into the molecular mechanisms that regulate CSC functioning. Studies on haematopoietic CSCs (leukaemias) have been the first to employ *in vitro* CSC models.

For solid tumours (i.e. breast, colon or lung cancer), we have had to wait for the optimization of culture systems capable to maintain CSCs alive and without phenotypic biases. In particular, primary cells deriving from a solid neoplastic tissue have to set in "low attachment" culture conditions (i.e. a condition that avoids the attachment of the cell to the surface of the plastic ware) where the majority of primary cells die, while a minor population of putative cancer stem cells survive. This latter population of cells is expected to give rise to spheroid structures rich in CSCs. This multicellular floating structure, if mechanically disaggregated to a single cell suspension, is expected to generate secondary, tertiary, and n-generation multicellular spheroids. It is relevant to note that such multicellular spheroids are not composed only of CSCs, but also by "daughter cells" which create a (hypoxic) microenvironment that facilitates the survival of CSCs (Figure 19.2). Neurospheres is the specific term that has been coined to describe this kind of primary CSC cultures from brain tumours. Similarly, for breast cancer or colon cancer, the terms "mammosphere" and "colonspheres" have been minted. These *in vitro* CSC models have been validated for many years, ascertaining their ability to propagate *in vitro* a minor population of cells endowed with a CSC phenotype (CD44⁺/ CD24⁻ or ALDH1⁺ in the case of mammospheres), and high capacity to self-renew. Lastly, it has been shown that cells with a higher tumorigenic potential with respect to adherent (traditional) cell culture systems are obtained from the specific tissue-derived spheroids. These studies have made it possible to investigate the activation of stem cell pathways and the action of molecules able to interfere with CSC suvival. Tissue-derived spheroids containing CSCs are endowed with a strong resistance to cell death induced by anti-tumoral molecules or ionizing radiations compared to cells grown in plastic-adherent culture conditions. Furthermore, several studies on tissue-derived spheroids led to the discovery of new pharmacological targets for novel anticancer drugs (Figure 19.2).

19.4 CSCs: hijacking of the normal stem cell programs

Normal stem cells are programmed for long-term survival destined to sustain tissue homeostasis and to preside over the repair of the healthy tissue in case of damage. For this purpose, normal stem cells are equipped with a variety of survival mechanisms, such as membrane proteins belonging to the ATP-binding cassette family (e.g. ABCG2). These membrane carriers are capable of extruding a large variety of endogenous or exogenous toxic compounds, including cytotoxic drugs, as well as fluorescent dyes (HOESCHT_3342) that

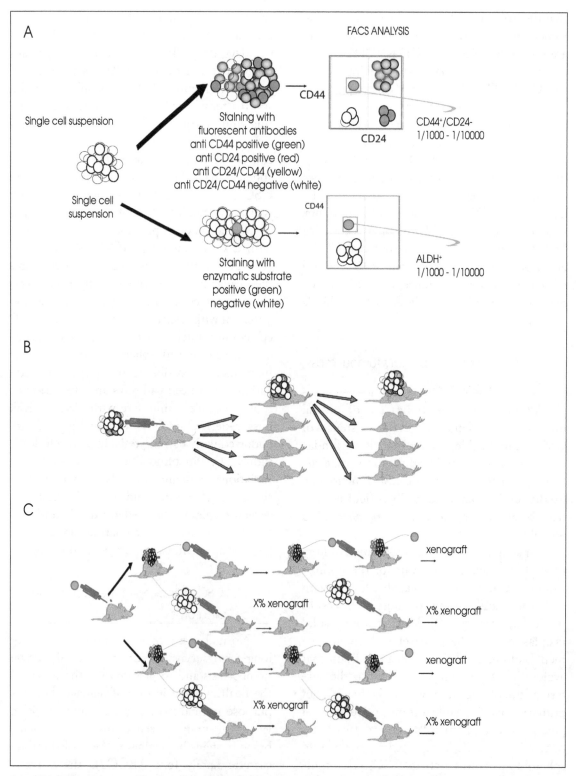

Figure 19.1 **CSCs characterization from a primary human neoplasia (the experiment depicted refers to breast cancer tissue)**.
A, cytofluorimetric analysis of the CD44+/CD24- or ALDH1 expressing cells; **B**, cancer cells are endowed with a different capability to induce tumor xenografts in immunocompromised mice; **C**, CSCs (green cells) are rare cells endowed with a highly efficient capability to induce tumor xenografts.

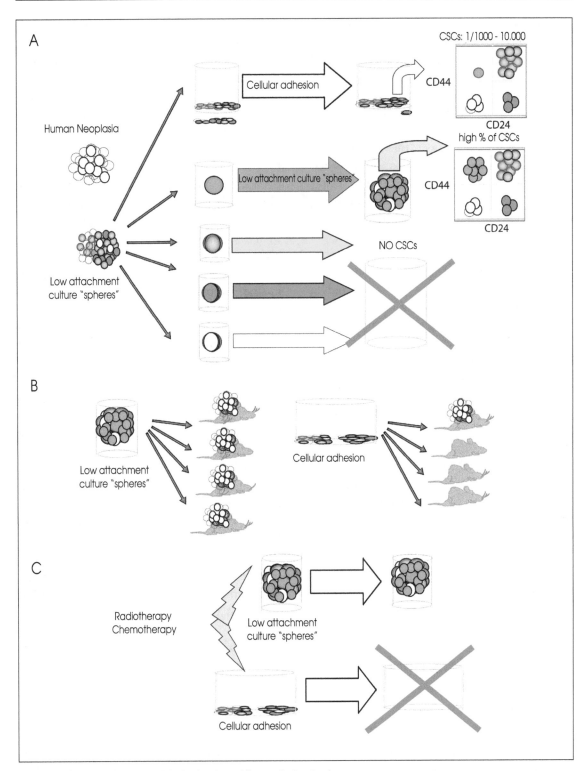

Figure 19.2 **Primary culture of CSCs by means of tissue-derived spheres**
A, if primary neoplastic tissue-derived cells are cultured *in vitro* they originate a canonic adherent cell population. If primary neoplastic tissue-derived cells are cultured in low attachment conditions, the cells do not adhere to plastic but they grow in suspension as cellular spheroids. CD44+/CD24- cells are preferentially capable of surviving in low attachment conditions and of propagating in culture; **B**, primary tumour tissue-derived spheroids are endowed with high tumorigenic capability in mice xenograft; **C**, tumour tissue -derived spheroids are more resistant to anti-cancer agents compared to adherent cells.

lead to the identification of the so-called side population. This latter is present in normal and tumour tissues, and in both cases is enriched in cells endowed with stem cell properties. Notably, the presence of such proteins confers survival advantage in the hypoxic environment. This is not surprising, because the normal stem cell niche is hypoxic. Hence, this intrinsic feature of the normal stem cells can be hijacked by CSCs, which become inherently resistant to harsh environmental conditions, including exposure to stringent tumour hypoxic environment and to chemo- and radiotherapy. Consistent with the mutation accumulation theory of cancer, it can be hypothesized that CSCs arise from normal stem cells, which accumulate genetic pro-tumorigenic mutations. Nevertheless, the similarity between CSCs and normal stem cells does not entail the notion that the former are generated from the latter. In fact, several studies performed in mice conveyed that the activation of specific oncogenes could generate CSCs starting from differentiating haematopoietic progenitor cells. More recent studies show a similar phenomenon in the mammary gland, where the overexpression of the SLUG gene generates CSCs starting from differentiated progenitors. This finding reveals that the stem cell program can be reactivated (hijacked) in differentiated cells that do not show intrinsic stem cell features (Figure 19.3). These models have vastly expanded the spectrum of the normal cells in which the stem cell potential can be reactivated by specific genetic lesions.

19.5 The role of the epithelial-mesenchymal transition and hypoxia in intra-tumoral heterogeneity

The reactivation of the CSC program recalls the concept of "plasticity" or "cellular reprogramming": both phenomena are epitomized by the mechanism of epithelial-mesenchymal transition. This process is well known by embryologists and describes the epithelial and the mesenchymal phenotype as two extremes of a continuum in which the cell assumes varying degrees of differentiation. Epithelial neoplastic cells can assume a mesenchymal phenotype through a genetic program (e.g. driven by the SLUG gene), which allows them to migrate throughout tissues and disseminate pro-metastatic cells at distant organs. Along with the migration capacity, the acquisition of CSC markers, such as CD44, ALDH1, CD133 protein expression is also promoted. This dedifferentiation process does not occur in all cells, but only in permissive subpopulations, such as cells carrying inactivation of onco-suppressor genes, e.g. the TP53 gene. It is worth noting that the SLUG gene is over-expressed in the hypoxic microenvironment where it confers a survival advantage. This observation suggests that cells with CSC phenotype can be originated by specific microenvironmental cues. Following this concept, heterogeneous populations of cells with CSC characteristics can be found in the same tumour. For instance, $CD44^+/CD24_-$ and $ALDH1^+$ CSC populations may coexist in breast cancer. Notably, the $ALDH1^+$ CSC population is enriched in hypoxic tissue regions and associates with luminal cell features, while the $CD44^+/CD24^-$ CSC population is more frequently associated with myoepithelial/basal cell features. The observation above allows to reconcile the CSC model with the presence of intra-tumoral cellular heterogeneity, i.e. the presence in the same tumour mass of different subpopulation of cells that are not genetically related to each other and that can behave as CSCs in different tumour microenvironments. Speculatively, some CSC subpopulations may give rise to proliferating compartments, others to dormant cells or to disseminating ones. As far as the hypoxic microenvironment is concerned, it has long been observed that tumour tissues contain areas with a low oxygen concentration (0.1-1% partial pressure of O_2) that are associated to chemo- and radio-resistance. These regions are enriched in CSCs, e.g. $ALDH1^+$ cells in breast cancer and CD133+ CSCs in brain cancers. The ability to survive in such conditions is an

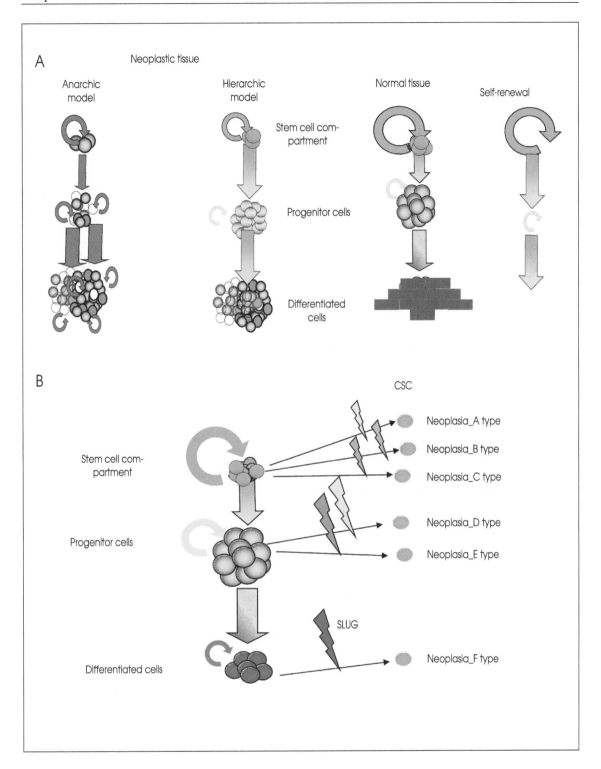

Figure 19.3 **The relationship between normal and cancer stem cells.**
A, The CSC model of cancer proposes a hierarchy in which a neoplastic tissue is fueled by an aberrant differentiation cascade that originates from a compartment of CSC population. Such process is strictly regulated in an efficient physiologic manner in the normal tissue, where normal stem cells asymmetrically generate progenitor cells and differentiated progeny; **B**, CSCs and normal stem cells share similar properties; however, CSCs do not necessarily derive from transformed normal stem cells. CSCs can originate from progenitor cells that harbour specific genetic lesions (e.g. ectopic expression of the SLUG gene).

evolutionary strategy, optimized for the preservation of normal stem cells from oxygen-dependent free radical-induced DNA damage. Moreover, the hypoxic microenvironment is a powerful inducer of the normal stem cell program. In CSCs, hypoxia elicits the genetic program of epithelial-mesenchymal transition and triggers the CSC phenotype (e.g. expression of CD44+, formation of mammospheres) particularly in breast cancer cells lacking the TP53 gene. The capability of CSCs to thrive in hypoxia may explain their inherent resistance to conventional chemo- and radiotherapy and their likelihood to survive anti-angiogenic therapy compared to other cancer cells. This therapeutic strategy is aimed at killing the tumour mass by halting blood vessel formation and thus by shortening oxygen supply. In fact, in the animal model, anti-angiogenic therapy may activate hypoxia survival mechanisms in putative CSCs leading to the enhancement of tumour aggressiveness (Figure 19.4).

19.6 The inflammatory addiction of cancer stem cells

The observation that cancer behaves as a "wound that never heals" underpins the tight similarity between the neoplastic growth and the inflammatory process. Normal stem cells are involved in the inflammatory response, because they have to repair/regenerate the damaged tissue, once the inflammatory process has been resolved. This phenomenon is a potential double-edged sword if normal stem cells are excessively overdriven by inflammatory stimuli and may give rise to an excessive response that may lead to neoplastic growth. In fact, CSCs seem to repair the neoplastic tissue as their normal counterparts would do in the presence of tissue damage. The evidence that inflammatory mediators play a pivotal role in CSC behavior was demonstrated by studies on Interleukin-6. This inflammatory cytokine is able to act on human breast CSCs grown as mammospheres by increasing a series of stem cell characteris-

tics, such as hypoxia survival, epithelial-mesenchymal transition and resistance to cell death on administration of anticancer drugs. The link between CSCs and inflammation could explain the role of chronic inflammation as a pre-cancerous condition. Indeed, it is known that people suffering from chronic inflammation or inflammatory diseases (e.g. chronic hepatitis) are affected by an increased incidence of liver cancer. Chronic inflammations include pathologies (e.g. gastritis, esophagitis) and chronic exposure to irritants/chemicals (e.g. asbestos, cigarette smoke). In this context, ageing itself is a cancer-predisposing condition because it is characterized by a progressive increase of systemic inflammation, a phenomenon called inflammageing (from the fusion of the words "inflammation" and "ageing"). In this light, the inflammatory microenvironment is of pivotal importance for facilitating and sustaining the growth of CSCs, which would gain an advantage over their normal counterparts, especially in the presence of genetic mutations. An example of this phenomenon is the loss of TP53, which, on the one hand, is able to facilitate the onset of the CSC phenotype (e.g. the epithelial-mesenchymal transition induced by the SLUG gene expression), while, on the other hand, it makes cells less sensitive to death induced by inflammatory environment (e.g. TNFalpha-induced cell death). In this regard, the relationship between inflammation and CSC behaviour brought to light a potential "Achilles heel" of this cell subpopulation. In fact, the so-called "inflammatory addiction" of the CSCs has been demonstrated in the mammary gland and in haematopoietic tissue. This means that CSCs not only take advantage of inflammation but their survival becomes dependent on the autocrine production of inflammatory molecules. Some autocrine cytokine circuits, such as interleukin 6, are promoted by the loss of important regulatory pathways (e.g. loss of TP53). Hence, on one side the inflammatory activation makes the CSCs autonomous from micro-environ-

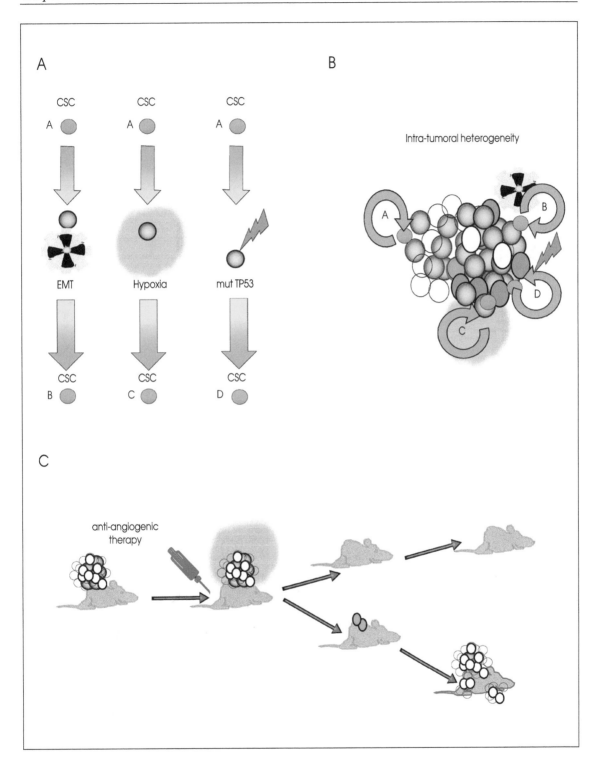

Figure 19.4 **CSCs and intra-tumoral heterogeneity.**
A, cancer cells can activate genetic programs, such as Epithelial-Mesenchymal Transition (MET), hypoxia response or harbour mutations in onco-suppressor genes (i.e. p53) that lead to CSC behaviour; **B**, the neoplastic tumour mass is constituted by different types of CSCs, some of which are originated from the process described in the previous panel. This model is more realistic in respect to the previous one (hierarchic origin of tumour tissues); **C**, anti-angiogenic therapy induces hypoxia response in cancer cells. Paradoxically, such stress may generate CSCs with a more aggressive phenotype.

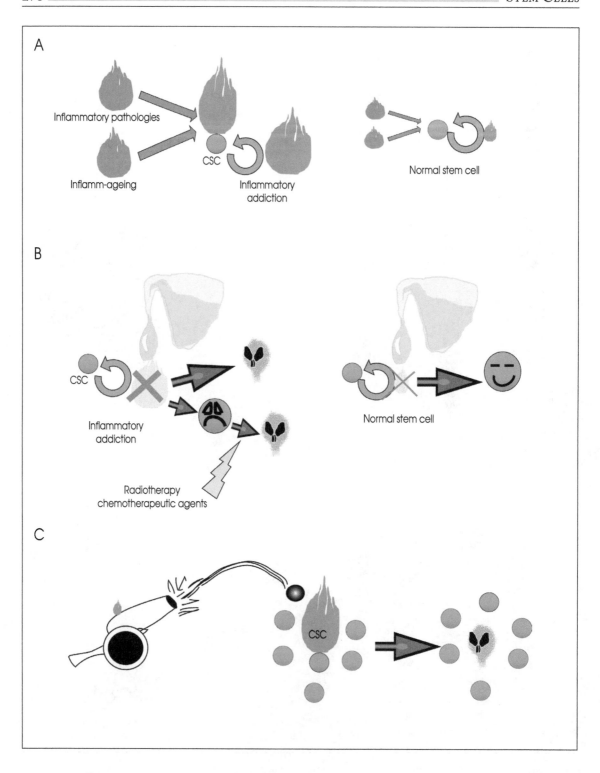

Figure 19.5 **Inflammation as the Achille's heel of CSCs.**
A, CSCs are characterized by an over-activation of the inflammatory pathways (autocrine loop) that favours their survival, a condition that can be defined as "Inflammatory addiction". Normal stem cells do not show the same behaviour, displaying a reduced inflammatory autocrine loop dependency; **B**, new anti-cancer drugs may target specifically this "inflammatory addiction" of CSCs, without killing normal stem cells; **C**, the main objective of cancer therapy is to eradicate CSCs avoiding to cause damage to healthy cells and tissues; for this reason CSCs are represented similarly to normal stem cells, due to the important similarities between these two cell populations.

mental signals, on the other it makes them vulnerable to the activity of anti-inflammatory molecules. As an example, natural origin molecules, such as parthenolide, which inhibits the activation of the NF-kB pathway, have been studied as potential CSC-specific drugs. In fact, such molecules are capable of killing CSCs at concentrations that are not harmful to their normal counterparts. A similar effect can be achieved also by inhibiting the autocrine Interleukin-6 molecular circuitry. Far from suggesting that the currently available anti-inflammatory drugs alone are able to fight the growth of an established neoplasia, current research studies how to exploit molecules capable of impinging upon inflammatory pathways to make CSCs more vulnerable to chemotherapy (Figure 19.5).

19.7 Final perspective

Current knowledge on CSC biology provides an interpretative model to understand cancer behaviour. Nevertheless, several other biological processes, such as cell plasticity, have be taken into account to fully explain the biology of cancer. In particular, we have progressively moved from a perspective in which CSCs arise from a normal stem cell due to accumulation of genetic mutations, to a perspective in which the interactions with the microenvironment are of primary importance in generating cells in which the CSC genetic program is activated. In particular, the inherent link between the functioning of CSCs and inflammation allows a better understanding of the connection between cancer, inflammation and ageing. In this regard, the use of specific drugs associated with nano-particles capable of releasing specific drugs only in the place of action (i.e. the tumour tissue) represents an already open challenge. Such technological tools, coupled with molecules that can target the potential "Achilles heel" of CSCs may constitute "magic bullets" to specifically target CSCs.

Recommended reading and references

1. Al-Hajj M et al. *Prospective identification of tumorigenic breast cancer cells.* Proc Natl Acad Sci U S A 2003 Apr 1;100(7):3983-3983.

2. Bonafè M et al. *Inflamm-aging of the stem cell niche: breast cancer as a paradigmatic example: breakdown of the multi-shell cytokine network fuels cancer in aged people.* Bioessays 2012 Jan;34(1):40-49.

3. Conley SJ et al. *Antiangiogenic agents increase breast cancer stem cells via the generation of tumor hypoxia.* Proc Natl Acad Sci USA 2012;109:2784–2789.

4. Cozzio A et al. *Similar MLL-associated leukemias arising from self-renewing stem cells and short-lived myeloid progenitors.* Genes Dev 2003;17:3029e3035.

5. Dalloul A. *Hypoxia_and visualization of the stem cell_niche.* Methods Mol Biol. 2013;1035:199-205.

6. Denison TA et al. *Tumor heterogeneity and its implication for drug delivery.* J Control Release 2012 Dec 10;164(2):187-191.

7. Dontu G et al. *In vitro propagation and transcriptional profiling of human mammary stem/progenitor cells.* Genes Dev 2003 May 15;17(10):1253-1270.

8. Franceschi C et al. *An evolutionary perspective on immunosenescence.* Ann N Y Acad Sci 2000 Jun;908:244-254.

9. Kelly PN et al. *Tumor growth need not be driven by rare cancer stem cells.* Science. 2007 Jul 20;317(5836):337.

10. Lapidot T et al. *A cell initiating human acute myeloid leukaemia after transplantation into SCID mice.* Nature 1994;367, 645e648.

11. Li X et al. *Intrinsic resistance of tumorigenic breast cancer cells to chemotherapy.* J Natl Cancer Inst 2008 May 7;100(9):672-679.

12. Liu S et al. *Breast cancer stem cells transition between epithelial and mesenchymal states reflective of their normal counterparts.* Stem Cell Reports 2013 Dec 27;2(1):78-91.

13. Marusyk A et al. *Intra-tumour heterogeneity: a looking glass for cancer?* Nature Reviews Cancer 2012 Apr 19;12(5):323-334.

14. McDermott SP et al. *Targeting breast cancer stem cells.* Mol Oncol 2010 Oct;4(5):404-419.

15. Ponti D et al. *Isolation and in vitro propagation of tumorigenic breast cancer cells with stem/progenitor cell properties.* Cancer Res 2005 Jul 1;65(13):5506-5511

16. Reynolds BA et al. *Neural stem cells and neurospheres—Re-evaluating the relationship.* Nat Methods 2005;2:333–336.

17. Rycaj K et al. *Cell-of-Origin of Cancer versus Cancer Stem Cells: Assays and Interpretations.* Cancer Res 2015 Oct 1;75(19):4003-4011.

18. Sansone P et al. *IL-6 triggers malignant features in mammospheres from human ductal breast carcinoma and normal mammary gland.* J Clin Invest 2007 Dec;117(12):3988-4002

19. Singh SK et al. *"Identification of a cancer stem cell in human brain tumours ".* Cancer Res 2003 63(1): 5821–5828.

20. Storci G et al. *The basal-like breast carcinoma phenotype is regulated by SLUG gene expression.* J Pathol 2008 Jan;214(1):25-37.

21. Tan TZ et al. *Epithelial-mesenchymal transition spectrum quantification and its efficacy in deciphering survival and drug responses of cancer patients.* EMBO Mol Med 2014 Sep 11;6(10):1279-1293.

22. Sansone P, Ceccarelli C, Berishaj M, Chang Q, Rajasekhar VK, Perna F, Bowman RL, Vidone M, Daly L, Nnoli J, Santini D, Taffurelli M, Shih NN, Feldman M, Mao JJ, Colameco C, Chen J, DeMichele A, Fabbri N, Healey JH, Cricca M, Gasparre G, Lyden D, Bonafé M, Bromberg J. *Self-renewal of CD133(hi) cells by IL6/Notch3 signalling regulates endocrine resistance in metastatic breast cancer.* Nat Commun. 2016 Feb 9;7:10442. doi: 10.1038/ncomms10442.

Index

CPSIA information can be obtained
at www.ICGtesting.com
Printed in the USA
LVHW060849060620
657564LV00010B/481